VEDIC MATHEMATICS
TEACHER'S MANUAL

ADVANCED LEVEL

Kenneth R. Williams

INSPIRATION BOOKS

Published by Inspiration Books, 2009.
Kensglen, Nr Carsphairn, Castle Douglas, DG7 3TE, Scotland, U.K.

ISBN 978-1-902517-18-6

First published in 2003 by Inspiration Books.
Revised edition 2009.

http://www.vedicmaths.org

PREFACE

This Manual is the third of three self-contained Manuals (Elementary, Intermediate and Advanced) and is designed for adults with a good understanding of basic mathematics to learn or teach the Vedic system. So teachers could use it to learn Vedic Mathematics, or it could be used to teach a course on Vedic Mathematics. This Manual is suitable for teachers of students in grades 9 to 14.

The eighteen lessons of this course are based on a series of one week summer courses given at Oxford University by the author to Swedish mathematics teachers between 1990 and 1995. Those courses were quite intensive consisting of eighteen, one and a half hour, lessons. Some of the material here is more advanced than would be given to the average 18 year old student but this is what the teachers wanted on the courses and so the same is given here.

The lessons in this book however probably contain more material than could be given in a one and a half hour lesson. The teacher/reader may wish to omit some sections, go through the material in a different sequence to that shown here or break up some sections.

All techniques are fully explained and proofs and explanations are given, the relevant Sutras are indicated throughout (these are listed at the end of the Manual) and, for convenience, answers are given after each exercise. Cross-references are given showing what alternative topics may be continued with at certain points.

It should also be noted that in the Vedic system a mental approach is preferred so we always encourage students to work mentally as long as it is comfortable. In the Cosmic Calculator Course pupils are given a short mental test at the start of most or all lessons, which makes a good start to the lesson, revises previous work and introduces some of the ideas needed in the current lesson. In the Vedic system pupils are encouraged to be creative and use whatever method they like.

CONTENTS

LESSON 1
LEFT TO RIGHT

SUMMARY

This Lesson shows addition, subtraction and multiplication from left to right and its advantages, checking devices, and also introduces the use of bar numbers.

1.1 **Introduction** - background information about Vedic Mathematics.
1.2 **Addition** – from left to right
1.3 **Multiplication** – from left to right
1.4 **Writing Left to Right Sums**
1.5 **Subtraction**
1.6 **Digit Sums** - reducing a number to a single digit.
1.7 **Checking Devices** – checking multiplication, addition and subtraction using the digit sums and by examining the first and last figures.
1.8 **All from 9 and the Last from 10** – for subtractions, and the use of bar numbers.

1.1 INTRODUCTION

Vedic Mathematics is the ancient system of mathematics which was rediscovered early last century by **Sri Bharati Krsna Tirthaji** (henceforth referred to as Bharati Krsna).

The Sanskrit word "veda" means "knowledge". The Vedas are ancient writings whose date is disputed but which date from at least several centuries BC. According to Indian tradition the content of the Vedas was known long before writing was invented and was freely available to everyone. It was passed on by word of mouth. The writings called the Vedas consist of a huge number of documents (there are said to be millions of such documents in India, many of which have not yet been translated) and these have recently been shown to be highly structured, both within themselves and in relation to each other (see Reference 2). Subjects covered in the Vedas include Grammar, Astronomy, Architecture, Psychology, Philosophy, Archery etc., etc.

A hundred years ago Sanskrit scholars were translating the Vedic documents and were surprised at the depth and breadth of knowledge contained in them. But some documents headed "Ganita Sutras", which means mathematics, could not be interpreted by them in terms of mathematics. One verse, for example, said "in the reign of King Kamse famine, pestilence and unsanitary conditions prevailed". This is not mathematics they said, but nonsense.

Bharati Krsna was born in 1884 and died in 1960. He was a brilliant student, obtaining the highest honours in all the subjects he studied, including Sanskrit, Philosophy, English, Mathematics, History and Science. When he heard what the European scholars were saying about the parts of the Vedas which were supposed to contain mathematics he resolved to study the documents and find their meaning. Between 1911 and 1918 he was able to reconstruct the ancient system of mathematics which we now call Vedic Mathematics.

He wrote sixteen books expounding this system, but unfortunately these have been lost and when the loss was confirmed in 1958 Bharati Krsna wrote a single introductory book entitled "Vedic Mathematics". This is currently available and is a best-seller (see Reference 1).

The present author came across the book "Vedic Mathematics" in 1971 and has been developing the content of that book, and applying the system in other areas not covered by Bharati Krsna. since then. Anything in this book which is not in "Vedic Mathematics" has been developed independently by the author in this way (with a few exceptions which are acknowledged in their place).

There are many special aspects and features of Vedic Mathematics which are better discussed as we go along rather than now because you will need to see the system in action to appreciate it fully. But the main points for now are:

1) The system rediscovered by Bharati Krsna is based on sixteen formulae (or Sutras) and some sub-formulae (sub-Sutras). These Sutras are given in word form: for example *Vertically and Crosswise* and *By One More than the One Before*. In this text they are indicated by italics. The Sutras can be related to natural mental functions such as completing a whole, noticing analogies, generalisation and so on.

2) Not only does the system give many striking general and special methods, previously unknown to modern mathematics, but it is far more coherent and integrated as a system.

3) Vedic Mathematics is a system of mental mathematics (though it can also be written down).

Many of the Vedic methods are new, simple and striking. They are also beautifully interrelated so that division, for example, can be seen as an easy reversal of the simple multiplication method (similarly with squaring and square roots). This is in complete contrast to the modern system. Because the Vedic methods are so different to the conventional methods, and also to gain familiarity with the Vedic system, it is best to practice the techniques as you go along.

1.2 ADDITION

The Vedic system is extremely flexible and teaches flexibility. Conventional addition of, say, 2-figure numbers works from right to left, but since we write and pronounce numbers from left to right it is not so easy to add numbers mentally this way. Vedic addition includes addition from left to right.

(You may prefer to begin with Section 1.4 which shows **written** calculations from left to right.)

Given   7 6
          8 8 +
          ___   for example, we can see that we have 7 + 8 = 15 in the left column.

And a glance at the right-hand column shows that there is a carry and so the first two figures of the answer must be 16. The right-hand total is 14 and since the 1 has been dealt with already we only have to put the 4 after the 16 to get 164 as the answer. The totals 15 and 14 are combined as shown below:

$$\begin{array}{r} 1\ 5 \\ 1\ \ 4\ + \\ \hline 1\ 6\ 4 \end{array}$$

This is an easy, direct and natural way of adding numbers.

          6 4 6
          6 7 8 +
          1 3 2 4   The first total is 12 which becomes 13 because there is a
                          carry in the next column. The 11 in the second column
means that we now have 131. Then remembering this 131 we look at the third column which adds up to 14. The 131 therefore becomes 132 and a 4 is placed at the end giving 1324 as the answer.

Mental mathematics obviously relies more on the memory than conventional methods where every step is written down. Young children have very good memories and mental mathematics helps to strengthen the memory further. (This means that Vedic Mathematics is good for adults too, whose memory may not be as good as it once was.) This also gives confidence and teaches self-reliance, showing that we do not need pencil and paper or calculator for every sum but can find an answer without any external help.

We can show the actual steps of this example more clearly as follows:

first $\begin{array}{r} 1\ 2 \\ 1\ 1\ + \\ \hline 1\ 3\ 1 \end{array}$ then $\begin{array}{r} 1\ 3\ 1 \\ 1\ \ 4\ + \\ \hline 1\ 3\ 2\ 4 \end{array}$

Or, even more compactly as: 12,11 = 131;

131,14 = **1324**.

Here the curved line under two numbers shows that they are to be added. This is the method we will use in this book to indicate which figures are to be mentally combined.

Similarly for

8 6 5 5
8 9 2 8 +   the totals give 16,15 = 175,

then   175,7 = 1757 (there is no carry here),
_____
then   1757,13 = **17583**.

✎ **Practice A**   Add the following, writing down only the answer:

a 8 6	b 4 7	c 7 3	d 3 7	e 6 7 8	f 8 3 6
_7 7_	_8 8_	_6 4_	_4 9_	_7 8 7_	_6 2 7_
___	___	___	___	_____	_____

It is also useful to practice adding sums after only hearing the numbers being added, for example:

g 7 7	h 6 7	i 3 8	j 8 2	k 7 7 7	l 2 8 8
_8 8_	_6 8_	_4 8_	_8 3_	_8 8 8_	_2 8 9_
___	___	___	___	_____	_____

a	163	b	135	c	137	d	86	e	1465	f	1463
g	165	h	135	i	86	j	165	k	1665	l	577

1.3 MULTIPLICATION

The same idea can be used for multiplication.

 Suppose we have the sum: 2 3 7
                                              2 ×
                                          _____

We multiply each of the figures in 237 by 2 starting at the left.
The answers we get are **4, 6, 14**.

Since the 14 has two figures the 1 must be carried leftwards to the 6.
So, 46,14 = **474**.

Again we build the answer up mentally from the left:
first 4, then 4,6 = 46, then 46,14 = **474**.

☆5☆   2 3 6   First we have 14.
             _____ 7 ×   then 14, 21 = 161.
             _____   then 161, 42 = **1652**.

☆6☆   For 73 × 7 we get 49, 21 = **511**. (because 49+2 = 51)

✎ **Practice B**   Multiply the following from left to right:

a 2 7   b 7 2   c 2 6   d 7 6   e 7 8   f 8 3
  __3 ×   __7 ×   __6 ×   __6 ×   __9 ×   __3 ×
  _____   _____   _____   _____   _____   _____

g 6 4 2   h 2 5 6   i 7 4 1   j 2 2 3
    __4 ×   __3 ×   __3 ×   __9
   _____   _____   _____   _____

a	81	b	504	c	156	d	456	e	702	f	249
g	2568	h	768	i	2223	j	2007				

These can also be practised when the sum is heard and not seen.

k 33 × 4   l 55 × 7   m 34 × 8   n 66 × 6   o 62 × 4

p 55 × 5   q 44 × 4   r 43 × 7   s 88 × 4   t 73 × 3

k	132	l	385	m	272	n	396	o	248
p	275	q	176	r	301	s	352	t	219

ADVANTAGES OF LEFT TO RIGHT CALCULATION

There are many advantages to left to right calculation as we pronounce and write numbers from left to right. Also, sometimes we only need the first two or three significant figures and would waste a lot of time and effort if we found all the figures of a long sum by starting at the right. Division is always done from the left, so all calculations can be done left to right, which means we can combine operations and, for example, find the square root of the sum of two squares in one line (see Lesson 13). For finding square roots, trig functions and so on there is no right-hand figure to start from anyway, so there is no option but to start at the left.

1.4 WRITING LEFT TO RIGHT SUMS

We have described the mental method of left to right addition and multiplication. Here we see how to proceed if the sums are written out instead.

7    $367 + 985 = 1352$.

$$
\begin{array}{r}
3\ 6\ 7 \\
9\ 8\ 5\ + \\
\hline
1_2 \\
\hline
\end{array}
$$

In this addition sum, if we add the left-hand column we get $3 + 9 = 12$. Since there will be a carried figure from the next column that will affect this total, we put down only the 1 and carry the 2 as forwards as shown. The middle column adds up to 14 and we add the carried 2, **as 20**, to this to get 34 and put down 3_4 as shown. Then the right-hand column adds up to 12, to which we add the carried 4, **as 40**, to get 52: which goes down to complete the answer.

$$
\begin{array}{r}
3\ 6\ 7 \\
9\ 8\ 5\ + \\
\hline
1_2 3_4 5\ 2 \\
\hline
\end{array}
$$

 8    $3457 \times 8 = 27656$.

$$
\begin{array}{r}
3\ \ 4\ \ 5\ \ 7 \\
8\ \times \\
\hline
2\ _47\ _26\ _05\ 6 \\
\hline
\end{array}
$$

We begin on the left: $3 \times 8 = 24$, put as shown;
$4 \times 8 = 32$, add the carried 4, **as 40**, $32 + 40 = 72$;
$5 \times 8 = 40$, add the carried 2, **as 20**, $40 + 20 = 60$;
$7 \times 8 = 56$, $56 + 0 = 56$, put as shown.

 9    $138 \times 4 = 0_45_252 = 552$.

In the previous two examples we started with a 2-figure product (12 and 24). Here we initially get $1 \times 4 = 4$, a single figure number. So we put down 0_4 as shown.

 10    $234 \times 3 = 0_66_9{}^{1}02 = 702$.

Here we get 0_6 and then 6_9 and then we add 12 to 90 to get 102.
As this is a 3-figure number the 1 in 102 is carried leftwards to the 6, so that it becomes 7.

✎ **Practice C**   Try the sums in Practice A and B from left to right like this.

This is also very easy.

 11   Find **35567 – 11828**.

$$
\begin{array}{r}
3\ 5\ 5\ 6\ 7 \\
1\ 1\ 8\ 2\ 8\ - \\
\hline
2 \\
\hline
\end{array}
$$

We set the sum out as usual:
Then starting on the **left** we subtract in each column.

$3 - 1 = 2$, but before we put **2** down we check that in the next column the top number is larger. In this case 5 is larger than 1 so we put **2** down.

In the next column we have $5 - 1 = 4$, but looking in the third column we see the top number is not larger than the bottom (5 is less than 8) so instead of putting 4 down we put **3** and the other 1 is placed *On the Flag,* as shown so that the 5 becomes 15.

```
3 5 ¹5 6 7
1 1  8 2 8 –
2 3
```

So now we have $15 - 8 = 7$. Checking in the next column we can put this down because 6 is greater than 2.
In the fourth column we have $6 - 2 = 4$, but looking at the next column (7 is smaller than 8) we put down only **3** and put the other one *On the Flag* with the 7 as shown.

```
3 5 ¹5 6 ¹7
1 1  8 2 8 –
2 3 7 3
```

Finally $17 - 8 = 9$:

```
3 5 ¹5 6 ¹7
1 1  8 2 8 –
2 3 7 3 9
```

 12 Find **535 – 138.**

Here we have $5 - 1 = 4$ in the first column.
But in the next column the figures are the same.
In such a case we must look one further column along.

```
5 3 5
1 3 8 –
```

And since in the third column the top number is smaller, we reduce the 4 to **3**:

```
5 ¹3 5
1 3 8 –
3
```

Then we proceed as before:

```
5 ¹3 ¹5
1 3 8 –
3 9 7
```

We subtract in each column starting on the left, but before we put an answer down we look in the next column.
   If the top is greater than the bottom we put the figure down.
   If not, we reduce the figure by 1, put that down and give the other 1 to the smaller
      number at the top of the next column.
If the figures are the same we look at the next column to decide whether to reduce or not.

✎ **Practice D**   Subtract the following from left to right.

a 4 4 4	b 6 3	c 8 1 3	d 6 9 5	e 7 6 5	f 5 0 4
1 8 3 –	2 8 –	3 4 5 –	3 6 8 –	3 6 9 –	2 7 5 –

g 5 1	h 3 4 5 6	i 7 1 1 7	j 8 0 0 8	k 5 1 6 1	l 9 8 7 6
3 8 –	2 8 1 –	1 7 7 1 –	3 8 3 9 –	1 8 3 8 –	6 7 8 9 –
___	___	___	___	___	___

a 261 (3–3=0=9)	b 35 (9–1=8)	c 468 (3–3=0=9)	d 327 (11–8=3)	e 396 (9–9=0=9)	f 229 (9–5=4)
g 13 (6–2=4)	h 3175 (9–2=7)	i 5346 (7–7=0=9)	j 4169 (7–5=2)	k 3323 (4–2=2)	l 3087 (3–3=0=9)

1.6 DIGIT SUMS

The **digit sum** of a number is found by adding the digits in a number and adding again if necessary until a single figure is reached.

Digit sums are useful for divisibility testing, and for checking calculations.

13   So, for example, for **21302** we get 2+1+3+0+2 = **8**.

And for **76** we first get 7+6 = 13, but 1+3 = 4, so 76 → **4**.

So every number, no matter how long, can be reduced to a single figure, its digit sum.

Furthermore, if any number contains a 9, that 9 can be 'cast out'.

14   So in 193 we can simply add the 1 and 3 to get a digit sum of 4.

This is because $9 = 1\bar{1}$ (writing 9 as $10 - 1$) and the digit sum of $1\bar{1}$ is 0.
So for 193 we can say $193 = 103 + 90 = 103 + 1\bar{1}0 \rightarrow 1 + 3 = 4$.

Similarly for the digit sum of **39979** we ignore the 9s, add the 3 and 7 and give the digit sum as **1** (10→1).

So if we have to find the digit sum of a number with a nine in it **we can delete the 9, or 9s.**

This can be taken further: **any pair or group of digits which add up to 9 can be deleted.**

15   For **3725** we can delete the 72 in the centre because they add up to 9. We just add 3 and 5 to get the digit sum of **8**.

For **613954** we see 6 and 3 which make 9, 5 and 4 which make 9 and also a 9.
Deleting all these we have only 1 left so 613954 → **1**.
The number **3251** also contains a 9 because 3+5+1 = 9, so deleting these 3251 → **2**.

✏ **Practice E**   Find the digit sum of the following numbers:

a 42   b 47   c 32101   d 777   e 2468

f 669   g 996   h 5194   i 237364

a	6	b	2	c	7	d	3	e	2
f	3	g	6	h	1	i	7		

We may prove that a pair of digits totalling 9 can be cast out as follows.
Two digits in a number whose sum is 9 can be expressed as $p(10^n)$ and $(9-p)(10^m)$, n>m say.
And so their sum is $p(10^n) + (9-p)(10^m)$

$$= (10^n - 10^m)p + 9(10^m)$$
$$= 10^m(10^{n-m} - 1)p + 9(10^m)$$
$$= 10^m(9k)p + 9(10^m)$$

which is clearly a multiple of 9.
And since we can cast out any number of 9s in a number, we can cast out any multiple of 9.

1.7 CHECKING DEVICES

There are various checking devices available in the Vedic system.

A One comes under the sub-Sutra *The First by the First and the Last by the Last* (see the list of Sutras at the end of this book).

Suppose we have found that $877 \times 3 = 2631$ and we want to check the answer. The above Sutra allows us to check the beginning and end of the answer.

Multiplying the first figure of 877 by the first figure of 3 we get $8 \times 3 = 24$ and our answer starts with 26, so this looks right. Then multiplying the last figure of 877 by the last figure of 3 we get $7 \times 3 = 21$, telling us that the answer must end with a 1, which it does.

This is a useful and very quick check. It does not tell us that the answer is right of course but it could tell us that the answer is wrong.

The sub-Sutra *The First by the First and the Last by the Last* is used in many ways. For example in measuring or drawing a line with a ruler (or an angle with a protractor) we line the first point of the line with the first mark on the ruler and note the position of the last point on the ruler.

B The Digit Sum Check.

The digit sums can be used to check sums. We simply replace all the numbers in the sum by their digit sums and check that the calculation is still true.

To check **877 × 3 = 2631** we replace 877 by its digit sum which is 4.
And similarly 2631 is replaced by 3.

Then 877 × 3 = 2631 becomes **4 × 3 = 3,**

and this is true in digit sum arithmetic as 4 × 3 = 12 and 12 is equivalent to 3:
(12 → 1+2 = 3).

The Vedic formula here is *The Product of the Sum is the Sum of the Products.*

It is worth while doing the check next to the sum:

$$
\begin{array}{r}
8\ 7\ 7 \\
3 \\
\hline
2\ 6\ 3\ 1
\end{array} \times
\qquad
\begin{array}{r}
4 \\
3 \\
\hline
3
\end{array} \times
$$

So we write the three digit sums to the right of the sum and check it forms a correct sum.

✐ **Practice F**   Use the methods above to check your answers to Practice B.

___

  Checking addition is also very easy

$$
\begin{array}{r}
8\ 7\ 5 \\
6\ 4\ 6 \\
\hline
1\ 5\ 2\ 1
\end{array} +
\quad
\begin{array}{r}
2 \\
7 \\
\hline
9
\end{array} +
\qquad \text{and} \qquad
\begin{array}{r}
7\ 3\ 5 \\
8\ 8 \\
\hline
8\ 2\ 3
\end{array} +
\quad
\begin{array}{r}
6 \\
7 \\
\hline
4
\end{array} +
$$

Note: a) because these are addition sums we **add** the digit sums (not multiply as before),
   b) the second sum is verified because 6+7 = 13 → 4 in digit sums.

✐ **Practice G**   Check your answers to Practice A using the digit sums.

___

The digit sum check does not prove the answer is correct: if you add 44 and 77 and give the answer as 211 instead of 121 the digit sum check will not detect it. The checks show that the answer is probably correct.
The sums can also be checked of course by doing the calculation from right to left instead of from left to right.

The Vedic formula *The Product of the Sum is the Sum of the Products* applies for all the digit sum checks. For addition it would be *The Total of the Digit Sums is the Digit Sum of the Total*. The formula has many other applications (see Reference 3), for example in finding areas of composite shapes (*The Area of the Whole is the Sum of the Areas*).

CHECKING SUBTRACTION SUMS

 18   Find **69 – 23** and check the answer.

         6 9   6   The answer is 46.
         2 3 –   5 –   The digit sums of 69 and 23 are 6 and 5.
         4 6   1   And 6 – 5 = 1, which confirms the answer because the
                            digit sum of the answer, 46, is also 1.

19   Find **56 – 29**.

         5 6   2
         2 9 –   2 –
         2 7   0

In this example, the digit sum of both 56 and 29 is 2 and subtracting gives us 0.
The digit sum of the answer is 9, but we have already seen that 9 and 0 are equivalent
as digit sums, so the answer is confirmed.
Alternatively, we can add 9 to the upper 2 before subtracting the other 2 from it:
11–2 = 9. This is because adding 9 to a number does not affect its digit sum.

The digit sum for 5454 is 9 by adding the digits, but if we delete the 9s (because 5+4 = 9) we
get 0 for the digit sum. Indicating again that in digit sums 9 and 0 are equivalent.

20   Find **679 – 233**.

         6 7 9   4
         2 3 3 –   8 –
         4 4 6   5

Here we have 4 – 8 in the digit sum check so we simply add 9 to the upper figure
(the 4) and continue: 13 – 8 = 5, which is also the digit sum of 446.

✐ Practice H

Check your answers to Exercise D by using the digit sum check.

Answers: see answers to previous exercise.

> *"These and many more interesting features*
> *there are in the Vedic decimal system, which*
> *can turn mathematics for the children from its*
> *present excruciatingly painful character to the*
> *exhilaratingly pleasant and even funny and*
> *delightful character it really bears."*
> From "Vedic Mathematics", Page 239.

1.8 *ALL FROM 9 AND THE LAST FROM 10*

1.8a SUBTRACTION FROM A BASE

Applying the Vedic Sutra *All From 9 and the Last From 10* to a number gives another number.

 If we apply the formula to **876** we get **124** because 8 and 7 are taken from 9 and 6 is taken from 10.

 Similarly

3883	64	98	6	10905
↓	↓	↓	↓	↓
6117	**36**	**02**	**4**	**89095**

 Applying the Sutra to **3450** or any number that ends in 0 we need to be a bit careful. If we take the last figure as 0 here, when we take it from 10 we get 10 which is a 2-figure number. To avoid this we **take 5 as the last figure**: we apply the Sutra to 345 and simply put the 0 on afterwards. So we get **6550**.

Similarly with 28160 we get **71840**,
and with 4073100 we get **5926900**.

Look again at the numbers in Examples 21, 22, 23 above.
If you add a number and its *All from 9...* number you should find that the total is always 10, 100, 1000, 10000 . . .
The total is always one of these unities, called **base numbers**.

This means that when we applied the Sutra to 876 we found how much it was below 1000.
Or, in other words, the Sutra gave the answer to the sum **1000 – 876**. The answer is **124**.

> The formula *All from 9 and the Last from 10*
> subtracts numbers from the next highest unity.

 1000 – 864 = 136   Just apply *All From 9 and the Last from 10* to 864,

1000 – 707 = 293,

10000 – 6523 = 3477,

100 – 76 = 24,

1000 – 580 = 420.   Remember: apply the Sutra just to 58 here.

In every case the number is being subtracted from the next highest unity (power of 10).

This kind of subtraction is frequently in use as we often need to subtract from a base number: in finding the change from a ten pound note for example, or in working with probabilities we need calculations like $1 - 0.5621$.

 Suppose we had **1000 – 43**.
This has three zeros, but 43 is only a 2-figure number.
We can use the above method by writing $1000 - 043 = $**957**.
We put the extra zero in front of 43, and then apply the Sutra to 043.

 10000 – 58.
Here we need to add two zeros: $10000 - 0058 = $**9942**.

 Now consider **600 – 77**.
We have 600 instead of 100.
In fact the 77 will come off one of those six hundreds, so that 500 will be left.
So $600 - 77 = $**523**.
The 6 is reduced by one to 5, and the Sutra is applied to 77 to give 23.

This reduction by one illustrates the Sutra *By One Less than the One Before*.

✎ **Practice I**   Subtract the following:

a $1000 - 481$	**b** $1000 - 309$	**c** $1000 - 892$	**d** $1000 - 976$
e $100 - 78$	**f** $100 - 33$	**g** $10000 - 8877$	**h** £10 – £6.12
i $1000 - 710$	**j** $1000 - 86$	**k** $600 - 88$	**l** $5000 - 74$

a	519	b	691	c	108	d	24
e	22	f	67	g	1123	h	£3.88
i	290	j	914	k	512	l	4926

1.8b BAR NUMBERS

Just as 9 can be written as $1\bar{1}$, so 19 can be written as $2\bar{1}$, 28 as $3\bar{2}$ and so on.
This gives us greater flexibility in representing numbers and enables us to remove digits over 5 from a calculation if we wish.

We pronounce $4\bar{2}$ as "four, bar two" because the 2 has a bar on top.

This is rather like telling the time: we often say 'quarter to seven' or 'ten to seven' instead of 6:45 or 6:50 and so on.

28      $86\bar{1}$ = 859, because $6\bar{1}$ = 59   (the 8 is unchanged),

        $127\bar{3}$ = 1267, because $7\bar{3}$ = 67.

✎ **Practice J**   Convert the following numbers:

a $6\bar{1}$	b $8\bar{2}$	c $3\bar{3}$	d $9\bar{1}$	e $46\bar{2}$	f $85\bar{1}$	g $774\bar{1}$	h $999\bar{1}$
i $1\bar{2}$	j $11\bar{1}$	k $12\bar{3}$	l $3\bar{4}0$				

a	59	b	78	c	27	d	89	e	458	f	849	g	7739	h	9989
i	8	j	109	k	117	l	260								

We may also need to **put numbers into bar form**.

29      $79 = 8\bar{1}$ because 79 is 1 less than 80,

        $239 = 24\bar{1}$ because $39 = 4\bar{1}$,

        $508 = 51\bar{2}$. 08 becomes $1\bar{2}$.

✎ **Practice K**   Put the following into bar form:

a 49	b 58	c 77	d 88	e 69	f 36	g 17
h 359	i 848	j 7719	k 328	l 33339	m 609	n 708

a	$5\bar{1}$	b	$6\bar{2}$	c	$8\bar{3}$	d	$9\bar{2}$	e	$7\bar{1}$	f	$4\bar{4}$	g	$2\bar{3}$
h	$36\bar{1}$	i	$85\bar{2}$	j	$772\bar{1}$	k	$33\bar{2}$	l	$3334\bar{1}$	m	$61\bar{1}$	n	$71\bar{2}$

30   How would you remove the bar number in $5\bar{1}3$?
        The best way is to split the number into two parts: $5\bar{1}/3$
        Since $5\bar{1}$ = 49, the answer is **493**.

If a number has a bar number in it, split the number after the bar.

$7\bar31 = 7\bar3/1 = \textbf{671}$,

$52\bar42 = 52\bar4/2 = \textbf{5162}$,

$3\bar215 = 3\bar2/15 = \textbf{2815}$ since $3\bar2 = 28$,

$5\bar13\bar2 = 5\bar1/3\bar2 = \textbf{4928}$, as $5\bar1 = 49$ and $3\bar2 = 28$,

$3\bar13\bar23\bar3 = 3\bar1/3\bar2/3\bar3 = \textbf{292827}$.

✎ **Practice L**   Remove the bar numbers:

a $6\bar14$ b $4\bar23$ c $5\bar25$ d $3\bar17$ e $45\bar23$ f $23\bar45$ g $2\bar22$

h $333\bar23$ i $5\bar132$ j $23\bar55$ k $5\bar44321$ l $4\bar13\bar1$ m $6\bar273$ n $2\bar1\bar1$

o $41\bar31$ p $52\bar33$ q $7\bar152$ r $\bar13\bar15\bar1$ s $9\bar283$ t $1\bar3\bar1$ u $13\bar151$

a	594	b	383	c	485	d	297	e	4483	f	2265	g	182
h	33283	i	4932	j	1755	k	464321	l	3929	m	5867	n	191
o	4071	p	5173	q	6952	r	7149	s	8877	t	71	u	12951

So far we have only had a bar on a single figure.
But we could have two or more bar numbers together.

Remove the bar numbers in $5\bar{\bar3}\bar3$.

The 5 means 500, and $\bar{33}$ means 33 is to be subtracted.
So $5\bar{33}$ means 500 – 33, and we have just seen sums of this type.

$500 - 33 = \textbf{467}$ because the 33 comes off one of the hundreds, so the 5 is reduced to 4.
And applying *All from 9 and the Last from 10* to 33 gives 67.

Similarly $7\bar{14} = \textbf{686}$. The 7 reduces to 6 and the Sutra converts 14 to 86.

$26\bar{21} = \textbf{2579}$. 26 reduces to 25.

$7\bar{02} = \textbf{698}$. The Sutra converts 02 to 98.

$50\bar3 = \textbf{497}$. 50 is reduced to 49   (alternatively, write $50\bar3$ as $5\bar{03}$: see previous example).

$4\bar{20} = 4\bar20 = \textbf{380}$.

$4\overline{23}1$ Here we can split the number after the bar: $4\overline{23}/1$.

$4\overline{23}$ changes to 377, and we just put the 1 on the end: $4\overline{23}1 = \mathbf{3771}$.

Similarly $5\overline{12}4 = 5\overline{12}/4 = \mathbf{4884}$,

$3\overline{11}33 = 3\overline{11}/33 = \mathbf{28933}$,

$5\overline{123} = \mathbf{4877}$,

$3\overline{1}4\overline{31} = 3\overline{1}/4\overline{31} = \mathbf{29369}$.

✐ **Practice M**   Remove the bar numbers:

a $6\overline{12}$	b $7\overline{33}$	c $2\overline{31}$	d $5\overline{11}$	e $9\overline{04}$	f $70\overline{6}$
g $55\overline{23}$	h $72\overline{41}$	i $333\overline{22}$	j $62\overline{14}$	k $53\overline{122}$	l $332\overline{244}$
m $7\overline{333}$	n $6\overline{123}$	o $5\overline{104}$	p $44\overline{112}$	q $74\overline{031}$	r $71\overline{031}$
s $63\overline{322}$	t $3\overline{1}10\overline{2}$	u $42\overline{223}$	v $3\overline{1}1\overline{41}$	w $32\overline{122}$	x 31023

a	588	b	667	c	169	d	489	e	896	f	694
g	5477	h	7159	i	33278	j	5794	k	46922	l	327844
m	6667	n	5877	o	4896	p	43888	q	73969	r	68971
s	56678	t	29098	u	37783	v	28939	w	28078	x	30977

ADVANTAGES OF BAR NUMBERS

Bar numbers are an ingenious device which we will be using in later work. Their main advantages are:
1. It gives us flexibility: we use the vinculum* when it suits us.
2. Large numbers, like 6, 7, 8, 9 can be avoided.
3. Figures tend to cancel each other, or can be made to cancel.
4. 0 and 1 occur twice as frequently as they otherwise would.

* The bar on top of a number is called a vinculum.

*"The Sutras are easy to understand, easy to apply
and easy to remember; and the whole work can be
truthfully summarised in one word "mental".
From "Vedic Mathematics", Page xvi.*

1.8c GENERAL SUBTRACTION

Pupils sometimes subtract in each column in a subtraction sum **regardless of whether the top** is greater than the bottom or not.
However this method can be used to give the correct answer.

36

$$
\begin{array}{r}
4\,4\,4 \\
2\,8\,6 \ - \\
\hline
\end{array}
$$

Subtracting in each column we get $4-2 = 2$, $4-8 = -4 = \overline{4}$, $4-6 = -2 = \overline{2}$.
Since these negative answers can be written with a bar on **top we can** write:

$$
\begin{array}{r}
4\,4\,4 \\
2\,8\,6 \ - \\
\hline
2\,\overline{4}\,\overline{2}
\end{array}
$$

and $2\overline{4}\overline{2}$ is easily converted into **158**.

37 Similarly

$$
\begin{array}{r}
6\,7\,6\,7 \\
1\,9\,0\,8 \ - \\
\hline
5\,\overline{2}\,6\,\overline{1}
\end{array}
= \ \mathbf{4859}.
$$

All subtraction sums can be dealt with by this method. We simply **subtract each number from** the number above it, putting a bar on the answer if the top is less **than the bottom.**
We then remove the bar numbers as shown before.

✎ **Practice N**   Subtract using bar numbers:

a $\begin{array}{r} 5\,4\,3 \\ 1\,6\,8 \ - \\ \hline \end{array}$ b $\begin{array}{r} 5\,6\,7 \\ 2\,7\,9 \ - \\ \hline \end{array}$ c $\begin{array}{r} 8\,0\,4 \\ 3\,8\,8 \ - \\ \hline \end{array}$ d $\begin{array}{r} 7\,3\,7 \\ 5\,5\,8 \ - \\ \hline \end{array}$

e $\begin{array}{r} 6\,4\,1\,3 \\ 1\,8\,7\,8 \ - \\ \hline \end{array}$ f $\begin{array}{r} 8\,0\,2\,4 \\ 5\,3\,3\,9 \ - \\ \hline \end{array}$ g $\begin{array}{r} 6\,5\,4\,3 \\ 2\,8\,8\,1 \ - \\ \hline \end{array}$ h $\begin{array}{r} 7\,1\,0\,3 \\ 3\,9\,9\,1 \ - \\ \hline \end{array}$

i $\begin{array}{r} 4\,5\,6\,5\,4 \\ 2\,7\,9\,8\,6 \ - \\ \hline \end{array}$ j $\begin{array}{r} 6\,3\,3 \\ 8\,8 \ - \\ \hline \end{array}$ k $\begin{array}{r} 8\,2\,2 \\ 5\,7\,7 \ - \\ \hline \end{array}$ l $\begin{array}{r} 5\,5\,5 \\ 2\,7\,5 \ - \\ \hline \end{array}$

a	375	b	288	c	416	d	179
e	4535	f	2685	g	3662	h	3112
i	17668	j	545	k	245	l	280

General multiplication and squaring from left to right are covered in Lessons 5 and 7.

LESSON 2
SPECIAL METHODS

SUMMARY

There are many special methods in the Vedic system which enable us to find particularly easy solutions to some problems.

2.1 **Multiplication near a Base** – multiplying numbers near 10, 100 etc.
2.2 **Mental Calculations** – advantages etc.
2.3 **Special Numbers** – used for multiplying and in later lessons.
2.4 **Division by Nine Etc.** – also algebraic quotients.

2.1 MULTIPLICATION NEAR A BASE

Another useful application of the Sutra **Nikhilam** Navatascharaman Dasatah (*All from 9 and the Last from 10*) is in multiplying numbers which are close to a base number, like 10, 100, 1000 etc. We call this **Nikhilam multiplication** or Base multiplication.

2.1a NUMBERS JUST BELOW THE BASE

 Usually a sum like **88 × 98** is considered especially difficult because of the large figures, 8 and 9.

But since the numbers 88 and 98 are close to the base of 100 you may think that there ought to be a simple way to find such a product and in the Vedic system there is a wonderfully easy way.

88 – 12	88 is 12 below 100, so we put –12 next to it,
98 – 2	98 is 2 below 100 so we put –2 next to it.
86 / 24	We call the 12 and 2 **deficiencies** as the numbers 88 and 98 are deficient from the unity of 100 by 12 and 2.

The answer 8624 is in two parts: 86 and 24.
The 86 is found by taking one of the deficiencies from the other number: that is
88–2 = **86**   or   98–12 = **86**   (whichever you like),
and the 24 is simply the product of the deficiencies: 12 × 2 = **24**.
So **88 × 98 = 8624**. It could hardly be easier.

Algebraic Proof: $(x - a)(x - b) = x(x - a - b) + ab$
where x is the base number, 100 in this case, and a and b are the deficiencies, 12 and 2.

For **93 × 96** we get deficiencies of 7 and 4, so

$$\begin{array}{r} 93 - 07 \\ 96 - \ 4 \\ \hline 89 \ / \ 28 \end{array}$$

The differences from 100 are 7 and 4,
93 – 4 = **89** or 96 – 7 = 89,
and 7 × 4 = **28**.

> In fact once we have got the deficiencies we apply the *Vertically and Crosswise* Sutra:
> **we cross-subtract** to get the left-hand part of the answer, and
> **we multiply vertically** in the right-hand column to get the right-hand part of the answer.

For **98 × 97:**

$$\begin{array}{r} 98 - 02 \\ 97 - 03 \\ \hline 95 \ / \ 06 \end{array}$$

Note the zero inserted here: the numbers being multiplied are near to 100, so two digits are required on the right, as in the other examples.

For **89 × 89:**

$$\begin{array}{r} 89 \ - 11 \\ 89 \ - 11 \\ \hline 78 \ /_1 21 \end{array} = \textbf{7921}$$

Here the numbers are each 11 below 100, and 11 × 11 = 121, a 3–figure number.
The hundreds digit of this is therefore carried over to the left.

✏ **Practice A**   Multiply the following:

a 94 × 94   b 97 × 89   c 87 × 99   d 87 × 98   e 87 × 95

f 95 × 95   g 79 × 96   h 98 × 96   i 92 × 99   j 88 × 88

k 97 × 56   l 97 × 63   m find a way of getting 92 × 196?

a	88/36	b	86/33	c	86/13	d	85/26	e	82/65
f	90/25	g	75/84	h	94/08	i	91/08	j	77/44
k	54/32	l	61/11	m	180/32 (find 92×98 and double the answer)		

The most efficient way to do these sums is to take one number and subtract the other number's deficiency from it. Then multiply the deficiencies together, mentally adjusting the first part of the answer if there is a carry figure.
This is so easy it is really just mental arithmetic.

5   568 × 998 = **566864**.

In this sum the numbers are close to 1000, and the deficiencies are 432 and 2.
The deficiency for 568 is found by applying the Nikhilam Sutra: *All from 9 and the Last from 10.*

           568 – 432
           998 –   2   The method here is just the same, but we allow 3 figures
           566 / 864   on the right as the base is now 1000.

The differences of the numbers from 1000 are 432 and 2.
Then cross-subtracting: 568 – 2 = **566**,
And vertically: 432 × 2 = **864**.

The number of spaces needed on the right is the number of 0s in the base number.

---

6   68778 × 99997 = **6877593666**.

Even large numbers like this are easily   68778 – 31222
and mentally multiplied by the same method.   99997 –   3
                                                68775 / 93666

7   7 × 8 = **56**.

In the Vedic system tables above 5×5 are not really essential: 7 – 3
                                                                      8 – 2
Exactly the same method gives us 7 × 8 = 56.   **5 / 6**

✏ **Practice B**   Multiply the following mentally:

a 667 × 998   b 768 × 997   c 989 × 998   d 885 × 997

e 883 × 998   f 8 × 6   g 891 × 989   h 8888 × 9996

i 6999 × 9997   j 90909 × 99994   k 78989 × 99997   l 9876 × 9989

---

a	665/666	b	765/696	c	987/022	d 882/345
e	881/234	f	4/8	g	881/199	h 8884/4448
i	6996/9003	j	90903/54546	k	78986/63033	l 9865/1364

2.1b ABOVE THE BASE

Suppose now that the numbers are not both below a base number as in all the previous examples, but above the base.

 8   **103 × 104 = 10712**.

$$
\begin{array}{r}
103 + 03 \\
104 + \ 4 \\
\hline
107 \ / \ 12
\end{array}
$$

This is even easier than the previous examples, but the method is just the same. The differences from the base are +3 and +4 since the numbers are now **above the base**.

103 + 4 = 107   or   104 + 3 = 107, and 4 × 3 = 12.

So now we **cross-add,** and multiply vertically.

✐ **Practice C**   Multiply mentally:

a   133 × 103   **b**   107 × 108   **c**   171 × 101   **d**   102 × 104

e   123 × 102   **f**   14 × 12   **g**   18 × 13   **h**   1222 × 1003

i   1051 × 1007   **j**   15111 × 10003   **k**   125 × 105   **l**   10607 × 10008

a	136/99	b	115/56	c	172/71	d	106/08
e	125/46	f	16/8	g	23/4	h	1225/666
i	1058/357	j	15115/5333	k	131/25	l	10615/4856

Algebraic Proof: $(x + a)(x + b) = x(x + a + b) + ab$, where $x = 10^n$.

2.1c   ABOVE AND BELOW

 9   Find **124 × 98**.

Here one number is over and the other is under 100:   124 + 24
The differences from 100 are +24 and –2.   98 – 2
Crosswise gives 122 (124–2 or 98+24).   122 / $\overline{48}$ = **12152**

So 122 is the left-hand part of the answer.

Then multiplying the differences we get –48, written $\overline{48}$ (since a plus times a minus gives a minus). This gives the answer as 122 $\overline{48}$.

To remove the negative portion of the answer we just take 48 from one of the hundreds in the hundreds column. This simply means reducing the hundreds column by 1 and applying *All From 9 and the Last From 10* to 48.

Thus 122 becomes 121 and $\overline{48}$ becomes 52.

So 124 × 98 = 122$\overline{48}$ = **12152**.

 1003 × 987 = 990/$\overline{039}$ = 989/961.

Similarly, we first get 1003 − 13 = 990 or 987 + 3 = 990,

and +3 × −13 = $\overline{039}$ (three figures required here as the base is 1000).

Then 990 is reduced by 1 to 989, and applying the formula to 039 gives 961.

So these sums are just like the others except that we need to clear the minus part at the end.

 121 × 91 = 112/$_i\overline{89}$ = 110/11.

Here we have a minus one to carry over to the left so that the 112 is reduced by 2 altogether.

✎ **Practice D**

a 104 × 91	**b** 94 × 109	**c** 103 × 98	**d** 92 × 112
e 91 × 111	**f** 106 × 89	**g** 91 × 103	**h** 91 × 107
i 91 × 105	**j** 991 × 1005	**k** 987 × 1006	**l** 992 × 1111

a	9464	**b**	10246	**c**	10094	**d**	10304
e	10101	**f**	9434	**g**	9373	**h**	9737
i	9555	**j**	995955	**k**	992922	**l**	1102112

Algebraic Proof: $(x + a)(x − b) = x(x + a − b) − ab$, where $x = 10^n$.

2.1d *PROPORTIONATELY*

The *Proportionately* formula considerably extends the range of this multiplication method.

 213 × 203 = 43239.

$$213 + 13$$
$$\underline{203 + \ 3}$$
$$2 × \ \underline{216} \ / \ 39 \ = \mathbf{43239}$$

We observe here that the numbers are not near any of the bases used before: 10, 100, 1000 etc.
But they are close to 200, with differences of 13 and 3 as shown above.

The usual procedure gives us 216/39 (213+3=216, 13×3=39).

Now since our base is 200 which is 100×2 we multiply **only the left-hand part** of the answer by 2 to get 43239.

Algebraic Proof: $(nx + a)(nx + b) = nx(x + a + b) + ab, x=10^n$.

13   **29 × 28 = 812**.

The base is 30 (3×10), and the deficiencies are –1 and –2.
Cross-subtracting gives 27,
then multiplying vertically on the right we get **2**,
and finally $3 \times 27 = 81$.

$$\begin{array}{r} 29 - 1 \\ \underline{28 - 2} \\ 3 \times \; \underline{27 \;/\; 2} = 812 \end{array}$$

So these are just like the previous sums but with an extra multiplication (**of the left-hand side only**) at the end.

14   **33 × 34**.

In this example there is a carry figure:

$$\begin{array}{r} 33 + 3 \\ \underline{34 + 4} \\ 3 \times 37 \;/\; _12 = 111/_1 2 = \mathbf{1122} \end{array}$$

Note that since the right-hand side does not get multiplied by 3 we **multiply** the left-hand side by 3 **before adding the carried figure**.

15   **88 × 49** = ½(88×98) = ½(8624) = **4312**.

This example shows a different application of *Proportionately*.
In 88 × 49 the numbers are not both close to 100, but since twice 49 is 98 we can find 88 × 98 and halve the answer at the end.

✎ **Practice E**   Multiply mentally:

a 41 × 42   **b** 204 × 207   **c** 321 × 303   **d** 203 × 208

e 902 × 909   **f** 48 × 47   **g** 188 × 196   **h** 199 × 198

i 189 × 194   **j** 207 × 211   **k** 312 × 307   **l** 5003 × 5108

m 23 × 24   **n** 44 × 98   **o** 48 × 98   **p** 192 × 98

a	172/2	b	422/28	c	972/63	d	422/24
e	8199/18	f	225/6	g	368/48	h	394/02
i	366/66	j	436/77	k	957/84	l	25555/324
m	55/2	n	43/12	o	47/04	p	188/16

2.1e WITH DIFFERENT BASES

 9998 × 94 = 9398/12.

Here the numbers are close to different bases: 10,000 and 100, and the deficiencies are −2 and −6.
We write, or imagine, the sum set out as shown:

$$\begin{array}{r} 9998 - 02 \\ 94\ \ -06 \\ \hline 9398\ /\ 12 \end{array}$$

It is important to line the numbers up as shown because the 6 is not subtracted from the 8, but from the 9 above the 4 in 94. That is, the second column from the left here.

Then multiply the deficiencies together: 2×6 = **12**.

Note that the number of figures in the right-hand part of the answer corresponds to the base of the lower number (94 is near 100, therefore there are 2 figures on the right).

 10007 × 1003 = 10037021.

Lining the numbers up:

$$\begin{array}{r} 10007 + 007 \\ 1003\ \ + 003 \\ \hline 10037\ /\ 021 \end{array}$$

we see that we need three figures on the right and that the surplus, 3, is added in the 4th column, giving 10037.

✎ **Practice F**   Find:

a 97 × 993	**b** 92 × 989	**c** 9988 × 98	**d** 9996 × 988
e 103 × 1015	**f** 106 × 1012	**g** 10034 × 102	**h** 1122 × 104

a	963/21	b	909/88	c	9788/24	d	9876/048
e	1045/45	f	1072/72	g	10234/68	h	1166/88

Algebraic Proof: $(x + a)(y + b) = (x + a)y + bx + ab$, where $x=10^m$, $y=10^n$.

Another application of this type of multiplication is in multiplying three or more numbers simultaneously which are close to a base (see Reference 3).

2.2 MENTAL CALCULATIONS

The Vedic techniques are so easy that the system of Vedic Mathematics is really a system of mental mathematics. This has a number of further advantages as pupils seem to make faster progress and enjoy mathematics more when they are permitted to do the calculation in their head. After all, the objects of mathematics are mental ones, and writing down requires a combination of mental and physical actions, so that the child's attention is alternating between the mental and physical realms. This alternation is an important ability to develop but working only with mental objects also has many advantages.

Mental mathematics leads to greater creativity and the pupils understand the objects of mathematics and their relationships better. They begin to experiment (especially if they are encouraged to do so) and become more flexible. Memory and confidence are also improved through mental mathematics.

SPECIAL METHODS

The special methods play a large part in encouraging mental mathematics. Everyone likes a short cut, whether it is a quick way to get from one place to another or an easy way of doing a particular calculation. Life is full of special methods: to tackle all similar situations in the same way is not the way most people like to function. Every mathematical calculation invites its own unique method of solution and we should encourage children to look at the special properties of each problem in order to understand it best and decide on the best way forward. This is surely the intelligent way to do mathematics.

2.3 SPECIAL NUMBERS

We have already seen the special methods for multiplying numbers near bases. There are many other special multiplication methods in the Vedic system some of which we show here.

2.3a REPEATING NUMBERS

Some multiplications are particularly easy. This type comes under the Sutra *By Mere observation*.

18   **23 × 101 = 2323.**

To multiply 23 by 101 we need 23 hundreds and 23 ones, which gives 2323.

The effect of multiplying any 2-figure by 101 is simply to make it repeat itself.

19   Similarly **69 × 101 = 6969.**

20   And **473 × 1001 = 473473.**

Here we have a 3-figure number multiplied by 1001 which makes the 3-figure number repeat itself.

21   **47 × 1001 = 47047.**

Here, because we want to multiply by 1001, we can think of 47 as 047.
So we get 047047, or just 47047.

22   **123 × 101 = 12423.**

Here we have 12300 + 123 so the 1 has to be carried over.

23   **28 × 10101 = 282828.**

⁂ **Practice G**   Find:

a 46 × 101   **b** 246 × 1001   **c** 321 × 1001   **d** 439 × 1001

e 3456 × 10001   **f** 53 × 10101   **g** 74 × 1001   **h** 73 × 101

i 29 × 1010101   **j** 277 × 101   **k** 521 × 101   **l** 616 × 101

a	4646	b	246246	c	321321	d	439439
e	34563456	f	535353	g	74074	h	7373
i	29292929	j	27977	k	52621	l	62216

"But, according to the Vedic system,
the multiplication tables are not
really required above 5×5."
From "Vedic Mathematics", Page 13.

2.3b *PROPORTIONATELY*

24 $43 \times 201 = 8643$.

Here we bring in the *Proportionately* formula: because we want to multiply by 201 rather than 101 we must put twice 43 (which is 86) then 43.

25 $31 \times 10203 = 316293$. We have 31×1, 31×2, 31×3.

✏ **Practice H**   Find:

a 54×201 **b** 32×102 **c** 333×1003 **d** 41×10201 **e** 33×30201

f 17×20102 **g** 13×105 **h** 234×2001 **i** 234×1003 **j** 43×203

a	10854	**b**	3264	**c**	333999	**d** 418241	**e**	996633
f	341734	**g**	1365	**h**	468234	**i** 234702	**j**	8729

2.3c DISGUISES

Now it is possible for a sum to be of the above type without it being obvious: it may be disguised.

If we know the factors of some of these special numbers (like 1001, 203 etc.) we can make some sums very easy.

Suppose for example you know that $3 \times 67 = 201$.

26 $93 \times 67 = 6231$.

$$\text{Since } 3 \times 67 = 201,$$
$$\text{therefore } 93 \times 67 = 31 \times 3 \times 67$$
$$= 31 \times 201$$
$$= 6231$$

In other words, we recognise that one of the special numbers (201 in this case) is contained in the sum (as 3×67 here).

Now suppose we know that $3 \times 37 = 111$.

24 × 37 = 888.

We know that $3 \times 37 = 111$, which is a number very easy to multiply.
So $24 \times 37 = 8 \times 3 \times 37$
$$= 8 \times 111$$
$$= 888.$$

Another useful result is $19 \times 21 = 399 = 40\bar{1}$.

 38 × 63 = 2394.

$38 \times 63 = 2 \times 19 \times 3 \times 21$
$$= 6 \times 19 \times 21$$
$$= 6 \times 40\bar{1}$$
$$= 240\bar{6}$$
$$= 2394.$$

If we know the factors of these special numbers we can make good use of them when they come up in a sum, and they arise quite frequently.

Below is a list of a few of these numbers with their factors:

$67 \times 3 = 201$	$17 \times 6 = 102$	$11 \times 9 = 10\bar{1}$
$43 \times 7 = 301$	$13 \times 8 = 104$	$19 \times 21 = 40\bar{1}$
$7 \times 11 \times 13 = 1001$	$29 \times 7 = 203$	$23 \times 13 = 30\bar{1}$
$3 \times 37 = 111$	$31 \times 13 = 403$	$27 \times 37 = 100\bar{1}$

 62 × 39 = 2418.

We see 31×13 contained in this sum: $62 \times 39 = 2 \times 31 \times 3 \times 13$
$$= 2 \times 3 \times 31 \times 13$$
$$= 6 \times 403$$
$$= 2418.$$

✎ **Practice I**   Use the special numbers to find:

a 29×28 **b** 35×43 **c** 67×93 **d** 86×63

e 77×43 **f** 26×77 **g** 34×72 **h** 57×21

i 58×63 **j** 26×23 **k** 134×36 **l** 56×29

m 93×65 **n** 54×74 **o** 39×64 **p** 51×42

a	812	b	1505	c	6231	d	5418
e	3311	f	2002	g	2448	h	1197
i	3654	j	598	k	4824	l	1624
m	6045	n	3996	o	2496	p	2142

These special numbers can also be useful in finding recurring decimals (see end of Section 3.8) and divisibility (see Lesson 9).

2.4 DIVISION BY NINE ETC.

As we have seen before, the number 9 is special. And there is a very easy way to divide by 9.

2.4a ADDING DIGITS

30 Find **23 ÷ 9**.

The first figure of 23 is the answer: 2.
And we add the figures of 23 to get the remainder: 2 + 3 = 5.
So **23 ÷ 9 = 2 remainder 5**.

It is easy to see why this works because every 10 contains a 9 with 1 left over.
So two tens contains two 9s with 2 left over.
And if 20 contains two 9s remainder 2, then 23 (which is 3 more) contains two 9s remainder 5.

Practice J Divide by 9:

a	51	b	34	c	17	d	44	e	60	f	71	g	46

a	5 r6	b	3 r7	c	1 r8	d	4 r8	e	6 r6	f	7 r8	g	4 r10 = 5 r1

This can be extended to the division of longer numbers.

Find **2311 ÷ 9**.

If the sum was written down it would look like this:

9)2 3 1 1
  2 5 6 r 7

9) 2 3 1 1
    ↓
   2

The initial **2** is brought straight down into the answer:

9) 2 3 1 1
   ⟋
  2 5

This 2 is then added to the 3 in 2311, and **5** is put down:

9) 2 3 1 1
     ⟋
  2 5 6

This 5 is then added to the 1 in 2311, and **6** is put down again:

9) 2 3 1 1
       ⟋
  2 5 6 rem 7

This 6 is then added to 1 to give the remainder, **7**:

> The first figure of the dividend is the first figure of the answer,
> and each figure in the answer is added to the next figure in the dividend
> to give the next figure of the answer.
> The last number we write down is the remainder.

 Find **1234 ÷ 9**.

9) 1 2 3 4
  1 3 6 r 10

In this example we get a remainder of 10, and since this contains another 9 we add 1 to 136 and get **137 remainder 1**.

✎ **Practice K**   Divide the following numbers by 9:

a 212	b 3102	c 11202	d 31	e 53
f 203010	g 70	h 114	i 20002	j 311101
k 46	l 234	m 56	n 444	o 713

a 23 rem 5	b 344 rem 6	c 1244 rem 6	d 3 rem 4	e 5 rem 8
f 22556 rem 6	g 7 rem 7	h 12 rem 6	i 2222 rem 4	j 34566 rem 7
k 5 rem 1	l 26	m 6 rem 2	n 49 rem 3	o 79 rem 2

33   **3172 ÷ 9.**

$$9)\underline{\;3\quad 1\quad 7\quad 2\;}$$
$$3\quad 4\quad 11\ r\ 13$$

Here we find we get an 11 and a 13: the first 1 in the 11 must be carried over to the 4, giving 351, and there is also another 1 in the remainder so we get **352 remainder 4.**

 34   Find **21.2 ÷ 9.**

$$9)\underline{\;2\quad 1\,.2\quad 0\quad 0\quad 0\;}$$
$$2\,.3\quad 5\quad 5\quad 5\ldots = 2.3\dot{5}$$

Here we have a decimal point and the answer is given as a decimal, without a remainder. Adding 5 to 0 repeatedly, gives the recurring 5.

✎ **Practice L**   Divide the following by 9:

a 6153	**b** 3272	**c** 555	**d** 8252
e 661	**f** 4741	**g** 5747	**h** 2938
i 12345	**j** 75057	**k** 443322	

a	683 rem 6	b	363 rem 5	c	61 rem 6	d	916 rem 8
e	73 rem 4	f	526 rem 7	g	638 rem 5	h	326 rem 4
i	1371 rem 6	j	8339 rem 6	k	49258		

2.4b A SHORT CUT

However, to avoid the build-up of 2-figure numbers like 11 and 13, in Example 33 above, we may notice, before we put the 4 down, that the next step will give a 2-figure number and so we put 5 down instead:

$$9)\underline{\;3\quad 1\quad 7\quad 2\;}$$
$$3\quad 5\quad 2\ r\ 4$$

Then add 5 to 7 to get 12, but as the 1 has already been carried over we only put the 2 down. Finally, 2+2 = 4.

 35   Find **777 ÷ 9.**

$$9)\underline{\;7\quad 7\quad 7\;}$$
$$8\quad 6\ r\ 3$$

If we put 7 for the first figure we get 14 at the next step, so we put 8 instead.
Now 8+7 = 15 and the 1 has already been carried over, but if we put the 5 down we see a 2-figure number coming in the next step, so we put 6 down instead.
Then 6+7 = 13 and the 1 has been carried over, so just put down the 3.

Practice M   Divide the following by 9:

a 6153	b 3272	c 555	d 8252
e 661	f 4741	g 5747	h 2938
i 12345	j 75057	k 443322	l 1918161

a	683 rem 6	b	363 rem 5	c	61 rem 6	d	916 rem 8
e	73 rem 4	f	526 rem 7	g	638 rem 5	h	326 rem 4
i	1371 rem 6	j	8339 rem 6	k	49258	l	213129

2.4c DIVIDING BY 8

36   Dividing by 8: $111 \div 8$.

$$8) \underline{1\ 1|1}$$
$$1\ 3|7$$

When dividing by 8 we can write 2 below it (not shown here), as this is its deficiency from 10. Then instead of putting each number in the answer into the next column, as before, we first double it.

That is: bring down **1**.
Twice that 1 plus 1 = **3**.
Twice that 3 plus 1 = **7**.

37    $3411 \div 8$.

$$8) \underline{3\ 4\ 1|1}$$
$$4\ 2\ 6|3$$

As in Example 35 we anticipate that the second column will be in excess of 9, and put down 4 initially instead of 3.
And similarly in the third column we put an extra unit.

2.4d ALGEBRAIC DIVISION

38    $(2x^2 + 5x + 7) \div (x - 1)$.

$$x - 1\ )\underline{2x^2 + 5x + 8}$$
$$2x + 7\ \text{rem } 15$$

$x-1$ is just like number 9 as it is 1 below x, just as 9 is 1 below 10.
This means that the same method can be used in this division as for division by 9.

We bring the first coefficient, 2, down into the answer. (Or dividing *the first by the first*, we get $2x^2 \div x = 2x$). Then we add this 2 to the 5 in the next column and put down 7. Finally adding this 7 to the 8 we get 15 as the remainder.

39 $(2x^2 + 5x + 8) \div (x - 2)$.

Here we are dividing by $x - 2$, which is just like dividing by 8.
That is, we double the answer digit before adding it in the next column:

$$x - 2 \;) \underline{2x^2 + 5x + 8}$$
$$2x \; + \; 9 \text{ rem } 26$$

This illustrates something we will see over and over again in the Vedic system: that an arithmetic process slides smoothly and perfectly into an algebraic process. This is rarely seen in the conventional system. We can extend this in other directions. For example:

40 $(2x^2 + 5x + 8) \div (x + 1)$.

Here we have $(x + 1)$ instead of $(x - 1)$. This means we subtract the last answer coefficient in the next column instead of adding it.

$$x + 1 \;) \underline{2x^2 + 5x + 8}$$
$$2x \; + \; 3 \text{ rem } 5$$

Bring down the 2x, then take this 2 from 5 in the next column and put down 3. Then 3 from 8 is 5 for the remainder.

✏ **Practice N**

a $101 \div 8$ b $1101 \div 8$ c $2121 \div 8$ d $11111 \div 8$ e $132 \div 8$

f $2x^2 + 3x + 4 \div x - 1$ g $2x^3 + 3x^2 - 4x + 4 \div x - 1$ h $2x^2 + 3x + 4 \div x - 2$

i $2x^2 + 3x + 4 \div x + 1$ j $x^3 - 3x + 1 \div x + 3$

---

a 12 rem 5	b 137 rem 5	c 265 rem 1	d 1388 rem 7 e 16 rem 4
f 2x + 5 rem 9	g $2x^2 + 5x + 1$ rem 5	h 2x + 7 rem 18	
i 2x + 1 rem 3	j $x^2 - 3x + 6$ rem -17		

This method can be further extended to deal with divisors like $2x + 3$.
For general algebraic division see Section 10.7.

2.4e DIVIDING BY 11, 12 etc.

From Example 40 we get the clue as to how to deal with division by 11, 12, 13 etc: we subtract the last answer digit at each step, instead of adding it.

 3411 ÷ 11 = 310 rem 1 or 310.0̇9̇.

$$11 \underline{) \ 3 \ \ 4 \ \ 1 \ \ 1}$$
$$ 3 \ \ 1 \ \ 0 \ r \ 1$$

We bring down the initial **3**.
Then 4 – 3 = **1**.
1 – 1 = **0**.
1 – 0 = **1**.

To decimalise the remainder we just continue the subtractions:

$$11 \underline{) \ 3 \ \ 4 \ \ 1 \ \ 1 \ . \ 0 \ \ 0 \ \ 0}$$
$$ 3 \ \ 1 \ \ 0 \ . \ 1 \ \ \bar{1} \ \ 1 \ \ \bar{1} \ldots = \textbf{310.0909}.....$$

 523 ÷ 11 = 47 rem 6.

$$11 \underline{) \ 5 \ \ 2 \ \ 3}$$
$$ 5 \ \ \bar{3} \ r \ 6 \ = \textbf{47 rem 6}$$

We get $2 - 5 = \bar{3}$ here. Then $3 - \bar{3} = 6$.

 3411 ÷ 12 = 284 rem 3.

$$12 \underline{) \ 3 \ \ 4 \ \ 1 \ \ 1}$$
$$ 3 \ \ \bar{2} \ \ 5 \ r \ \bar{9} \ = 285 \ \text{rem} \ \bar{9} = \textbf{284 rem 3}$$

To divide by 12 we subtract double the last answer digit.
So after bringing down the 3 we have $4 - 2 \times 3 = \bar{2}$.
Then $1 - 2 \times \bar{2} = \textbf{5}$.
And $1 - 2 \times 5 = \bar{9}$.

Since the 285 is 285 twelves we take one of these twelves (leaving 284 of them) to add to the $\bar{9}$ to give a remainder of 3.

✐ **Practice O**

a 345 ÷ 11   b 543 ÷ 11   c 20304 ÷ 11   d 81726 ÷ 11

e 1489 ÷ 12   f 333 ÷ 12   g 5151 ÷ 12   h 9184 ÷ 12

a 31 r4	b 49 r4	c 1845 r9	d $8\overline{6}3\overline{1}$ r7 = 7429 r7
e 124 r1	f 27 r9	g 429 r3	h $8\overline{4}6$ r$\overline{8}$ = 765 r4

This method is capable of extension to larger divisors like 89, 787, 123 etc. See Manual 2. Lesson 10 or References 1, 3.

 44   **83 ÷ 19 = 4 rem 7.**

$$19\overline{)\,8\quad 3}$$
$$\text{4 rem 7}$$

The number of 19s in 83 will be the number of 20s in 80, so we can just divide 8 by 2 and put down **4**. Since every 20 in 80 will have one 19 and one remainder, this answer, 4, is also the remainder after dividing 80 by 19. Then with the 3 the full remainder is 7.

In other words we divide similarly to division by 9, except that we divide by 2 at each step. This explains the method introduced in the next lesson.

45   **151.2 ÷ 19 = 7.957...**

$$19\overline{)\,1\quad 5\quad 1\,.\,2}$$
$$_{\,|}7\,.\,9_{\,|}5_{\,|}7...$$

Similarly here, we divide 15 by 2, put down 7 and prefix the remainder, 1, as 17 is the remainder on dividing 150 by 19. Then 17 + 1 (in the units column) gives 18 to divide by 2 at the next step.

> *"On seeing this kind of work actually being performed by the little children, the doctors, professors and other "big-guns" of mathematics are wonder struck and exclaim: "Is this mathematics or magic?" And we invariably answer and say: "It is both. It is magic until you understand it; and it is mathematics thereafter"; and then we proceed to substantiate and prove the correctness of this reply of ours!"*
> From "Vedic Mathematics", Page xvii.

LESSON 3
RECURRING DECIMALS

SUMMARY

Here we see the super-fast Vedic method of converting fractions into their decimal form.

A fraction can be converted to a decimal by dividing the numerator by the denominator.
This can be quite time consuming however if the denominator is not small, but the Vedic system gives us some really easy and beautiful methods which are also extremely fast.

This is in fact just an extension of the method given in the last lesson for dividing by 9.

3.1 DENOMINATOR ENDING IN 9

 Convert the fraction $\frac{1}{19}$ to its decimal form.

Dividing by 19 is normally not too easy but here we can use the formula *By One More than the One Before.*
This means one more than the number before the 9 in this fraction.
Since there is a 1 before the 9, one more than this is **2**.
So for this fraction the Sutra says *By 2*.

We call 2 the **Ekadhika** (the number *one more*) and we keep dividing by this 2 (rather than dividing by 19). 'Ekadhika' is pronounced with two long syllables followed by two short syllables, the long syllables being twice the length of the short ones.

We start with 0 and a decimal point. $\qquad \frac{1}{19} = 0.$
Then dividing **2** into 1 (the numerator) goes 0 remainder 1.
Note carefully that we put the remainder **before** the answer, 0. $\quad \frac{1}{19} = 0._10$

We now have 10 in front of us ($_1$0) and we divide this by **2**: $\frac{1}{19} = 0._105$

We then divide this 5 by **2**.

This gives 2 remainder 1 so we now have: $\frac{1}{19} = 0._105_12$

Again we put the remainder, 1, before the 2.

> At every step we divide the last answer figure by the Ekadhika, **2**,
> and put the answer down as the next answer figure.
> Any remainder is put before that answer figure.

Then we divide 12 by **2** and put down 6.

$$\frac{1}{19} = 0._10 5_1263_11_15_17_189_147_13_168421$$

We find that after 18 figures the answer figures are starting to repeat themselves (we get 10 to divide and then 5, which is how we started the sum).

To show that the 18 figures repeat endlessly we put a dot over the first and last figures.

The answer is $\frac{1}{19} = 0.\dot{0}5263157894736842\dot{1}$, the remainder figures are not part of the answer.

Dividing by 2 like this is very much easier than dividing by 19 of course!

 2   Convert $\frac{11}{19}$ to a recurring decimal.

The Ekadhika is still **2** because we still have 19 in the denominator.
But we begin by dividing **2** into 11 (the numerator) this gives 5 remainder 1:
$$\frac{11}{19} = 0._15$$

Next we divide **2** into 15: $\frac{11}{19} = 0._15_17$

Continuing the division until it starts to repeat we get:

$$\frac{11}{19} = 0.\dot{5}7894736842105263\dot{1}$$

There are two important things which you may have noticed as you worked out $\frac{11}{19}$.

It also has 18 figures recurring like $\frac{1}{19}$.

In fact the figures are the same as $\frac{1}{19}$ but they just start in a different place.

3   Note that the decimal for $\frac{11}{19}$ can be obtained from the decimal for $\frac{1}{19}$ because

$\frac{11}{19} = \frac{10}{19} + \frac{1}{19}$ and $\frac{10}{19}$, being ten times $\frac{1}{19}$ will be $\frac{10}{19} = 0.\dot{5}26315789473684210\dot{}$. So we can just add these two decimals, which can be done by adding pairs of digits in the decimal for $\frac{1}{19}$: 0+5=**5**, 5+2=**7**, 2+6=**8** . . .

PROOF

In dividing 19 into an even figure followed by a zero:

$$\frac{\quad 1r1 \quad}{19)20} \qquad \frac{\quad 2r2 \quad}{19)40} \qquad \frac{\quad 3r3 \quad}{19)60} \qquad \text{etc.}$$

we find the quotient is equal to the remainder, and half the even number.

This is because $19 = 2\bar{1}$. And since in decimal division the remainder with zero appended becomes the next dividend, we can divide into the quotient instead. If the dividend is an odd number we carry one to the right, as 10.

\#   Consequently the digit you write down, with its preceding subscript if there is one, is also the remainder at that point.

So when you have completed the first three digits for $\frac{1}{19}$ and put down $0._10\,5_12$, the 12 is the remainder at that stage. And a consequence of this is that the digits that follow on after $0._10\,5_12$ are the digits for $\frac{12}{19}$.

An alternative explanation is supplied by the well-known result: $\dfrac{1}{x-1} = \dfrac{1}{x} + \dfrac{1}{x^2} + \dfrac{1}{x^3} + \ldots$

which, for x = 20 becomes: $\dfrac{1}{19} = \dfrac{1}{20} + \dfrac{1}{20^2} + \dfrac{1}{20^3} + \ldots$ Here each term is obtained from the previous term by dividing it by 2 and putting it one place to the right (dividing by 10).

4   Convert $\frac{17}{29}$ to decimal form.

Here the number before the 9 is 2 so *One More than the One Before* means one more than 2, which is **3**. So **the Ekadhika is now 3**.

This means we start by dividing 17 (the numerator) by **3**, and keep on dividing by **3**: 3 into 17 goes 5 remainder 2.

$$\frac{17}{29} = 0._25$$

Then **3** into 25 goes 8 remainder 1; and **3** into 18 goes 6 and so on.

The full recurring decimal for $\frac{17}{29}$ is $0.\dot{5}862068965517241379310344827\dot{}$.

There are 28 figures here.

\# You may notice that the number of figures in the recurring decimals seen so far is one less than the denominator: (N=D–1). This is often the case, but not always: $\frac{9}{39}$ has six recurring figures, not 38.

But the number of figures cannot exceed D–1. In dividing 1 by 19, for example, there can be only 18 possible different remainders and so there cannot be more than 18 figures in the recurring decimal.

3.2 A SHORT CUT

You have now worked out three recurring decimals: $\frac{1}{19}$, $\frac{11}{19}$, $\frac{17}{29}$ using the Ekadhika method. The first two have 18 recurring figures and the third has 28.

If you write out the three recurring decimals but with $\frac{1}{19}$ and $\frac{11}{19}$ in two rows of 9 figures and $\frac{17}{29}$ with two rows of 14 figures you may notice something:

$$\frac{1}{19} = 0.\,0\,5\,2\,6\,3\,1\,5\,7\,8$$
$$9\,4\,7\,3\,6\,8\,4\,2\,1$$

$$\frac{11}{19} = 0.\,5\,7\,8\,9\,4\,7\,3\,6\,8$$
$$4\,2\,1\,0\,5\,2\,6\,3\,1$$

$$\frac{17}{29} = 0.\,5\,8\,6\,2\,0\,6\,8\,9\,6\,5\,5\,1\,7\,2$$
$$4\,1\,2\,3\,7\,9\,3\,1\,0\,3\,4\,4\,8\,2\,7$$

In each case the total of every column is the same: every column adds up to 9. This means that when we have got half way through a sum we can write down the second half from the first half: we just take every figure in the first half from 9 and this gives us the second half!

Now you may ask "how do I know when I am half way through?" and there is a simple way to find out. Take the numerator of the given fraction from the denominator: 19 – 1 = 18.
When 18 comes up you are half way through. In your recurring decimal for $\frac{1}{19}$ you should see 18 (written ₁8) at the end of the first line!

Similarly for $\frac{11}{19}$, since 19–11 = 8 you should find 8 at the end of your first line.
And for $\frac{17}{29}$, 29–17 = 12 (written as ₁2) which comes up after 14 figures.

This is because $\frac{17}{29} + \frac{12}{29} = 0.99....9$, and the figures of $\frac{12}{29}$ are therefore complementary to the figures of $\frac{17}{29}$. Since the figures are complementary 12 must come up half way because there must be as many figures after 12 as there are up to 12.

> If the difference of numerator and denominator comes up in a recurring decimal you are half way through and you can get the second half by taking all the figures in the first half from 9.
> (The difference of numerator and denominator does not always appear however).

If fact, if you include the remainder digits (the subscripts) each column adds up to the denominator.

 Convert $\frac{9}{39}$ to a decimal.

First we note that the Ekadhika is **4** now (1 more than 3); we can write **E = 4**.
Also the half way number is 30 (39–9=30): **H = 39–9= 30**.

We begin by dividing the Ekadhika, 4, into the numerator, 9: $\frac{9}{39}=0._1 23_30$
The first three steps give us 12, 3 and 30 and so we find that the half way number has come up after just 3 figures.
So we just take each of the first three figures from 9 to get the full answer:

$$\frac{9}{39}=0._1\dot{2}3_30769$$

\# You can of course find $\frac{9}{39}$ without using the half way number: just keep dividing by **4**.

❋ Find the recurring decimal for $\frac{10}{39}$. (E=4 and H=29)
You should get a 6-figure recurring decimal for this just as you did in Example 5 above, but in this case the half way number does not come up.

 Answer: $\frac{10}{39}=0._2\dot{2},5_16\,4\,1_1\dot{0}$

✐ **Practice A**   Find the recurring decimal for:

a $\frac{25}{29}$ b $\frac{24}{39}$ c $\frac{29}{39}$ d $\frac{3}{49}$ e $\frac{44}{69}$ f $\frac{44}{79}$

g $\frac{1}{99}$ h $\frac{1}{9}$ (E will be 1 here because there is zero before the 9)

i plot your answers from **b** to **f** above on 9-point circles.

---

a $\frac{25}{29}=0._1\dot{8}62_30,6_38_19_16_155_117_124/13793103448275$ b $\frac{24}{39}=0.\dot{6}_21_15/38\dot{4}$ c $\frac{29}{39}=0._1\dot{7}_14,3_35,8_2\dot{9}$

d $\frac{3}{49}=0._3\dot{0}6_11_22_22_24_44_48_19_47_29_459_41_18_33_16_17_23_34_46/93877551020408163265\dot{3}$

e $\frac{44}{69}=0._2\dot{6}_53_17_568_11_14_25_19_142_10_22_48_59_38_55_50_17_32_4\dot{4}$

f $\frac{44}{79}=0._4\dot{5}_55_56_49_162_20_42_55_33_16_4\dot{4}$ g $\frac{1}{99}=0.\dot{0}\dot{1}$ h $\frac{1}{9}=0.\dot{1}$

3.3 PROPORTIONATELY

So far all our fractions have had 9 as the last figure of the denominator.
In fact the special method we have been using can only be applied when the denominator ends in 9. However there are various other devices we can apply so that the method will work with other denominators.
One of these is to use the *Proportionately* formula.

 6 Find the recurring decimal for $\frac{7}{13}$.

The denominator does not end in 9 here, it ends in 3.
However we know we can multiply the top and bottom of a fraction by any number we like without changing its value.

To get a 9 in the denominator we can multiply the numerator and denominator of $\frac{7}{13}$ by 3 to get: $\frac{7}{13} = \frac{21}{39}$.

And we now find the decimal for $\frac{21}{39}$ exactly as before: $\frac{21}{39} = 0._1\dot{5}_3,8\,4\,6\,\dot{1}$

The half way number is 18, and it comes up after 3 figures.

✳ What will $\frac{1}{7}$ need to be multiplied by on top and bottom so that the denominator ends in 9?
Answer: 7

In the next exercise each fraction will need to be multiplied so that the denominator ends in a 9.

✎ **Practice B**   Convert to recurring decimals:

a $\frac{1}{7}$ b $\frac{2}{13}$ c $\frac{5}{23}$ d $\frac{17}{33}$ e $\frac{9}{11}$ f $\frac{3}{17}$

a $\frac{1}{7} = \frac{7}{49} = 0._2\dot{1}_1,4_2 8\,5\,7\,\dot{7}$ b $\frac{2}{13} = \frac{6}{39} = 0._2\dot{1}_1 5_3 3/846$ c $\frac{5}{23} = \frac{15}{69} = 0._1\dot{2}_1,7_6 39,13_3 0,4_3 3_5 478260869565$

d $\frac{17}{33} = \frac{51}{99} = 0.\overline{51}$ e $\frac{9}{11} = \frac{81}{99} = 0.\overline{81}$ f $\frac{3}{17} = \frac{21}{119} = 0._0\dot{1}_1,7_6 6_8 47_7 0_{10} 5_9 8/82352941$

✎ **Practice C**   Find correct to 4 decimal places:

a $\frac{18}{59}$ b $\frac{67}{89}$ c $\frac{100}{109}$ d $1\frac{3}{7}$ e $\frac{20}{13}$ f $\frac{99}{49}$

a 0.3051   b 0.7528   c 0.9174   d 1.4286   e 1.5385   f 2.0204

3.4 LONGER NUMERATORS

We are not restricted to denominators where the numerator is a whole number between 0 and the denominator. This method can work for any numerator.

  Find **1.23 ÷ 19**.

We find $\frac{1}{19}$ and simply add 2 when we deal with the tenths and add 3 when we deal with the hundredths:

$$\tfrac{1.23}{19} = 0._1 0\ 6_1 4\ 7_1 3 \ldots$$

We begin with 2 divided into 1 (as with $\frac{1}{19}$) and put $_1 0$.

Next instead of dividing 2 into 10 we divide 2 into 12 because we add on the 2 in 1.23. This gives 6 which we put down.

Then the 3 in 1.23 is added to the 6, so we divide 2 into 9 and put down $_1 4$.

From here on we just divide by 2 as before: 2 into 14 is 7 etc.

This considerably opens up the range of application of this method.

  Find **2345 ÷ 49**.

$$\frac{2345}{49} = {}_3 4_3 7._2 8_3 5 \ldots$$

The steps are: 23 ÷ 5 = 4 rem 3, put $_3 4$.
Now we add the 4 in 2345 to 34 to get 38, 38 ÷ 5 = 7 rem 3, put $_3 7$.
Now add the 5 in 2345 to 37 to get 42, 42 ÷ 5 = 8 rem 2, put $_2 8$.
From here on we divide as normal: 28 ÷ 5 = 5 rem 3 etc.

  Find **72.7 ÷ 29**.

$$\frac{72.7}{29} = {}_1 2._2 4_1 {}^1 0_2 6 \ldots = 2.506 \ldots$$

Here we get 10 in the third place and have to carry 1 to the left.

Alternatively, at the second step

put $14 \div 3 = 5$ rem $\bar{1}$:
$$\frac{72.7}{29} = {}_12._{\bar{1}}5_20_26\ldots = 2.506\ldots$$

Then ${}_{\bar{1}}5 = \bar{5}$ and we add the 7 in the tenths place of the numerator to this to get 2:
$2 \div 3 = 0$ rem 2, put ${}_20$. And so on.

Or, thirdly to avoid the last 7 in 72.7,

start with $72.7 = 73.\bar{3}$:
$$\frac{73.\bar{3}}{29} = {}_12.5_20_26\ldots$$

✎ **Practice D**   Find to 4 S.F.

a $5.67 \div 19$ b $67.8 \div 29$ c $555 \div 39$ d $0.0135 \div 79$

e $321 \div 13$ f $33 \div 9.5$ g $19.19 \div 59$ h $18.88 \div 19$

a	0.2984	b	2.338	c	14.23	d	0.0001709
e	24.69	f	3.474	g	0.3253	h	0.9937

3.5 DENOMINATORS ENDING IN 8, 7, 6

If a denominator ends not with a 9 but with a number close to it (8, 7 or 6) we can use the same method as for denominators ending in 9 but multiply the last figure at each step by 2, 3 or 4 before dividing.

  $\frac{7}{48} = 0._21_43_58_1\dot{3}$.

We begin by dividing 5 into 0.7.
This gives us 0.1 remainder 2: $\frac{7}{48} = 0._21$

So far this is just what we would have done for $\frac{7}{49}$. But from now on, before we divide by 5 we must **double the last figure**, because 48 is **2** below 50.

Looking at ${}_21$ we double the last figure and therefore divide 5 into 22 rather than 21. This gives 4 remainder 2, written ${}_24$ so we now have: $\frac{7}{48} = 0._21_24$
We again double the last figure and divide 5 into 28 to get ${}_35$.
Then doubling the 5 in 35 we divide 5 into 40, and so on.

Note how the 3 repeats itself at the end: we keep dividing 5 into 16 and get ${}_13$ over and over again.

We can summarise the whole process as follows:

> 1. Find the Auxiliary Fraction.   E.g. $\frac{0.7}{5}$ in the example above.
> 2. Divide the bottom of the AF into the top, writing any remainder **before** the answer figure. E.g. 0.21
> 3. From now on **double** the last figure of the number pair before dividing. E.g. 5 into 22 (not 21)

\# When a fraction is converted to a decimal the resulting decimal may terminate or it may not. (e.g. $3 \div 4 = 0.75$ which terminates). If the division does not terminate three things can happen:

1. the decimal has a single recurring figure (e.g. $2 \div 3 = 0.6666... = 0.\dot{6}$)

2. the decimal has a block of figures recurring (e.g. $2 \div 7 = 0.\dot{2}8571\dot{4}$)

3. the decimal has some non-recurring figures followed by a recurring figure or a block of recurring figures (e.g. $7 \div 30 = 0.2\dot{3}$ or $15 \div 28 = 0.53\dot{5}7142\dot{8}$)

Every factor of 2 or 5 in the denominator of a fraction contributes one non-recurring figure to the decimal (but 2 and 5 together, i.e. a factor of 10, contribute one figure). So $\frac{1}{22}$ and $\frac{1}{15}$ will have one non-recurring figure and a recurring part.

✐ **Practice E**   Find the full recurring decimal for:

a $\frac{5}{38}$ b $\frac{5}{78}$ c $\frac{7}{18}$

d Find the first 5 figures (after the decimal point) of the decimal for $\frac{13}{28}$.

---

a 0.1315789473684210526 b $0.064102\dot{5}$ c $0.3\dot{8}$ d 0.46428

⁂ 11 $\frac{78}{87} = 0._68_3 9_36 35\ 5_61\ 7_32\ 4_31 6_36 7\ 9\ 3\ 1_30 3_33 4_64\ 8_62 3_76 5_38\ 6\ 2_60_6\ 6$

We start with 9 into 7.8 goes 0.8 remainder 6 giving: $0._68$

We now see 68 but because 87 is 3 below 90 we must treble the last figure at each step. So the 8 in 68 becomes 24, and added to 60 makes 84.

Dividing 84 by 9 we get 9 remainder 3 giving: $0._68_39$
We now have 39. We treble the 9 to 27 and add the 30 which gives 57.
Then 57 divided by 9 goes 6 remainder 3 giving $0._68_39_36$ and so on.

✐ **Practice F**   Find the full recurring decimal for:

a $\frac{9}{37}$ b $\frac{34}{77}$ c Find the first 6 figures of the decimal for $\frac{22}{57}$

---

a $0.\dot{2}4\dot{3}$ b $0.\dot{4}4155\dot{8}$ c 0.385964

Find $\frac{9}{28}$ giving 7 figures after the decimal point.

In finding $\frac{9}{28}$ you should have arrived at $_15$ in the 7th decimal place.

If you continue from here you get 3 into 20 (because the 5 is doubled) which goes 6 remainder 2.

This gives us $_15_26$.
Then 3 into 32 gives a 2-figure answer (10 rem 2).

This means that the 6 in $_26$ needs to be a 7 because 1 will be carried back from the next place.

So we do not write 3 into 20 goes 6 remainder 2 but write 7 remainder $\bar{1}$.

So we now have $_15_{\bar{1}}7$.

This works nicely because we double 7 to get 14 and add this to $\overline{10}$ to get 4.
Then 3 into 4 goes 1 remainder 1 and the decimal is starting to repeat.

This gives $0.3\,2_1\dot{1}4_2\,2\,8_1\dot{5_{\bar{1}}}\,7$ as the full answer.

✎ **Practice G**   Find the first 9 figures of the decimal for:

a $\frac{20}{47}$ b $\frac{19}{67}$

---

a   0.425531914   b   0.283582089

3.6 DENOMINATORS ENDING IN 1

So far all the denominators we have encountered have been just **below** a multiple of ten, like 29, 38, 47 etc.

On Page 38 we saw:
In dividing 19 into an even figure followed by a zero:

$$\frac{1r1}{19)20} \qquad \frac{2r2}{19)40} \qquad \frac{3r3}{19)60} \qquad \text{etc.}$$

we find the quotient is equal to the remainder, and half the even number.

Suppose now that we are dividing by 21 (one unit over 20 rather than one unit under it). The above divisions become:

$$\frac{1r\bar{1}}{21)2\,0} \qquad \frac{2r\bar{2}}{21)4\,0} \qquad \frac{3r\bar{3}}{21)6\,0} \qquad \text{etc.}$$

So the quotient is again half the even number and the remainder is the negative of the quotient.

This tells us we can use the same method for finding $\frac{1}{21}$ as we used for $\frac{1}{19}$ except that each answer digit is considered negative as far as calculating the next digit is concerned.

 $\frac{4}{21} = 0.2\,\bar{1},0\,5,_{\bar{i}}\bar{2}\,\bar{4} = 0.\dot{1}9047\dot{6}.$

We begin with numerator, $4 \div 2 = 2$:   0.2

Then taking this answer digit, 2, as $\bar{2}$ we divide this by 2 and put: $0.2\,\bar{1}$

The $\bar{1}$ then becomes 1 and is divided by 2: $0.2\,\bar{1},0$

Now divide 2 into 10: $0.2\,\bar{1},0\,5$

Then 2 into $\bar{5}$: $0.2\,\bar{1},0\,5,_{\bar{i}}\bar{2}$

And now as the $\bar{2}$ is taken as 2 we have $\bar{8}$ ($\bar{1}2 = \bar{8}$) to divide by 2: $0.2\,\bar{1},0\,5,_{\bar{i}}\bar{2}\,\bar{4}$

From here the digits will recur.

This method follows nicely from the earlier one but is rather cumbersome with all the negatives. In fact Bharati Krsna uses a clever device for simplifying this: as the answer digits are to be considered negative at each step he expresses the numerator, N, as $(N-1) + 0.\dot{9}$. This gives a series of nines in the numerator so that every negative remainder is changed to a positive number when 9 is added to it.

So $\frac{4}{21}$ becomes $\frac{3.\dot{9}}{21}$. This means each answer digit can be subtracted from 9 and then divided by, in this case, 2.

 $\frac{4}{21} = 0.{}_{,1}\dot{1}\,9\,0,_14,7\dot{6}.$

We divide 2 into 3 (one less than the numerator): $= 0.{}_{,1}1$

Then in 11 the 1 in the units place is taken from 9 to give 18, which we divide by 2:

$0.{}_{,1}19$

This 9 is now taken from 9 to give $0 \div 2 = 0$ $0.{}_{,1}19\,0$

Next we take 0 from 9 and so divide 9 by 2: $0.{}_{,1}19\,0,_14$

And so on

(15) $\frac{19}{31} = 0.6\ 1_29\ 0\ 3\ 2_12\ \ldots$

We begin by dividing 3 into 18. This gives: 0.6

From now on we take each answer figure (but not any of the small remainder figures) from 9 before dividing.

So we take 6 from 9 to get 3. Then 3 divided by 3 gives **1**:   0.61

Take this 1 from 9 to get 8. $8 \div 3 = 2$ rem **2**, so we now have: 0.61_22

Take the last 2 in 22 from 9 to get 27. $27 \div 3 = $ **9**: 0.61_229

Take 9 from 9 to get 0. $0 \div 3 = $ **0**: 0.61_2290

Take 0 from 9 to get 9, $9 \div 3 = $ **3**, and so on.

✱ Check you agree with the figures shown above and continue the division. The decimal begins to recur after 15 figures.

· **Answer:** $0.\dot{6}1290322580645\dot{1}$

> To summarise:
> 1. Divide the tens digit of the denominator into N – 1, where N is the numerator, and put down the result, prefixing any remainder.
> 2. Take the last digit of the last number pair from 9 and divide again.

✐ **Practice H**   Find the full recurring decimal for:

a $\frac{13}{21}$ b $\frac{22}{31}$ c $\frac{1}{21}$ d $\frac{17}{41}$ e $\frac{8}{51}$ f $\frac{4}{91}$ g $\frac{1}{81}$

---

a $0.\dot{6}1904\dot{7}$ b $0.\dot{7}09677419354838$ c $0.\dot{0}4761\dot{9}$ d $0.\dot{4}146\dot{3}$

e $0.\dot{1}568627450980392$ f $0.\dot{0}4395\dot{6}$ g $0.\dot{0}1234567\dot{9}$

"There are methods whereby ... we can easily transform any miscellaneous or non-descript denominator in question by simple multiplication etc., to the requisite standard form which will bring them within the jurisdiction of the Auxiliary Fractions hereinabove explained.

In fact, the very discovery of these Auxiliaries and of their wonderful utility in the transmogrification of frightful-looking denominators of vulgar fractions into such simple and easy denominator-divisors must suffice and prepare the scientifically-minded seeker after Knowledge, for the marvellous devices still further on in the offing"
From "Vedic Mathematics", Page 272.

3.7 DENOMINATORS ENDING IN 2, 3, 4

$\frac{5}{42}=0.1\,{}_31\,{}_19\,{}_04\,{}_37\,{}_16\,{}_31$. (with dots over the first 1 and the 6)

We simply follow the procedure for denominators ending in 1, but, as in the previous section we double (for denominators ending in 3 we treble, and so on) the last digit **before** taking the complement from 9.

Here we start with $4 \div 4 = 1$: $\frac{5}{42}=0.1$

Then double the 1 and take its complement, which gives 7 and $7 \div 4 = {}_31$: $\frac{5}{42}=0.1\,{}_31$

Doubling 1 and taking the complement gives 7 again, so $37 \div 4 = {}_19$: $\frac{5}{42}=0.1\,{}_31\,{}_19$

Next we double 9 to get 18, take this from 9 to get $\overline{9}$. So we now have ${}_1\overline{9}$ which is 1, and this we divide by 4: $\frac{5}{42}=0.1\,{}_31\,{}_19\,{}_10$
And so on.

$\frac{7}{32}=0.2\,{}_21\,9\,\overline{3}\,5\,{}_10\,{}_10\ldots = \mathbf{0.21875}$.

Here we have a terminating decimal (ending is a series of zeros).
Note the $\overline{3}$ that comes up in the 4th place. Following this, we double $\overline{3}$ to $\overline{6}$, take $\overline{6}$ from 9 to get 15, which we divide by 3.

$\frac{12}{53}=0.{}_12\,{}_32\,{}_36\,{}_14\,{}_21\,{}_15\,{}_40\,{}_49\,{}_24\,{}_23\ldots$

This is very similar except that as 53 is 3 over 50 we **treble** the last answer digit before taking the complement.

$\frac{1234}{51}={}_12\,4.{}_41\,{}_39\ldots$

Here note that there will be two figures before the decimal point and we start the calculation from $\frac{12}{51}$.

So $11 \div 5 = {}_12$: $\frac{1234}{51}={}_12$
Then we take the complement of 2 to get 17, but add to this the 3 in the numerator.
So $20 \div 5 = 4$: $\frac{1234}{51}={}_12\,4$
Complement of 4 is 5, add the 4 in the numerator to get 9, $9 \div 5 = {}_41$.
And so on.

✏ **Practice I**   Find the recurring decimal for:

a $\frac{19}{52}$ b $\frac{5}{22}$ c $\frac{89}{92}$ (5 figures)   d $\frac{16}{43}$ (9 figures)

e $\frac{1}{63}$ f $\frac{232}{41}$ (5 figures)   g $\frac{13.54}{52}$ (5 figures)

---

a $0._{,}3_{,}6_{,}5\,{,}3_{,}8_{,}4_{,}6_{,}\dot{1}_{,}5$ b $0.2_{,}\dot{2}_{,}\dot{7}$ c $0._{,}9_{,}6_{,}7_{,}8_{,}3_{,}9$ d $0._{,}3_{,}7\,2_{,}0_{,}9\,3\,0_{,}2_{,}3$

e $0._{,0}\dot{0}_{,}1\,6_{,}\overline{1}\,\overline{3}\,\dot{3}=0.\dot{0}1\,5\,8\,7\,\dot{3}$ f $_{,}5._{,}6_{,}5_{,}8_{,}5$ g $0._{,}2\,6_{,}0_{,}3_{,}8$

3.8 WORKING 2, 3 ETC. FIGURES AT A TIME

It is possible to speed up the calculation even further by working
with groups of 2, 3, 4, 5, 6 or more figures at a time.

  20

$\frac{1}{199}$ = 0._{,1}0 0/5 0/2 5/_{,1}1 2/5 6/2 8/1 4/0 7/_{,1}0 3 . . . .

Because we have two 9s in the denominator we can get the answer **two figures at a time**.

We start with 2 into 1 goes **00** remainder **1**, so we put down:

$$0._{,1}00$$

This gives 100, and 2 into 100 goes **50**, which we put down: 0._{,1}00/50

(Note each pair of answer figures are separated by an oblique line only to help show the method)

Then 2 into 50 is **25**:   0._{,1}00/50/25

Then 2 into 25 is **12** remainder **1**, so we put _{,1}12:   0._{,1}00/50/25/_{,1}12

Then 2 into 112 and so on.

We get the answer at least as fast as we can write it down.

21

$\frac{59}{133} = \frac{177}{399}$ = 0._{,1}4 4/3 6/0 9/_{,1}0 2/_{,2}2 5/_{,1}5 6 . . . .

Here we see 133 in the denominator and so we multiply the top and bottom of $\frac{59}{133}$ by
3 to get $\frac{177}{199}$ to get 9s in the denominator.

We therefore divide by 4, two figures at a time.

4 into 177 goes 44 remainder 1 etc.

22 $\frac{108}{2001}$ = 0. $_1$0 5 3/9 7 3/0 1 3/4 9 3 . . . .

Here we work with groups of 3 figures and because we are above the base of 2000 we begin by dividing into 107 and use complements from 9:

107 ÷ 2 = **53** remainder **1** so we put down: 0.$_1$053

Next take each of the figures 053 from 9 to get 946,
                                         so 2 into 1946 = **973**:   0.$_1$053/973

Then 973 becomes 026, and dividing by 2 we get **013**.
Etc.

23   Convert $\frac{63}{298}$ into its recurring decimal form.

Here we can divide by 3 in groups of two, but we need double each group as 298 is 2 below 300.

$$\frac{63}{298} = 0.21/14/_1 09/_1 39/_1 59/_2 72 \ldots$$

✐ Practice J   Find the first 5 groups of digits in the following:

a $\frac{88}{199}$ b $\frac{45}{299}$ c $\frac{535}{4999}$ (groups of 3 here)

d $\frac{70}{233}$ (multiply by 3)   e $\frac{57}{201}$ (groups of 2 and take from 9 after the first group)

f $\frac{222}{19999}$

g $\frac{37}{198}$ (divide by 2 in groups of 2 and double the last 2 figures after the first step)

a 0.44/22/11/05/52	b 0.15/05/01/67/22	c 0.107/021/404/280/856
d 0.30/04/29/18/45	e 0.28/35/82/08/95	
f 0.0111/0055/5027/7513/8756		
g 0.18/68/68/68/68		

Special numbers like 201, 399, 1001 (used in the last lesson) which are not prime and are near a base can be very useful here.

For example $\frac{8}{67}$ can be written as $\frac{24}{201}$ giving the answer two figures at a time.

$$\frac{8}{67} = \frac{24}{201} = 0._111/94/_102/_198/_150/_174\ldots$$

Alternatively $\frac{8}{67} = \frac{4776}{39999}$ which means we can get the answer four figures at a time!

$$\frac{8}{67} = \frac{4776}{39999} = 0.1194/_20298/_25074\ldots$$

✎ Practice K   Use the products given below to find the recurring decimals for the given fractions using groups of digits. Give three groups in each case.

$93 \times 43 = 3999$	$7 \times 43 = 301$	$87 \times 23 = 2001$	$13 \times 23 = 299$
$53 \times 17 = 901$	$47 \times 17 = 799$	$37 \times 27 = 999$	$7 \times 157 = 1099$
$131 \times 229 = 29999$	$409 \times 489 = 200001$	$3 \times 367 = 1101$	$19 \times 421 = 7999$

a $\frac{1}{43}$ 2 ways   b $\frac{10}{23}$ 2 ways   c $\frac{3}{17}$ 2 ways

d $\frac{5}{27}$ e $\frac{8}{157}$ f $\frac{4}{229}$

g $\frac{2}{489}$ h $\frac{17}{367}$ i $\frac{20}{421}$

---

a $\frac{93}{3999} = 0._1023/_3255/_3813$ $\frac{7}{301} = 0.02/_132/_255$

b $\frac{130}{299} = 0._143/_247/_182$ $\frac{870}{2001} = 0._1434/_1782/_1608$

c $\frac{141}{799} = 0._517/_564/_470$ $\frac{159}{901} = 0._517/_664/_570$

d $\frac{185}{999} = 0.\overset{..}{1}8\overset{..}{5}$ e $\frac{56}{1099} = 0._105/_609/_455$ f $\frac{524}{29999} = 0._20174/_26724/8908$

g $\frac{818}{200001} = 0._100408/_199795/50102$ h $\frac{51}{1101} = 0._604/_263/_521$ i $\frac{380}{7999} = 0._4047/_7505/_1938$

These recurring decimals can be useful in trigonometry.
For example the angle A in the triangle shown is $\frac{1}{29}$ radians to 4 decimal places.

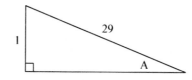

And the angle B is $\frac{2}{29}$ radians to 4 decimal places.

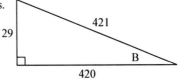

Though this is not taken further in this book see Reference 4 for further explanation.

LESSON 4
TRIPLES

SUMMARY

Here triples are introduced and a method for combining them. This is developed further in Lessons 8, 12 and 16.

4.1 **Definitions** – of a triple, triple angle etc.
4.2 **Triples for 45°, 30° and 60°**
4.3 **Triple Addition** – adding two triples together.
4.4 **Double Angle** – getting a triple with twice the angle of a given triple.
4.5 **Variations of 3,4,5** – one triple can specify eight directions.
4.6 **Quadrant Angles** – special triples for these angles.
4.7 **Rotations** – using triples to rotate points.

4.1 DEFINITIONS

A **triple** is a set of three numbers in which the sum of the squares of the first two numbers is equal to the square of the third number.

One example of a triple is **3, 4, 5** because $3^2 + 4^2 = 5^2$.

If a triangle had sides of 3, 4 and 5 units it would be right-angled, so the numbers can represent the lengths of the sides of a right-angled triangle.

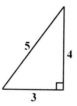

And let us say that the first number in the triple is always the base of the triangle, the second number is always the height and the third is always the hypotenuse.

So **4, 3, 5** represents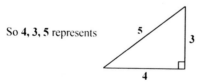

Similarly 2, 1½, 2½; $\sqrt{5}$, $\sqrt{6}$, $\sqrt{11}$; 2, $\sqrt{5}$, 3 are also triples.

Note: triples that have the same shape are called **equal triples**.
So 36, 15, 39 = 12, 5, 13 = 6, 2½, 6½.

If each of the elements (parts) of a triple are rational numbers then the triple is a **perfect triple**.

So, 2, $\sqrt{5}$, 3 is a triple but not a perfect triple as $\sqrt{5}$ is not a rational number.
And 4, 6, 7 is not a perfect triple as it is not even a triple: $4^2 + 6^2$ does not equal 7^2.

The **angle in a triple** is the angle between the **base** and the **hypotenuse**.
So for the **3, 4, 5** triple we can write: **A) 3, 4, 5**

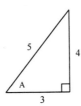

We write the angle first, then a bracket, then the sides of the triple.

Every triangle contains two triples. In this example we also have: **90°–A)4, 3, 5**.

 Write down the triple which has angle A:

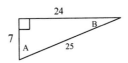

The angle A is between the sides 7 and 25, so 7 must be the base and 25 the hypotenuse.
We therefore put the 7 first: **A)7, 24, 25**.

Similarly if the angle B above was to be described in triple terms it would be:
B)24, 7, 25.

4.2 TRIPLES FOR 45°, 30° AND 60°

The angles 45°, 30° and 60° are simple angles which frequently occur and can easily be expressed with triples.

If you take a square of side 1 unit and draw a diagonal you will get a triangle with an angle of 45° because the diagonal cuts the right angle in half.

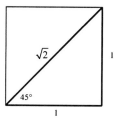

Pythagoras' theorem gives the diagonal length as $\sqrt{2}$ so a triple for 45° will be:

$$45°)\ 1,\ \ 1,\ \ \sqrt{2}$$

Similarly we can take an equilateral triangle of side 2 units and cut it in half:

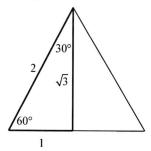

The base of the bold triangle above is 1 unit as the equilateral triangle is cut in half. For the same reason the 60° angle is cut in half to give 30° at the top.
And Pythagoras' theorem gives the height as $\sqrt{3}$.

✱ From the diagram above write down a triple for 60° and a triple for 30°.
   Answers: 60°)1, $\sqrt{3}$, 2, 30°)$\sqrt{3}$, 1, 2.

4.3 TRIPLE ADDITION

Now suppose we have two triples:

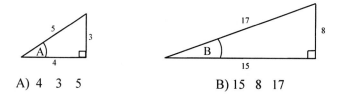

A) 4   3   5   B) 15   8   17

and suppose that we wish to add them in the way shown below, so that the angles are added.

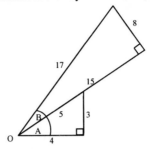

We want the sum of two triples to be itself a triple so we want a triple that contains the angle A+B.

This is obtained as follows:

A	4	3	5	
B	15	8	17	+
A+B	$(4 \times 15 - 3 \times 8)$,	$(3 \times 15 + 4 \times 8)$,	(5×17)	
=	36	77	85	

There is a simple pattern here which we can use to add the two triples.

That is, we multiply vertically in the first two columns and subtract to get the first element of the triple for (A+B).
Then we cross-multiply in the first two columns and add to get the second element.
And we multiply vertically in the third column to get the third element.

These *Vertical and Crosswise* products are shown diagrammatically below:

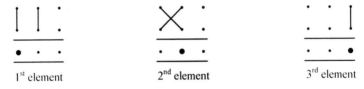

1st element   2nd element   3rd element

Algebraically we can say, for two triples A) x   y   z and B) X   Y   Z   the triple containing the angle (A+B) is given by:

A	x	y	z	
B	X	Y	Z	+
A+B	$(xX - yY)$,	$(yX + xY)$,	(zZ)	

This can be proved as follows.

The triple which contains the angle (A+B) is the triangle OQP below.

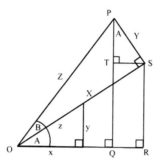

So the required triple is: A+B)OQ,   QP,   OP
                         = OR – QR,   QT + TP,   OP
                         = OR – TS,   RS + TP,   OP

But comparing $\triangle$ORS and triple x, y, z, which have similar triangles, OR = $\dfrac{xX}{z}$, RS = $\dfrac{yX}{z}$.

And comparing $\triangle$PTS and triple x, y, z, which have similar triangles, TS = $\dfrac{yY}{z}$, TP = $\dfrac{xY}{z}$.

So the triple is: A+B) $\dfrac{xX}{z} - \dfrac{yY}{z}$, $\dfrac{yX}{z} + \dfrac{xY}{z}$,   Z

                 = xX – yY,   yX + xY,   zZ

A	12	5	13
B	3	4	5
A+B	16	63	65

+

using the *vertical and crosswise* pattern shown above

Of course we can multiply (or divide) the elements of this triple by any number we like and it will still represent the same angle.
For example, if we want the hypotenuse of the triple 16, 63, 65 to be 13 we can divide through by 5 to get 3.2, 12.6, 13.

A	4	3	5
B	24	7	25
A+B	75	100	125
=	3	4	5

+

any common factor can be divided out

A	4	3	5	
B	4	3	5	+
A+B	7	24	25	

✏ **Practice A**   Add the following triples:

a	3 4 5	b	24 7 25	c	40 9 41	d	12 5 13	e	8 15 17
	15 8 17 +		3 4 5 +		4 3 5 +		8 15 17 +		4 3 5 +

---

a   13, 84, 85   b   44, 117, 125   c   133, 156, 205   d   21, 220, 221   e   −13, 84, 85

4.4 DOUBLE ANGLE

A	12	5	13	
A	12	5	13	+
2A	119	120	169	

It will be seen from this example and the previous one that the procedure simplifies when finding the triple for a double angle:

A	12	5	13
2A	$(12^2 - 5^2), (2 \times 12 \times 5), (13^2)$		

And in general:

A	x	y	r
2A	$(x^2 - y^2), (2xy), (r^2)$		

A	3	4	5
2A	−7	24	25

Here we find that the first element is negative. We can interpret this by considering the addition of two 3,4,5 triangles:

The sum of the two angles is obtuse and the resultant triangle OPQ has its base, OQ, extended in the opposite direction to the base OS.

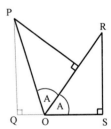

So the triple X) –7, 24, 25
looks like this:

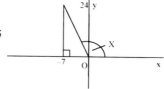

This is rather like the coordinate system we are familiar with, where O is the origin, OS along the x-axis and angles are measured anticlockwise from the positive x-axis.

So if the first element of a triple is negative, and the second positive as we have here, the angle is obtuse (between 90° and 180°).

And conversely, if the angle is obtuse the first two elements are negative and positive respectively.

✎ **Practice B**   Find a triple for 2A (note, in f and j below the dash indicates a number that is not given, but you can find it from the other two numbers):

a A)4, 3, 5   b A)15, 8, 17   c A) 21, 20, 29   d A) 5, 12, 13   e A)8, 15,17

f A)9, - , 15   g A)1, 2, $\sqrt{5}$ h A) $\sqrt{40}$, 3, 7   i A)5, $\sqrt{39}$, 8   j A)2, - , 5

k Given A)4, 3, 5, find a triple for 3A.

a 7, 24, 25	b 161, 240, 289	c 41, 840, 841	d –119, 120, 169	e –161, 240, 289
f –7,24,25	g –3,4,5	h 31,6√40,49	i -14,10√39,64	j -17,4√21,25
k –44,117,125				

One triple, like 3,4,5, can be use to define eight directions in a plane by being put in different positions.

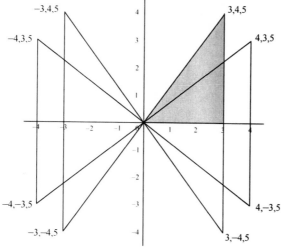

So a triple with only its first element negative, like –3,4,5 is in the second quadrant;
and triple with only its middle element negative, like 3,–4,5 is in the fourth quadrant, because
it has a negative height;
and a triple with the first two elements both negative, like –3,–4,5, is in the third quadrant as
its base and height are both extended in the negative direction.

So for –5,12,13 the sketch is: for –12,–5,13 the sketch is:

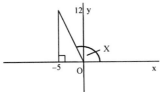   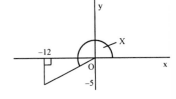

and for 15,–8,17 the sketch is:

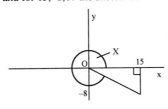

✎ **Practice C**   Sketch the following triples:

a 8,–15,17   **b** –7,24,25   **c** –2,–3,$\sqrt{13}$ **d** –2, $\sqrt{5}$,3

4.6 QUADRANT ANGLES

A quadrant is a quarter of a circle:

The quadrant angles, **0°, 90°, 180°, 270°** can also be expressed by triples.

Suppose we add the triples **A)4 3 5** and **B)3 4 5**:

A	4	3	5
B	3	4	5 +
A+B	0	25	25
=	0	1	1

We can divide 0,25,25 by 25 to get 0,1,1.

In this case we get a triangle with no base and height and hypotenuse equal.

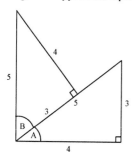

We see that because the triples are complementary A+B = 90°, so that the triple 0, 1, 1 represents an angle of 90°:

90°) 0   1   1

And if 90°) 0 1 1 we can double this triple to get a triple for an angle of 180°:

90°	0	1	1
180°	−1	0	1

Next we can double the 180° triple to get a triple for 360°, which is also a triple for 0°:

180°	−1	0	1
360°	1	0	1

And for 270° we can add 180° and 90°:

180°	−1	0	1
90°	0	1	1
270°	0	−1	1

These results can be summarized:

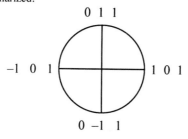

We can now use these triples in combination with others.

8   Given **A) 4 3 5** find a triple for **A+90°**.

$$
\begin{array}{c|ccc}
\text{A} & 4 & 3 & 5 \\
90° & 0 & 1 & 1 \\ \hline
\text{A+90°} & -3 & 4 & 5
\end{array} +
$$

9   Given **A) 4 3 5** find a triple for **A+180°**.

$$
\begin{array}{c|ccc}
\text{A} & 4 & 3 & 5 \\
180° & -1 & 0 & 1 \\ \hline
\text{A+180°} & -4 & -3 & 5
\end{array} +
$$

That is, we reverse the signs of the first two elements when adding 180°.

✎ Practice D

a Given A) 3, 4, 5 find triples for   i) 270°+ A,
                                            ii) A + 90°,
                                            iii) 2A + 90°.
b Given A) 4, 3, 5 find A+45°.
c Given A) 5, 12, 13 find a triple for 2A+ 180°.

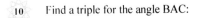

a   i) 4, –3,5   ii) –4,3,5   iii) –24,–7,25
b   1,7,5√2   c   119,–120,169

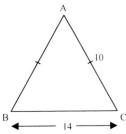

10   Find a triple for the angle BAC:

If we call the required angle 2x, then we can
get a triple for the half triangle and double it.

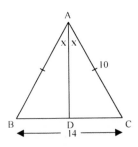

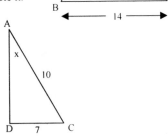

x) -, 7, 10 = √51, 7, 10

$\therefore$ 2x) 2, 14$\sqrt{51}$, 100 = 1, 7$\sqrt{51}$, 50.

✐ **Practice E**   Find a triple for the angle BAC in each of the following triangles.

a
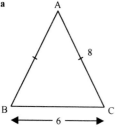

b
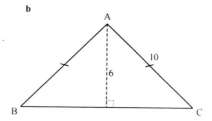

c In a rectangle ABCD side AB = 8cm and side BC = 5cm. If M is the mid point of CD find a triple for angle AMB.

d ABCD is a square and M and N are mid-points.

Find a triple for angle MDN.

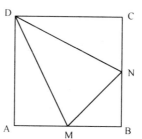

a   23,3$\sqrt{55}$,32   b   −7,24,25   c   9,40,41   d   4,3,5

4.7 ROTATIONS

We will assume all rotations to be anticlockwise unless otherwise stated.

 11   **Rotate P(7,3) through an angle of 90° using the origin as centre of rotation.**

We are effectively adding two triangles, one a 7, 3, $\sqrt{58}$ triangle and the other 0,1,1 (triple for 90°).

$$\begin{array}{ccc} 7 & 3 & \sqrt{58} \\ 0 & 1 & 1 \\ \hline -3 & 7 & \sqrt{58} \end{array} \ +$$

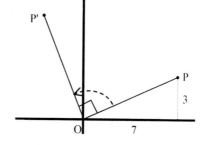

So the position of the rotated point, P', is (–3,7).
Note that since OP=OP' the third column is superfluous.

 Rotate the point P(5,2) through an angle A) 4,3,5 about the origin.

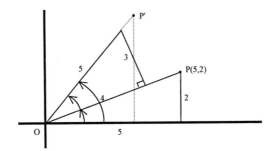

The point (5,2) gives us a right-angled triangle: $5, 2, \sqrt{29}$.
As the diagram shows, rotating through A) 4,3,5 is equivalent to adding these triples.

$$
\begin{array}{ccc}
5 & 2 & \sqrt{29} \\
4 & 3 & 5 \\
\hline
14 & 23 & 5\sqrt{29}
\end{array} +
$$

But we want the hypotenuse of the resulting triangle to be equal to OP, which is $\sqrt{29}$.
We therefore divide through by 5 which gives P' $(\frac{14}{5},\frac{23}{5})$ or P'(2.8, 4.6).

Note that the third column in the calculation above is unnecessary as we consistently divide through by the third element of the rotation triple.

 Rotate P(3,5) through A) –4,3,5 about the origin.

Here we are rotating by an obtuse angle but the method is the same:

$$
\begin{array}{ccc}
3 & 5 & - \\
-4 & 3 & 5 \\
\hline
-27 & -11 & -
\end{array} +
$$

∴ P'(–5.4,–2.2).

✏ **Practice F**   Rotate about the origin:

a (3,5) through an angle of 90°

b (−7,2) 180°

c (2,1) by the angle 7,24,25

d (−2,3) by 3,4,5

e (−4,6) by 30°

---

a (−5,3)   b   (7,−2)   c   (−0.4,2.2)   d   (−3.6,0.2)   e $(-2\sqrt{3}-3, 3\sqrt{3}-2)$

 Rotate P(6,5) through A) 3,4,5 about the point (4,1).

First we transpose the origin to (4,1).
If the origin is at (4,1) then the coordinates of P(6,5) become P'(2,4).

Then we rotate (2,4) by A)3,4,5:

$$\begin{array}{ccc} 2 & 4 & - \\ 3 & 4 & 5\ + \\ \hline -10 & 20 & - \end{array}$$

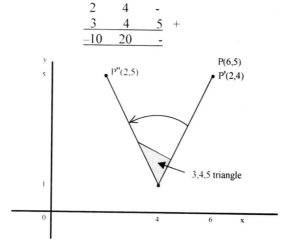

So the rotated point (relative to (4,1) as origin) is (−2,4).
And returning to the original origin by adding (4,1) back on we get **P'(2,5)**.

✏ **Practice G**   Rotate:

a (11,4) 90° about the point (3,5).

b (1,–2) 270° about the point (5,5).

c (1,–3) by 4,3,5 about the point (–2,3).

d (–3,1) by 3,–4,5 about (1,2).

---

a (4,13)   b (–2,9)   c (4,0)   d (–2.2,4.6)

Clockwise rotations involve triple subtraction: see Lesson 8.

An extension of this method allows easy rotation of points, lines and curves in 2 and 3-dimensional space. See Reference 4. Such rotations can save computer time as we avoid the need to evaluate sines, cosines, square roots etc.

The triple method unifies many areas of mathematics. Many problems that require a special formula of their own can be easily solved by addition or subtraction of triples or their 3-dimensional equivalent.

LESSON 5
GENERAL MULTIPLICATION

SUMMARY

This lesson shows the general Vedic method for multiplying numbers and algebraic expressions, using the *Vertically and Crosswise* Sutra.

5.1 **Two-Figure Numbers** – Multiplying 2-figure numbers.
5.2 **Moving Multiplier** – Multiplying numbers with different numbers of digits.
5.3 **Algebraic Products**
5.4 **Three-figure Numbers**
5.5 **Four-figure Numbers**
5.6 **Writing Left to Right Sums** – writing answers on paper.
5.7 **From Right to Left** – calculating from he right-hand side.
5.8 **Using Bar Numbers** – using these to remove digits 6, 7, 8, 9 when required.

5.1 TWO-FIGURE NUMBERS

 21 × 23.

Think of the numbers set out one below the other:

$$\begin{array}{cc} 2 & 1 \\ \underline{2} & \underline{3} \times \end{array}$$

There are 3 steps:

A. **multiply vertically** in the left-hand column: $2 \times 2 = 4$, so 4 is the first figure of the answer.

$$\begin{array}{cc} 2 & 1 \\ | & \\ \underline{2} & \underline{3} \times \\ 4 & \end{array}$$

B. **multiply crosswise** and add:
$2 \times 3 = 6$,
$1 \times 2 = 2$, $6 + 2 = 8$,
so 8 is the middle figure of the answer.

$$\begin{array}{cc} 2 & 1 \\ & \times \\ \underline{2} & \underline{3} \times \\ 4 & 8 \end{array}$$

C. **multiply vertically** in the right-hand column: $1 \times 3 = 3$,
3 is the last figure of the answer.

$$\begin{array}{cc} 2 & 1 \\ & | \\ \underline{2} & \underline{3} \times \\ 4 & 8 \; 3 \end{array}$$

$$\begin{array}{cc} 1 & 4 \\ \underline{2} & \underline{1} \times \\ 2 & 9 \; 4 \end{array}$$

A. vertically on the left: $1 \times 2 = 2$,
B. crosswise: $1 \times 1 = 1$, $4 \times 2 = 8$ and $1 + 8 = 9$,
C. vertically on the right: $4 \times 1 = 4$.

So the pattern for the three steps is: **vertical crosswise vertical**

This is of course very easy and straightforward, and we can now practice this vertical and crosswise pattern to establish the method.

✎ **Practice A**   Multiply mentally:

a 2 2	b 2 1	c 2 1	d 2 2	e 6 1	f 3 2	g 3 1	h 1 3
3 1 ×	3 1 ×	2 2 ×	1 3 ×	3 1 ×	2 1 ×	3 1 ×	1 3 ×
—	—	—	—	—	—	—	—

a 682	b 651	c 462	d 286
e 1 891	f 672	g 961	h 169

The previous examples involved no carry figures, so let us consider this next.

3

```
2  3
4  1 ×
9 4 3
```
The 3 steps give us: $2 \times 4 = 8$,
$2 \times 1 + 3 \times 4 = 14$,
$3 \times 1 = 3$.

The 14 here involves a carry figure, so in building up the answer mentally from the left we merge these numbers as before.

The mental steps are: 8
8,14 = 94   (the 1 is carried over to the left)
94,3 = 943
So **23 × 41 = 943**.

4

```
2  3
3  4 ×
7 8 2
```
The steps are: 6
6,17 = 77
77,12 = **782**.

5

```
3  3
4  4 ×
1 4 5 2
```
The steps are: 12
12,24 = 144
144,12 = **1452**.

We can now multiply any two 2-figure numbers together in one line.

The bar numbers can be used to remove digits over 5, see Section 5.8.

✎ **Practice B**   Multiply the following mentally:

a 2 1	b 2 3	c 2 4	d 2 2	e 2 2	f 3 1
4 7	4 3	2 9	2 8	5 3	3 6

g 2 2	h 3 1	i 4 4	j 3 3	k 3 3	l 3 4
5 6	7 2	5 3	8 4	6 9	1 9

a	987	b	989	c	696	d	616	e	1 166	f	1 116
g	1 232	h	2 232	i	2 332	j	2 772	k	2 277	l	646

You may have found in this exercise that you prefer to start with the crosswise multiplications, and put the left and right vertical multiplications on afterwards.

For **writing** these sums see Section 5.6.
For **right to left** calculations see Section 5.7.

EXPLANATION

It is easy to understand how this method works.
The vertical product on the right multiplies units by units and so gives the number of units in the answer. The crosswise operation multiplies tens by units and units by tens and so gives the number of tens in the answer. And the vertical product on the left multiplies tens by tens and gives the number of hundreds in the answer.

THE DIGIT SUM CHECK

This is also available for checking all these calculations.
For example to check **33 × 44 = 1452** we convert these three numbers to digit sums and get:
$6 \times 8 = 3$. This is correct in digit sum arithmetic as $6 \times 8 = 48$ and the digit sum of 48 is 3.

5.2 MOVING MULTIPLIER

In multiplying a long number by a single figure, for example 4321×2, we multiply each of the figures in the long number by the single figure.
We may think of the 2 moving along the row, multiplying each figure vertically by 2 as it goes.

Find **4321 × 32**.

4 3 2 1	Similarly here we put 32 first of all at the extreme left.
3 2	Then vertically on the left, $4 \times 3 = 12$.
	And crosswise, $4 \times 2 + 3 \times 3 = 17$.
4 3 2 1	Then move the 32 along and multiply crosswise:
3 2	$3 \times 2 + 2 \times 3 = 12$.
4 3 2 1	Moving the 32 once again:
3 2	multiply crosswise, $2 \times 2 + 1 \times 3 = 7$.
	Finally the vertical product on the right is $1 \times 2 = 2$.

These 5 results (in bold), 12,17,12,7,2 are combined mentally, as they are obtained, in the usual way:

$$12,17 = 137$$

$$137,12 = 1382$$

$$1382,7,2 = \mathbf{138272}$$

So we multiply crosswise in every position, but we multiply vertically also at the very beginning and at the very end.

 Find **31013 × 21**.

Here the 21 takes the positions:

3 1 0 1 3	3 1 0 1 3	3 1 0 1 3	3 1 0 1 3
2 1	2 1	2 1	2 1

The 6 mental steps give: 6,5,1,2,7,3 so the answer is **651273**.

✐ **Practice C**   Multiply using the moving multiplier method:

a	3 2 1	b	3 2 1	c	4 2 1	d	3 2 1	e	1 2 1 2
	2 1		2 3		2 2		4 1		2 1

f	1 3 3 1	g	1 3 1 3	h	1 1 2 2 1	i	3 4 5 2 6
	2 2		3 1		2 2		1 1

a	6 741	b	7 383	c	9 262	d	13 161	e	25 452
f	29 282	g	40 703	h	246 862	i	379786		

5.3 ALGEBRAIC PRODUCTS

The same Vertical and Crosswise pattern can be used to find the product of two binomials.

8   Multiply: $(2x + 5)(3x + 2)$.

$$
\begin{array}{ll}
2x \qquad\quad + 5 \\
\underline{3x \qquad\qquad + 2} \\
6x^2 + 19x + 10
\end{array}
$$

Vertically on the left: $2x \times 3x = 6x^2$.
Crosswise: $4x + 15x = 19x$.
Vertically on the right: $5 \times 2 = 10$.

✐ **Practice D**   Multiply:

a $(x + 3)(x + 5)$ b $(x + 7)(x - 2)$ c $(x - 4)(x + 5)$

d $(x - 5)(x - 4)$ e $(2x - 3)(3x + 6)$ f $(3x - 1)(x + 7)$

g $(4x + 3)(2x - 5)$ h $(x + 1)(9x - 1)$ i $(2x + 1)(2x - 1)$

a	$x^2+8x+15$	b	$x^2+5x-14$	c	x^2+x-20
d	$x^2-9x+20$	e	$6x^2+3x-18$	f	$3x^2+20x-7$
g	$8x^2-14x-15$	h	$9x^2+8x-1$	i	$4x^2-1$

So, unlike the current system, the same method is used for algebraic products as for arithmetic ones.

THE DIGIT SUM CHECK

The algebraic form of the digit sum check can be used.
If, for example, we wanted to check Example 8 above: $(2x + 5)(3x + 2) = 6x^2 + 19x + 10$
we check that the product of the sum of the coefficients in the brackets on the left-hand side equals the sum of the coefficients on the right-hand side.

That is $(2 + 5)(3 + 2) = 6 + 19 + 10$.
Since both sides come to 35 this confirms the answer.

5.4 THREE-FIGURE NUMBERS

We can extend the Vertical and Crosswise multiplication to products of any size. The answer can always be found in one line.

Find **504 × 321**.

```
        5   0   4
        3   2   1
      1 6 1 7 8 4
```

The extended pattern for multiplying 3-figure numbers is as follows.

A Vertically on the left, 5×3 = **15**.

```
        5   0   4
        |
        3   2   1
        1 5
```

B Then crosswise on the left,
5×2 + 0×3 = 10.
Combining the 15 and 10, as before:
15,10 = **160**.

```
        5   0   4
          ×
        3   2   1
        1 6 0
```

C Next we take 3 products and add them up,
5×1 + 0×2 + 4×3 = 17. And 160,17 = **1617**.

(actually we are gathering up the hundreds
by multiplying hundreds by units, tens by
tens and units by hundreds)

```
        5   0   4
           ✳
        3   2   1
        1 6 1 7
```

D Next we multiply crosswise on the right,
0×1 + 4×2 = 8: 1617,8 = **16178**.

```
        5   0   4
          ×
        3   2   1
      1 6 1 7 8
```

E Finally, vertically on the right,
4×1 = 4: 16178,4 = **161784**.

```
        5   0   4
              |
        3   2   1
      1 6 1 7 8 4
```

Note the symmetry in the 5 steps:
first there is 1 product, then 2, then 3, then 2, then 1.

We may summarise these steps as follows:

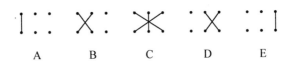

A   B   C   D   E

```
      3 2 1
      3 2 1  ×
    1 0 3 0 4 1
```

The five results are   9,12,10,4,1.
The mental steps are   9

9,12 = 102

102,10 = 1030

1030,4,1 = 103041.

11   Find **123 × 45**.

This can be done with the moving multiplier method or by the smaller vertical and crosswise pattern, treating 12 in 123 as a single digit .

Alternatively, we can put 045 for 45 and use the extended vertical and crosswise pattern:

$$
\begin{array}{ccc}
1 & 2 & 3 \\
0 & 4 & 5 \\
\hline
\multicolumn{3}{c}{5\,5\,3\,5}
\end{array}
$$

For the 5 steps we get 0,4,13,22,15.

Mentally we think 4; 53; 552; 5535.

Similarly we can multiply trinomials etc.

12 $(2x^2 + 3x + 4)(x^2 + 6) = 2x^4 + 17x^3 + 37x^2 + 46x + 24$.

This is just like multiplying two 3-figure numbers.

$$
\begin{array}{r}
2x^2 + 3x + 4 \\
x^2 + 0x + 6 \\
\hline
2x^4 + 3x^3 + 16x^2 + 18x + 24
\end{array}
$$

Note that we put 0x for the missing x-term.

We multiply vertically on the left: $2x^2 \times x^2 = 2x^4$.

Crosswise in the first two columns: $(2x^2 \times 0x) + (3x \times x^2) = 3x^3$.

Next we have: $(2x^2 \times 6) + (3x \times 0x) + (4 \times x^2) = 12x^2 + 0x^2 + 4x^2 = 16x^2$.

Looking at the last two columns: $(3x \times 6) + (4 \times 0x) = 18x$.

And vertically on the right: $4 \times 6 = 24$.

The five steps automatically gather up the same powers of x.

🖉 **Practice E**   Multiply (there are no carries in the first few sums):

a 1 2 1 1 3 1	**b** 1 3 1 2 1 2	**c** 1 2 1 2 2 2	**d** 3 1 3 1 2 1	**e** 2 1 2 3 1 3	**f** 1 2 3 3 2 1
g 2 1 2 4 1 4	**h** 2 2 2 3 3 3	**i** 2 4 6 3 3 3	**j** 1 0 5 5 0 7	**k** 1 0 6 2 2 2	**l** 5 1 5 5 5 5

m $(2x^2 + 2x + 3)(3x^2 + 5x + 1)$ **n** $(x^2 + 6x - 3)(2x^2 + 3x + 4)$

o $(2x^2 + 2xy + 3y^2)(x^2 + 5xy + y^2)$ **p** $(5x^2 - 3x - 8)(5x + 2)$

---

a 15 851	b 27 772	c 26 862	d 37 873	e 66 356	f 39 483
g 87 768	h 73 926	i 81 918	j 53 235	k 23 532	l 285 825
m $6x^4 + 16x^3 + 21x^2 + 17x + 3$			n $2x^4 + 15x^3 + 16x^2 + 15x - 12$		
o $2x^4 + 12x^3y + 15x^2y^2 + 17xy^3 + 3y^4$			p $25x^3 - 5x^2 - 46x - 16$		

5.5 FOUR-FIGURE NUMBERS

Once the vertical and crosswise method is **understood** it can be extended to multiply numbers of any size. We here extend the **pattern one stage further**, and multiply two 4-figure numbers.

13

$$
\begin{array}{cccc}
3 & 2 & 0 & 1 \\
4 & 3 & 0 & 2 \times \\
\hline
1\,3\,7\,7\,0\,7\,0\,2
\end{array}
$$

The 7 steps are illustrated as follows:

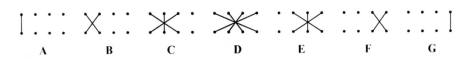

A   B   C   D   E   F   G

Working from left to right we get: **A.** 3×4 = 12

B. 3×3 + 2×4 = 17

C. 3×0 + 2×3 + 0×4 = 6

D. 3×2 + 2×0 + 0×3 + 1×4 = 10

E. 2×2 + 0×0 + 1×3 = 7

F. 0×2 + 1×0 = 0

G. 1×2 = 2

The mental steps are therefore: 12,17 = 137

137,6 = 1376

1376,10 = 13770

13770,7,0,2 = **13770702**

✎ **Practice F**   Multiply the following from left to right or from right to left:

a 2 1 3 1   b 2 0 2 1   c 3 2 0 1   d 5 1 1 3
  3 0 2 2   1 1 2 2   4 0 1 2   5 3 3 1

a   6,439,882   b   2,267,562   c   12,842,412   d   27,257,403

*"We thus follow a process of ascent and descent (going
forward with the digits on the upper row and coming
rearward with the digits on the lower row)."*
From "Vedic Mathematics", Page 42.

5.6 WRITING LEFT TO RIGHT SUMS

This is a continuation of the method introduced in Section 1.3 and will be found useful later for doing combined operations .

 63 × 74 = 662.

$$
\begin{array}{r}
6\ 3 \\
7\ 4 \\
\hline
4\ _2 6\ _5 6\ 2
\end{array}
$$

6 × 7 = 42, put down **4** and carry **2**;

(6 × 4) + (3 × 7) = 45, add carried 2, **as 20**,

45 + 20 = 65, put down **6**, carry **5**;

3 × 4 = 12, add carried 5, **as 50**,

12 + 50 = 62, put down **62**.

 61 × 83 = 5063.

$$
\begin{array}{r}
6\ 1 \\
8\ 3 \\
\hline
4\ _8{}^1 0\ _6 6\ 3
\end{array} = \textbf{5063}
$$

Here if we start with 4_8 we get 106 next and have to carry 1 to the left.

$$
\begin{array}{r}
6\ 1 \\
8\ 3 \\
\hline
5\ _{\bar 2} 0\ _6 6\ 3
\end{array}
$$

Alternatively, if we put $5_{\bar 2}$ instead of 4_8 we get 06 next.

$$
\begin{array}{r}
4\ 3\ 2\ 1 \\
3\ 2 \\
\hline
1\ _2 3\ _7 8\ _2 2\ _7 7\ 2
\end{array}
$$

The moving multiplier method can be used for sums like this.

17 **243 × 316 = 76788.**

$$
\begin{array}{r}
2\ 4\ 3 \\
3\ 1\ 6 \\
\hline
0\ _6 7\ _4 6\ _5 7\ _7 8\ 8
\end{array}
$$

2 × 3 = 6, put down **0** and carry **6**, etc.

18 **3201 × 4302 = 13770702.**

$$
\begin{array}{r}
3\ 2\ 0\ 1 \\
4\ 3\ 0\ 2 \\
\hline
1\ _2 3\ _7 7\ _6 7\ _0 0\ _7 7\ _0 0\ 2
\end{array}
$$

Later lessons (13, 17, 18) will use this method of finding and writing products

✎ **Practice G**

a 47×36	**b** 62×71	**c** 56×65	**d** 41×14	**e** 73×84
f 35×23	**g** 3434×42	**h** 567×82	**i** 444×321	**j** 765×321
k 357×223	**l** 135×531	**m** 5103×3221		

a 1_26_592	**b** 4_24_002	**c** 3_06_140	**d** 0_45_774	**e** $6_{\overline{4}}1_232$ or $5_6{}^1 1_232 = 6132$
f 0_68_105 or $0_67_9{}^1 05 = 805$		**g** 144228	**h** 46494	**i** $1_24_02_45_224$	**j** $2_14_25_45_665$
k $0_67_69_36_{\overline{1}}11$	**l** $0_57_{\overline{1}}1_56_885$	**m** 16436763		

5.7 FROM RIGHT TO LEFT

We can also calculate from right to left if we prefer, though for mental calculations left to right is better.

 86 × 23 = 1978.

$$\begin{array}{r} 8\ 6 \\ \underline{2\ 3} \\ 1\ 9{}_3 7{}_1 8 \end{array}$$

The steps are:
1) $6 \times 3 = 18$,
2) $(8 \times 3) + (6 \times 2) = 36$, $36 + 1 = 37$,
3) $8 \times 2 = 16$, $16 + 3 = 19$.

 4321 × 32 = 138272.

$$\begin{array}{ccccc} 4 & 3 & 2 & 1 \\ & & 3 & 2 \end{array} \qquad \begin{array}{ccccc} 4 & 3 & 2 & 1 \\ & 3 & 2 & \end{array} \qquad \begin{array}{ccccc} 4 & 3 & 2 & 1 \\ 3 & 2 & & \end{array}$$

The 32 takes the three positions shown (moving multiplier method: see Section 5.2).

$$\begin{array}{r} 4\ 3\ 2\ 1 \\ \underline{3\ 2} \\ 1\ 3{}_1 8{}_1 2\ 7\ 2 \end{array}$$

The steps (starting at the right are:
1) $1 \times 2 = 2$,
2) $2 \times 2 + 1 \times 3 = 7$,
3) $3 \times 2 + 2 \times 3 = 12$, write ${}_1 2$,
4) $4 \times 2 + 3 \times 3 = 17$, $17 +$ carried $1 = 18$, put ${}_1 8$,
5) $4 \times 3 = 12$, $12 +$ carried $1 = 13$.

⚜ 21
$$
\begin{array}{r}
2\ 3\ 4 \\
2\ 3\ 4\ \times \\
\hline
5_{\,1}4_{\,2}7_{\,2}5_{\,1}6
\end{array}
$$

We simply do the same operations (see Section 5.4) but start at the right side:
4×4 = **16**, put down 6 and carry 1 to the left.
3×4 + 4×3 = 24, 24 + carried 1 = **25**, put down 5 and carry 2.
And so on.

⚜ 22   Calculating Example 18 from right to left we get the numbers from G to A (Page 74) shown:

$$
\begin{array}{r}
3\ 2\ 0\ 1 \\
4\ 3\ 0\ 2 \\
\hline
1\ 3_{\,1}7\ 7_{\,1}0\ 7\ 0\ 2
\end{array}
$$

✎ **Practice H**   Multiply the following from right to left:

a 33 × 41   b 52 × 62   c 37 × 43   d 73 × 14

e 444 × 333   f 543 × 345   g 707 × 333   h 623 × 32

i 3231 × 2342

a	1353	b	3224	c	1591	d	1022
e	147852	f	187335	g	235431	h	19936
i	7567002						

SETTING THE SUMS OUT

In Example 21 each of the five steps had a center of symmetry.
The five dots on the right show these five centers and as we move
from left to right or right to left through the sum it is as if there is a dot
moving through the sum.
In the calculation shown here the units figure of the result of each of
the five steps is placed under the dot for that step

$$
\begin{array}{r}
2\ \ 3\ \ 4 \\
\bullet\ \bullet\ \bullet\ \bullet\ \bullet \\
2\ \ 3\ \ 4\ \times \\
\hline
5\ 4\ 7\ 5\ 6
\end{array}
$$

Other ways of setting the sums and answers out are possible and may be preferred.

5.8 USING BAR NUMBERS

 Find **34 × 19**.

This is the last sum from Practice B, but suppose here we would like to use bar numbers to remove the large digit 9.

So we change **34 × 19** to **34 × 2$\bar{1}$** :

$$
\begin{array}{r}
3 \ \ 4 \\
2 \ \ \bar{1} \\
\hline
6 \ 5 \ \bar{4} = \textbf{646}
\end{array}
$$

So the bar numbers can be quite useful in removing all digits 6, 7, 8, and 9 from a calculation. This gives us a choice about how to do a calculation (and in fact to facilitate cancellations of positive and negative digits it is sometimes best to leave some digits over 5 in a sum, but this needs some practice to get a feel for what works best).

✎ Practice I

a 19 × 24   **b** 59 × 23   **c** 28 × 31   **d** 19 × 49   **e** 38 × 38

f 292 × 398   **g** 309 × 279

---

a 456   **b** 1357   **c** 868   **d** 931   **e** 1444
f 116216   **g** 86211

Further algebraic products will be found in Lesson 13.

LESSON 6
SOLUTION OF EQUATIONS

SUMMARY
Here we see general and special methods of solving various types of equations.

6.1 **Transpose and Apply**
6.2 **Simultaneous Equations**
6.3 **Quadratic Equations**
6.4 **One in Ratio the Other One Zero** – special types of equation.
6.5 **Mergers** – merging the RHS of special types of equation into the LHS.
6.6 **When the Samuccaya is the Same it is Zero** – special types solved with this Sutra.
6.7 **The Ultimate and Twice the Penultimate** – a special type.
6.8 **Only the Last Terms** – a special type.
6.9 **Summation of Series** – special algebraic and numerical series.

6.1 TRANSPOSE AND APPLY

There are various special types of equation which are solved quickly and easily by special methods in the Vedic system. And there is the general method which comes under the Sutra *Transpose and Apply*.

6.1a SIMPLE EQUATIONS

 Solve $3x + 5 = 17$.

We apply the *Transpose and Apply* formula and write the answer straight down:

$$x = \frac{17 - 5}{3} = 4.$$

No intermediate steps are required, we just take 5 from 17, divide by 3 and we have the answer.

 Solve $\dfrac{x}{2} + 3 = 4$. $x = (4 - 3) \times 2 = \mathbf{2}$ (mentally).

 Solve $\dfrac{2x - 1}{3} = 5$. $x = \dfrac{5 \times 3 + 1}{2} = \mathbf{8}$.

4 Solve $\dfrac{2x^2+17}{5}=7.$ $x=\pm\sqrt{\dfrac{7\times5-17}{2}}=\pm3.$

Practice A   Solve:

a $3x+7=19$

b $4x-5=7$

c $\dfrac{x}{3}+4=6$

d $\dfrac{2x}{3}=8$

e $\dfrac{x+4}{7}=5$

f $\dfrac{2x}{3}+4=8$

g $\dfrac{5x+2}{3}=9$

h $3(5x-2)=54$

i $\dfrac{6}{x}-7=-10$

j $\dfrac{2x}{3}+\dfrac{1}{4}=1$

k $2x^2+3=53$

a	4	b	3	c	6	d	12
e	31	f	6	g	5	h	4
i	−2	j	$\frac{9}{8}$	k	±5		

6.1b MORE THAN ONE X-TERM

If x occurs more than once in an equation we can still get the answer mentally.

5 Solve $5x+3=3x+17.$

We mentally find 2x on the LHS and 14 on the RHS once like terms are combined.
So $2x=14$ and $x=7.$

Equations with fractions can be easily solved using *Vertically and Crosswise*.

6 Solve $\dfrac{x}{3}+\dfrac{2x}{5}=1.$

We cross-multiply and add on the LHS to get the new LHS and we multiply the denominators with the RHS to get the new RHS:

$x\times5+2x\times3=3\times5\times1.$

$\therefore 11x=15,\ x=\dfrac{15}{11}.$

This can be done in one line.
Numerical fractions can also be added in this way, as shown in Manuals 1 and 2. Current mathematical methods for adding and subtracting arithmetic expressions are different from algebraic ones, so we see once again the more unified Vedic approach.

✎ Practice B

a $7x - 5 = 4x + 10$ **b** $5 + 4x = 13 + 2x$ **c** $10x + 1 = 25 - 2x$

d $2(3x + 1) = x + 27$ **e** $\dfrac{2x}{3} + \dfrac{x}{2} = 21$ **f** $\dfrac{4x}{5} - \dfrac{2x}{3} = 4$

---

a 5	**b** 4	**c** 2	
d 5	**e** 18	**f** 30	

In fact Bharati Krsna (Reference 1, Chapter XI) recommends four types of equation as being important and common enough to merit assimilation of the general solution:

1) $ax + b = cx + d$ $x = \dfrac{d - b}{a - c}$

2) $(x + a)(x + b) = (x + c)(x + d)$ $x = \dfrac{cd - ab}{(a + b) - (c + d)}$

3) $\dfrac{ax + b}{cx + d} = \dfrac{p}{q}$ $x = \dfrac{dp - bq}{aq - cp}$

4) $\dfrac{m}{x + a} + \dfrac{n}{x + b} = 0$ $x = \dfrac{-mb - na}{m + n}$

We will be making use of some of these later in this lesson.

6.2 SIMULTANEOUS EQUATIONS

6.2a   GENERAL SOLUTION

Solution of pairs of simultaneous linear equations are solved as follows, also using *Transpose and Apply*:

Given $ax + by = p$

         $cx + dy = q$ then $x = \dfrac{bq - pd}{bc - ad}$ and $y = \dfrac{pc - aq}{bc - ad}$.

> *"The underlying principle behind all of them is Paravartya Yojayet which means: 'Transpose and adjust'. The applications, however, are numerous and splendidly useful."*
> From "Vedic Mathematics", Page 103.

⟨7⟩   Solve $2x + 3y = 13$,
              $5x + 2y = 16$.

$$x = \frac{3 \times 16 - 13 \times 2}{3 \times 5 - 2 \times 2} = \mathbf{2}, \text{ and } y = \frac{13 \times 5 - 2 \times 16}{3 \times 5 - 2 \times 2} = \mathbf{3}.$$

The simple pattern here enables us to put the answer straight down. The method is similar to the current one involving determinants and is easily derived.

✎ **Practice C**

a $3x + 5y = 19$ **b** $2x + 3y = 14$ **c** $4x - 3y = 20$ **d** $2x - y = -15$
     $2x + 3y = 12$ $5x + 7y = 33$ $5x - 2y = 32$ $3x + 7y = 37$

---

a x=3, y=2   **b** x=1, y=4   **c** x=8, y=4   **d** x=−4, y=7

The above method is not recommended for all types of linear simultaneous equations.
It may be considered that the solution to **d** above is better achieved by adding 7 times the first equation to the second (using *Proportionately*). And equations of the form y = f(x) and y = g(x) are usually best solved by equating the right-hand sides.

6.2b SPECIAL TYPES

    Solve $x + y = 6$,
              $x - y = 2$.

Here we use *By Addition and By Subtraction*.

Adding the equations gives $2x = 8$, so $\mathbf{x = 4}$,
and subtracting the equations gives $2y = 4$, so $\mathbf{y = 2}$.

    Solve $19x - 7y = 119$,
              $7x - 19y = 11$.

Notice the patterns in the coefficients of x and y and the signs here: $ax - by = c$
                                                                                $bx - ay = d$.

When we see such a pattern as this then two applications of *By Addition and By Subtraction* will solve the equations.

Adding the equations gives: $26x - 26y = 130$,
                        which on division by 26 gives: $\mathbf{x - y = 5}$.
Subtracting the equations gives: $12x + 12y = 108$,
                        which on division by 12 gives: $\mathbf{x + y = 9}$.

We now apply addition and subtraction to $x + y = 9$,

$x - y = 5$ to get $x = 7, y = 2$.

Another special type comes under the Vedic Sutra *If One is in Ratio the Other is Zero.*

10 Solve $3x + 2y = 6$,
$9x + 5y = 18$.

We notice that the ratio of the x coefficients is the same as the ratio of the coefficients on the right-hand side: **3:9 = 6:18**.
This tells us that since x is in ratio the other one, y, is zero: **y = 0**.
If y=0 we can easily find x by putting y=0 in the first (or the second) equation:
$3x + 0 = 6$. Therefore x=2.
So **x = 2, y = 0**.

So we look out for where the ratio of the x or y coefficients is the same as the ratio on the right: the other unknown is then equated to zero.

11 Solve $2x + 3y - 4z = 4$,
$3x + y + 2z = 6$,
$5x + 4y + 3z = 10$.

Here we see that 2:3:5 = 4:6:10, which means that **y = z = 0** and **x = 2**.

12 Solve $x^2 + xy - 9 = 2y$,
$2x^2 + 3xy - 18 = 4y$.

$-9:-18 = 2:4$ here so **x = 0** and **y = −4.5** is a solution.

Since such special types are not recognised under the current system a lot of extra unnecessary is done in solving them.

Practice D Solve (look out for the special types):

a $x + y = 10$
$x - y = 4$

b $x + y = 22$
$x - y = 4$

c $2x + 3y = 16$
$2x - 3y = 4$

d $5x + 2y = 42$
$5x - 2y = 18$

e $3x + 4y = 32$
$3x - 4y = 4$

f $x + y = 5$
$y + z = 10$
$x + z = 9$

g $a - b = 6$
$a^2 - b^2 = 96$

h $4x - 3y = 18$
$3x - 4y = 10$

i $7x - 4y = 48$	**j** $3x + 2y = 6$	**k** $3x + 8y = 6$	**l** $2x + y + 3z = 8$
$4x - 7y = 18$	$2x + 3y = 9$	$5x + 3y = 10$	$3x + 4y + z = 32$
			$4x + 3y + 2z = 24$

m $2x + y = 2$	**n** $x^2 + y^2 = 9$	**o** $xy + 3y + 4x = 3$
$y + 3z = 2$	$2x^2 + 3y^2 = 27$	$2xy + 6y + 5x = 6$
$3x + 4z = 0$		

a $x=7, y=3$	**b** $x=13, y=9$	**c** $x=5, y=2$	**d** $x=6, y=6$
e $x=6, y=3\frac{1}{2}$	**f** $x=2, y=3, z=7$	**g** $x=11, y=5$	**h** $x=6, y=2$
i $x=8, y=2$	**j** $x=0, y=3$	**k** $x=2, y=0$	**l** $x=z=0, y=8$
m $x=z=0, y=2$	**n** $x=0, y=\pm3$	**o** $x=0, y=1$	

6.3 QUADRATIC EQUATIONS

There is a simple relationship between the differential and the discrimminant in a quadratic equation:

> The differential is equal to the square root of the discrimminant.

The **discrimminant** of a quadratic expression is defined as follows:

> The discrimminant of a quadratic expression is
> **the square of the coefficient of the middle term minus the product of**
> **twice the coefficient of the first (x^2) term and twice the last term.**

That is, in the quadratic expression $ax^2 + bx + c$, the first differential is $2ax + b$ and the discrimminant is $b^2 - 4ac$.

So that $2ax + b = \pm\sqrt{b^2 - 4ac}$.

This is equivalent to the usual form of the formula for solving quadratic equations, $x = \dfrac{-b \pm \sqrt{b^2 - 4ac}}{2a}$, but is much simpler.

    Solve $3x^2 + 8x - 3 = 0$.

The differential is the square root of the discrimminant gives $6x + 8 = \pm\sqrt{100}$.
So $6x + 8 = \pm 10$.
$6x + 8 = 10$ gives $x = \frac{1}{3}$. And $6x + 8 = -10$ gives $x = -3$.

Solve $x^2 - 3x - 1 = 0$ giving the exact answer.

The differential is the square root of the discrimminant gives $2x - 3 = \pm\sqrt{13}$.

Adding 3 on the right and then halving gives an exact answer of $x = \frac{1}{2}(\pm\sqrt{13} + 3)$.

Evaluating square roots is covered in Lesson 11.

✎ **Practice E**   Solve:

a $2x^2 + x - 6 = 0$ b $x^2 - 2x - 4 = 0$ c $x^2 + 5x - 2 = 0$ d $2x^2 + 8x + 1 = 0$

a $x = \frac{3}{2}, -2$ b $x = \frac{1}{2}(\pm\sqrt{20} + 2)$ c $x = \frac{1}{2}(\pm\sqrt{33} - 5)$ d $x = \frac{1}{4}(\pm\sqrt{56} - 8)$

Some special types of quadratic equation are shown in later parts of this lesson.
Another method of solving quadratic equations is shown in Lesson 14.

6.4 ONE IN RATIO THE OTHER ONE ZERO

We have just seen an application of this Sutra in solving a special type of simultaneous
equation. Here is another type of equation solved by this formula.

 Solve $\dfrac{2}{x+4} + \dfrac{3}{x+6} = \dfrac{5}{x+5}$.

In the numerators we see $2 + 3 = 5$. This shows that the equation is linear.

[Multiplying the equation through by $(x+4)(x+6)(x+5)$ gives:
$2(x+6)(x+5) + 3(x+4)(x+5) = 5(x+4)(x+6)$, which shows that because this condition
is satisfied the x^2 terms vanish.]

And since also $\dfrac{2}{4} + \dfrac{3}{6} = \dfrac{5}{5}$ therefore $x = 0$.

 Solve $\dfrac{9}{x+3} + \dfrac{16}{x+4} = \dfrac{14}{x+2}$.

Similarly $\dfrac{9}{3} + \dfrac{16}{4} = \dfrac{14}{2}$ and so $x = 0$.

But $9 + 16 \neq 14$ so this equation is not linear and there is therefore another solution.

17   Solve $\dfrac{3}{2x+3}+\dfrac{5}{2x+5}=\dfrac{4}{x+2}$.

This is also the same type, but it is disguised. Multiplying top and bottom of the RHS by 2 we get:

$$\frac{3}{2x+3}+\frac{5}{2x+5}=\frac{8}{2x+4}$$

and the equation is seen to be linear.

Also $\dfrac{3}{3}+\dfrac{5}{5}=\dfrac{8}{4}$ so we get $2x = 0$ and **x = 0** as the only solution.

✎ **Practice F**

a $\dfrac{1}{x+1}+\dfrac{5}{x+5}=\dfrac{6}{x+3}$ **b** $\dfrac{1}{x+1}+\dfrac{3}{x+3}-\dfrac{4}{x+2}=0$ **c** $\dfrac{2}{x+4}-\dfrac{5}{x+5}=\dfrac{-3}{x+6}$

d $\dfrac{2}{2x+1}+\dfrac{6}{2x+3}=\dfrac{4}{x+1}$ **e** $\dfrac{2}{x+2}+\dfrac{8}{8-x}=\dfrac{6}{3-x}$

---

a x=0   **b** x=0   **c** x=0
d x=0   **e** x=0

There are many special types of equation. Spotting a particular characteristic which makes an equation linear or easy to solve can save a lot of time as well as making the solution process more fun. Each equation should be examined on its own merits: maybe we will find that the solution is obvious once we look carefully at the equation instead of using the same general method every time.

6.5 MERGERS

Here we use *Transpose and Apply* to simplify an equation.

18   Solve $\dfrac{3}{x+4}+\dfrac{2}{x+1}=\dfrac{5}{x+6}$.

As already shown, because the sum of the numerators on the LHS is equal to the numerator on the RHS the equation is linear.

But it does not satisfy the second condition in the last section, as $\dfrac{3}{4}+\dfrac{2}{1}\neq\dfrac{5}{6}$ so $x=0$ is not a solution.

As $3+2=5$ however we can merge the RHS into the LHS to produce a simpler equation.

We take the transposed value of the number in the denominator on the RHS (i.e. -6), add this to each of the numbers in the denominators on the LHS, multiply each result by the numerator of the fraction and put them down as the new numerators:

$$(4-6)\times 3 = -6,\ (1-6)\times 2 = -10.$$

This gives: $\dfrac{-6}{x+4}+\dfrac{-10}{x+1}=0$, or $\dfrac{3}{x+4}+\dfrac{5}{x+1}=0$.

This is one of the four standard types mentioned earlier and so the answer can be put straight down:

$$x = -\frac{23}{8}.$$

Proof

$$\frac{3}{x+4}+\frac{2}{x+1}=\frac{5}{x+6}=\frac{3}{x+6}+\frac{2}{x+6}.$$

Therefore $\dfrac{3}{x+4}-\dfrac{3}{x+6}=\dfrac{2}{x+6}-\dfrac{2}{x+1}$

Therefore $\dfrac{3(x+6-x-4)}{(x+4)(x+6)}=\dfrac{2(x+1-x-6)}{(x+6)(x+1)}$

Therefore $\dfrac{6}{x+4}=\dfrac{-10}{x+1}$ which gives $\dfrac{-6}{x+4}+\dfrac{-10}{x+1}=0$ as before.

An algebraic proof

Given $\dfrac{p}{x+a}+\dfrac{q}{x+b}=\dfrac{p+q}{x+c}$ we have to show that $\dfrac{p(a-c)}{x+a}+\dfrac{q(b-c)}{x+b}=0$.

Splitting the RHS: $\dfrac{p}{x+a}+\dfrac{q}{x+b}=\dfrac{p}{x+c}+\dfrac{q}{x+c}$.

Therefore $\dfrac{p}{x+a}-\dfrac{p}{x+c}=\dfrac{q}{x+c}-\dfrac{q}{x+b}$.

Therefore $\dfrac{p(x+c-x-a)}{(x+a)(x+c)}=\dfrac{q(x+b-x-c)}{(x+c)(x+b)}$.

Therefore $\dfrac{p(c-a)}{x+a}=\dfrac{q(b-c)}{x+b}$ which gives the required result.

✳(19) Solve $\dfrac{2}{2x+1}+\dfrac{6}{3x+2}=\dfrac{9}{3x+4}$.

This does not appear to be the above type, but multiplying the fractions (top and bottom) by 3, 2, 2 respectively we get:

$\dfrac{6}{6x+3}+\dfrac{12}{6x+4}=\dfrac{18}{6x+8}$, in which we now have $6+12=18$.

That a merger is possible is readily seen from the original equation because:
$\dfrac{2}{2}+\dfrac{6}{3}=\dfrac{9}{3}$.

Dividing through by 6: $\dfrac{1}{6x+3}+\dfrac{2}{6x+4}=\dfrac{3}{6x+8}$.

Then using the above merger method the transposed number is –8 and $(3-8)\times1=-5$, $(4-8)\times2=-8$ so that the merged equation is:

$\dfrac{-5}{6x+3}+\dfrac{-8}{6x+4}=0$.

The solution to this is $6x=\dfrac{20+24}{-13}$ and so $\mathbf{x}=-\dfrac{22}{39}$.

✎ **Practice G**   Merge and solve:

a $\dfrac{3}{x+1}+\dfrac{2}{x+3}=\dfrac{5}{x+2}$ b $\dfrac{4}{x+3}+\dfrac{1}{x+1}=\dfrac{5}{x+4}$ c $\dfrac{3}{x-2}+\dfrac{4}{x+1}=\dfrac{7}{x-1}$

d $\dfrac{3}{3x-1}+\dfrac{6}{2x+3}=\dfrac{4}{x+2}$ e $\dfrac{4}{2x-1}+\dfrac{9}{3x-1}=\dfrac{25}{5x-1}$

---

a $x=-7$ b $x=-\frac{13}{7}$ c $\frac{19}{5}$

d $x=-\frac{18}{23}$ e $x=\frac{2}{5}$

There are also complex merger types in which two or more fractions appear on the RHS (Reference 1) and can all be merged into the LHS.

"There, however, are several cases which really belong to this type but come under various kinds of disguises (thin, thick or ultra-thick)! But however thick the disguise may be, there are simple devices by which we can penetrate and see through the disguises and apply the 'Sunyam Samuccaya' formula."
From "Vedic Mathematics", Page 111.

6.6 WHEN THE SAMUCCAYA IS THE SAME IT IS ZERO

The term "Samuccaya" has several meanings.

6.6a SAMUCCAYA AS A COMMON FACTOR

20 Solve $2x + 3x = 4x$.

Clearly here the common factor, x, on each side, shows us that $x = 0$.

21 Solve $4(x - 1) = x - 1$.

Here there is a common factor of $(x-1)$ on both sides. So $x - 1 = 0$ and $x = 1$.

22 Solve $\dfrac{1}{2x+1} + \dfrac{2}{x+3} = x+1$.

By cross-multiplication on the left we see the numerator is $5x + 5$ and so $(x+1)$ is a common factor. So $x + 1 = 0$ and $x = -1$.

6.6b SAMUCCAYA AS THE PRODUCT OF THE INDEPENDENT TERMS

23 Solve $(x + 4)(x + 6) = (x + 3)(x + 8)$.

The product of the independent terms is the same on each side: $4 \times 6 = 3 \times 8$.
So $x = 0$.

24 Solve $(x + 1)(x + 2)(x + 3) = (x + 1)^2(x + 6)$.

Again $1 \times 2 \times 3 = 1 \times 1 \times 6$, therefore $x = 0$.

Also by the first meaning above $x + 1 = 0$, so $x = -1$.

> *"We begin this section with an exposition of several special types of equations which can be solved practically at sight, with the aid of a beautiful special Sutra which reads Sunyam Samyasamuccaya and which, in cryptic language (which renders it applicable to a large number of different cases) merely says: 'when the Samuccaya is the same, that samuccaya is zero' i.e. it should be equated to zero."*
> From "Vedic Mathematics", Page 107.

6.6c SAMUCCAYA AS THE SUM OF THE DENOMINATORS
of two fractions having the same numerical numerator.

 Solve $\dfrac{1}{2x-3}+\dfrac{1}{5x+1}=0$.

The numerators are the same and we have zero on the right so:

$(2x-3)+(5x+1)=0$ and $x=\dfrac{2}{7}$.

 Solve $\dfrac{3x}{x+1}+\dfrac{3x}{x+2}=0$.

Therefore $(x+1)+(x+2)=0$ and $x=-\dfrac{3}{2}$ or $\mathbf{0}$.

6.6d SAMUCCAYA AS A COMBINATION OR TOTAL

 Solve $\dfrac{2x-3}{2x-5}=\dfrac{4x-9}{4x-7}$.

It can be seen by mental cross-multiplication that the equation is linear ($2x \times 4x = 4x \times 2x$), and according to the Sutra, since the sum of the numerators = the sum of the denominators, this total is zero.
That is $6x-12=0$ and $\mathbf{x=2}$.

 Solve $\dfrac{2x+5}{x+3}=\dfrac{6x+35}{3x+17}$.

Here we have $8x+40$ as the sum of the numerators and $4x+20$ as the sum of the denominators. Dividing out the common factor we get $x+5$ for both.

Therefore $x+5=0$ and $\mathbf{x=-5}$.

 Solve $\dfrac{2x-3}{x+4}=\dfrac{x-9}{2x-16}$.

Here the total of the numerators and the denominators are both $3x-12$.
So $3x-12=0$ and $\mathbf{x=4}$.

But mental cross-multiplication reveals that this equation is not linear, but quadratic.

However the samuccaya formula will give us the other solution also: the difference between numerator and denominator on either side is the same, and this we equate to zero.

$x-7=0$, therefore $\mathbf{x=7}$ is the other solution.

PROOF

That the sum of the numerators equals the sum of the denominators can be expressed by:

$$\frac{Ax+B}{Cx+D} = \frac{Ex+F}{(A+E-C)x+B+F-D}. \qquad \qquad \text{- - - (1)}$$

Cross-multiplication and factorisation of this leads to

$$[(A+E)x + B + F][(A-C)x + B - D] = 0$$

in which the first factor is the sum of the numerators in (1) (and is therefore also the sum of the denominators).

The second factor is the difference between the numerator and denominator on the LHS of (1), and it is easily seen that this is also the difference on the right.

EXTENSION

The following generalisation of this application of this Sutra is due to Thomas Dahl of Skona University, Sweden.

 Solve $\dfrac{2\sin x}{\sin x + \cos x} = \dfrac{\cos x}{\sin x}$.

Here we have $2\sin x + \cos x$ as the total of both numerators and denominators, so
$2\sin x + \cos x = 0$ and $\sin x - \cos x = 0$.
So $\tan x = -\frac{1}{2}$ and $\tan x = 1$.

Proposition:

If $\dfrac{A(x)}{B(x)} = \dfrac{C(x)}{D(x)}$ - - - (2)

and if $A(x) + C(x) = B(x) + D(x)$,

then i) solutions of $A(x) + C(x) = 0$
and ii) solutions of $A(x) - B(x) = 0$, are also solutions of (2)

Proof:

Write A for A(x) etc.
Suppose $A + C = B + D$
and suppose that $A + C = 0$ (so that also $B + D = 0$)   - - - (3)
then $AD + CD = 0$,
and since by (3) $D = -B$ we have: $AD - BC = 0$
$\Leftrightarrow \dfrac{A}{B} = \dfrac{C}{D}$.   Q.E.D.

6.6e OTHER TYPES

31   Solve $\dfrac{1}{x-3}+\dfrac{1}{x-5}=\dfrac{1}{x-2}+\dfrac{1}{x-6}$.

With the same meaning, total, of the word samuccaya we can also solve an equation of this type in which we see that the numerators are all equal, and that the sum of the denominators on each side are equal, i.e. $2x - 8$.

Therefore we say $2x - 8 = 0$ and **x = 4.**

Explanation

Mentally adding the fractions on each side of the given equation we find that we have the same numerator, $2x - 8$, on each side. And by the first meaning of samuccaya above we can say that this is equal to zero.

And there are no other solutions because adding the fractions like this gives

$$\frac{1}{(x-3)(x-5)}=\frac{1}{(x-2)(x-6)}$$ which means $(x–3)(x–5) = (x–2)(x–6)$.

The x^2-terms are the same on each side, and the x-terms are the same on each side (because of the property peculiar to this type of equation).

32   Solve $\dfrac{2x}{2x-1}+\dfrac{2x}{x+13}=\dfrac{2x}{x+8}+\dfrac{2x}{2x+4}$.

Similarly $3x + 12$ is the total of the denominators on each side, so **x = –4, 0.**

33   Solve $\dfrac{3}{x+3}+\dfrac{5}{x+5}=\dfrac{1}{x+1}+\dfrac{7}{x+7}$.

This is a quadratic equation. First we observe that $\dfrac{3}{3}+\dfrac{5}{5}=\dfrac{1}{1}+\dfrac{7}{7}$ which means that one is in ratio and so $x = 0$.

Observing that the sum of the denominators on each side is the same we can, by the present formula, equate this to zero.

Therefore $2x + 8 = 0$, and **x = –4, 0.**

"The Sutras are very short; but, once one
understands them and the modus operandi
inculcated therein for their practical application,
the whole thing becomes a sort of children's play
and ceases to be a 'problem'."
From "Vedic Mathematics", Page 13.

Explanation
A general form of an equation of the above type is:

$$\frac{a}{x+a}+\frac{b}{x+b}=\frac{c}{x+c}+\frac{a+b-c}{x+a+b-c}$$ in which the sum of the numerators is a+b on each side,

and the sum of the denominators is 2x+a+b on each side.

That $x = \dfrac{-a-b}{2}$ can be seen by substituting this into the above equation.

 34 Solve $(x-4)^3 + (x-10)^3 = 2(x-7)^3$.

Here we observe that, disregarding the cube powers, the sum of the binomials on the LHS is twice the binomial on the right, i.e. (x–4) + (x–10) = 2(x–7).

Therefore we can say $x - 7 = 0$ and **x = 7**.

Explanation
Since the binomial on the right is the average of the binomials on the left the number that brings the RHS to zero will bring the two terms on the LHS to equal but opposite numbers, and it will therefore also be zero.

The above solution is in fact the only solution to this equation and this will hold for all equations of the form: $(x-a)^3 + (x-b)^3 = 2(x - \frac{a+b}{2})^3$.

 35 Solve $\dfrac{(x+2)^3}{(x+3)^3} = \dfrac{x+1}{x+4}$.

Here we see that, disregarding the powers:
the sum of the numerator and denominator on the LHS
         = the sum of the numerator and denominator on the RHS
         =2x + 5.
Therefore $2x + 5 = 0$ and **x = –2½**.

In fact, like the previous example, such equations are linear.

Explanation
Again the solution is minus the average of the numbers 2, 3 and of 1, 4 on each side, so that the ratios $\dfrac{x+2}{x+3}$ and $\dfrac{x+1}{x+4}$ are both equal to –1.

It will be seen that the numbers 1, 2, 3, 4 in the equation are in arithmetic progression and this is a characteristic of this type. If however the extreme terms in the progression are under the cubes, i.e. $\dfrac{(x+1)^3}{(x+4)^3} = \dfrac{x+2}{x+3}$ then x = –2½ is still a solution, but it is not the only one, the equation being in fact a cubic.

✏ **Practice H**   Use the *Samuccaya* Sutra to solve:

a $3x + 3 = 12x + 12$
b $\dfrac{1}{x-4} + \dfrac{1}{x+10} = 0$
c $\dfrac{3}{x-4} - \dfrac{3}{6-x} = 0$

d $\dfrac{x+2}{x+3} + \dfrac{x+2}{x+7} = 0$
e $\dfrac{x+3}{x+4} = \dfrac{2x+5}{2x+4}$
f $\dfrac{x+2}{2x+1} = \dfrac{x+1}{2x+5}$

g $\dfrac{2x+1}{x+2} = \dfrac{2x-3}{3x-4}$
h $\dfrac{1}{x+3} + \dfrac{1}{x+7} = \dfrac{1}{x+1} + \dfrac{1}{x+9}$
i $\dfrac{1}{2x+9} + \dfrac{1}{2x+3} = \dfrac{1}{2x+5} + \dfrac{1}{2x+7}$

j $\dfrac{2}{x+2} + \dfrac{5}{x+5} = \dfrac{1}{x+1} + \dfrac{6}{x+6}$
k $(x-3)^3 + (x-9)^3 = 2(x-6)^3$
l $\dfrac{(x+3)^3}{(x+5)^3} = \dfrac{x+1}{x+7}$

a $x+1=0, \therefore x = -1$
b $2x+6=0, \therefore x = -3$
c $2x-10=0, \therefore x = 5$
d $x+2=0, \therefore x = -2$
e $3x+8=0, \therefore x = -\frac{8}{3}$
f $2x+3=0, \therefore x = -\frac{3}{2}$
  $2x+10=0, \therefore x = -5$
g $4x-2=0, \therefore x = \frac{1}{2}$
h $2x+10=0, \therefore x = -5$
i $4x+12=0, \therefore x = -3$
  $x-1=0, \therefore x = 1$
j $x=0$
k $2x-12=0, \therefore x = 6$
l $2x+8=0, \therefore x = -4$
  $2x+7=0, \therefore x = -\frac{7}{2}$

This Sutra, *When the Samuccaya is the Same it is Zero*, was in fact in use when we were casting out nines or figures that total nine in Lesson 1. For example, to get the digit sum of 425 we can cast out the 4 and 5, as they total nine, and give the digit sum as 2: *when the total is the same (as 9) it is zero (can be cast out).*

The Sutra also applies in cancelling a common factor from the top and bottom of a fraction.

6.7 THE ULTIMATE AND TWICE THE PENULTIMATE

 36 Solve $\dfrac{1}{(x+1)(x+2)} + \dfrac{1}{(x+1)(x+3)} = \dfrac{1}{(x+1)(x+4)} + \dfrac{1}{(x+2)(x+3)}$.

The Sutra *The Ultimate and Twice the Penultimate* applies for the solution of an equation of the form $\dfrac{1}{AB} + \dfrac{1}{AC} = \dfrac{1}{AD} + \dfrac{1}{BC}$ where the factors A, B, C, D are in arithmetical progression.

Then $(x+4) + 2(x+3) = 0$ and $x = -\dfrac{10}{3}$.

Practice I   Solve: $\dfrac{1}{(x+7)(x+5)} + \dfrac{1}{(x+7)(x+3)} = \dfrac{1}{(x+7)(x+1)} + \dfrac{1}{(x+5)(x+3)}$

Answer: $(x+1) + 2(x+3) = 0, \therefore x = -\frac{7}{3}$

A proof of this will be found in Reference 1. Page 148.

6.8 ONLY THE LAST TERMS

37   Solve $\dfrac{x^2 + 2x + 3}{x^2 + 4x + 9} = \dfrac{x+2}{x+4}$.

We see that the first two terms of the numerator and denominator on the LHS have the same ratio as the terms on the RHS.

That is, $\dfrac{x^2 + 2x}{x^2 + 4x} = \dfrac{x+2}{x+4}$.

Only the Last Terms tells us that in such a case we can equate the RHS to the last terms on the left.

So $\dfrac{x+2}{x+4} = \dfrac{3}{9}$ from which by cross-multiplication we find **x = –1**.

Explanation
By cross-multiplication of the original equation we see that the x^3 terms cancel out, as do the x^2 terms. The equation is therefore linear.

The equation is of the form $\dfrac{AC+D}{BC+E} = \dfrac{A}{B}$ and by cross-multiplication of this we get:

$ABC + DB = ABC + AE$ and from this we get $\dfrac{A}{B} = \dfrac{D}{E}$.

38   Solve $(x+1)(x+6)(x+8) = (x+3)(x+5)(x+7)$.

This is a disguised example as the equation can be re-written: $\dfrac{(x+1)(x+6)}{(x+3)(x+5)} = \dfrac{x+7}{x+8}$

or $\dfrac{x^2+7x+6}{x^2+8x+15}=\dfrac{x+7}{x+8}$.

This is of the above type and so $\dfrac{x+7}{x+8}=\dfrac{6}{15}$ and $x=-\dfrac{19}{3}$.

✎ Practice J

a $\dfrac{x^2+5x+1}{x^2-x+3}=\dfrac{x+5}{x-1}$　　b $\dfrac{2-2x-3x^2}{2-5x-6x^2}=\dfrac{3x+2}{6x+5}$　　c $\dfrac{58x^2+87x+7}{87x^2+145x+11}=\dfrac{2x+3}{3x+5}$

---

a $x=-8$　　　b $x=-1$　　　c $x=2$

6.9 SUMMATION OF SERIES

The same Sutra *Only the Last Terms* enables us to sum certain types of series.

 Find the sum of the first three terms of the series:

$$\frac{1}{(x+1)(x+2)}+\frac{1}{(x+2)(x+3)}+\frac{1}{(x+3)(x+4)}+\dots$$

Let S_3 denote the sum of the first three terms.
We note the special characteristic here: that the terms in the denominator are in arithmetic progression.

The formula says that therefore S_3 is a fraction whose numerator is the sum of the numerators and whose denominator is the product of the first and last terms.

Therefore $S_3=\dfrac{3}{(x+1)(x+4)}$.

Similarly $S_5=\dfrac{5}{(x+1)(x+6)}$ and $S_{31}=\dfrac{31}{(x+1)(x+32)}$.

 Find S_4 for $\dfrac{1}{(x+2)(3x+1)}+\dfrac{1}{(3x+1)(5x+0)}+\dfrac{1}{(5x+0)(7x-1)}+\dots$

The arithmetic progression is there and so $S_4=\dfrac{4}{(x+2)(9x-2)}$.

41 Solve: $\dfrac{3}{(x+2)(x+3)}+\dfrac{3}{(x+3)(x+4)}=2$

Summing the series on the LHS we get: $\dfrac{6}{(x+2)(x+4)}=2$, which leads to the solutions $x=-1,\ x=-5$.

 42 Find S_4 for $\dfrac{1}{5\times9}+\dfrac{1}{9\times13}+\dfrac{1}{13\times17}+\ldots$

The same characteristic being present we can say $S_4=\dfrac{4}{5\times21}$.

43 Find $\dfrac{1}{15}+\dfrac{1}{35}+\dfrac{1}{63}$.

Since $\dfrac{1}{15}+\dfrac{1}{35}+\dfrac{1}{63}=\dfrac{1}{3\times5}+\dfrac{1}{5\times7}+\dfrac{1}{7\times9}$ we can therefore say the sum is $\dfrac{3}{3\times9}=\dfrac{1}{9}$.

44 Find S_3 for $\dfrac{3}{(x+5)(x+8)}+\dfrac{7}{(x+8)(x+15)}+\dfrac{8}{(x+15)(x+23)}+\ldots$

This is a different variety, the special characteristic being that each numerator is the difference of the binomial terms in the denominator.

Therefore $S_3=\dfrac{18}{(x+5)(x+23)}$.

✎ **Practice K**

a $\dfrac{1}{(x+3)(x+5)}+\dfrac{1}{(x+5)(x+7)}+\dfrac{1}{(x+7)(x+9)}+\ldots$ find S_3

b $\dfrac{1}{(x+2)(3x+1)}+\dfrac{1}{(3x+1)(5x+0)}+\dfrac{1}{(5x+0)(7x-1)}+\ldots$ find S_4

c $\dfrac{1}{2\times7}+\dfrac{1}{7\times12}+\dfrac{1}{12\times17}+\ldots$ find S_5

d $\dfrac{1}{(x+7)(x+8)}+\dfrac{2}{(x+8)(x+10)}+\dfrac{14}{(x+10)(x+24)}+\ldots$ find S_3

e Solve: $\dfrac{3}{(x+5)(x+8)} + \dfrac{7}{(x+8)(x+15)} = \dfrac{10}{11}$

---

a $\dfrac{3}{(x+3)(x+9)}$ **b** $\dfrac{4}{(x+2)(9x-2)}$ **c** $\dfrac{5}{2\times 27}$ **d** $\dfrac{17}{(x+7)(x+24)}$ **e** $x = -4, x = -16$

6.10 FACTORISATION

The Vedic method of factorising quadratic expressions in one unknown is not given here (see Reference 1 or 3).

45   Factorise: $2x^2 + 6y^2 + 3z^2 + 7xy + 11yz + 7zx$.

We apply *By Alternate Elimination and Retention*, which means we can first eliminate z, by putting z = 0, and retain x and y: $2x^2 + 7xy + 6y^2 = (x + 2y)(2x + 3y)$.

Next put y = 0 to eliminate y and retain x and z: $2x^2 + 7zx + 3z^2 = (x + 3z)(2x + z)$. So, filling in the gaps we get: $(x + 2y + 3z)(2x + 3y + z)$.

46   Factorise: $a(b + c)^2 + b(c + a)^2 + c(a + b)^2 - 3abc$.

Again here we can alternately put a, b and c = 0.
This gives: $bc^2 + cb^2 = bc(b + c)$,
$ac^2 + a^2c = ac(a + c)$,
$ab^2 + a^2b = ab(a + b)$, respectively.

We can combine these as: $(a + b + c)(ab + ac + bc)$.

The alternative possibility here, $(a + b)(a + c)(b + c)$, can be discounted as it does not give the last term of the given expression.

Sometimes more than one variable can usefully be equated to zero.

LESSON 7
SQUARES AND SQUARE ROOTS

SUMMARY
This lesson shows the neat and easy general method for squaring numbers (from left to right or right to left) and square roots of perfect squares. It also sets things up for general square roots (Lesson 11) which has applications in other sections of this book.

7.1 Squaring 2-Figure Numbers
7.2 Algebraic Squaring – squaring binomials.
7.3 Squaring Longer Numbers – squaring 3 and 4-figure numbers.
7.4 Written Calculations – writing squaring sums, left to right and right to left.
7.2 Square Roots of Perfect Squares – square roots of numbers up to 40,000.

The *Vertically and Crosswise* formula simplifies nicely when the numbers being multiplied are the same, and gives us a really easy method for squaring numbers.

7.1 SQUARING 2-FIGURE NUMBERS

We will use the term **Duplex**, D, as follows:

for 1 figure **D is its square**,   e.g. $D(4) = 4^2 = 16$;

for 2 figures **D is twice their product**, e.g. $D(43) = 2 \times 4 \times 3 = 24$.

🖉 **Practice A**   Find the Duplex of the following numbers:

a 5	b 23	c 55	d 2	e 14	f 77	g 26	h 90
a 25	b 12	c 50	d 4	e 8	f 98	g 24	h 0

> The square of any number is just the total of its Duplexes,
> combined in the way we have been using for mental multiplication.

1    $43^2 = 1849$.

Working from left to right there are three duplexes in 43: D(4), D(43) and D(3).
$D(4) = 16$, $D(43) = 24$, $D(3) = 9$.

Combining these three results in the usual way we get: 16
                                                        $16, 24 = 184$
                                                        $184, 9 = \mathbf{1849}$

 $64^2 = 4096$.

D(6) = **36**, D(64) = **48**, D(4) = **16**,
So mentally we get: 36
                        $36, 48 = 408$
                        $408, 16 = \mathbf{4096}$

✎ **Practice B**   Square the following:

a 31   b 14   c 41   d 26   e 23   f 32   g 21

h 66   i 81   j 91   k 56   l 63   m 77

a	961	b	196	c	1681	d	676	e	529	f	1024	g	441
h	4356	i	6561	j	8281	k	3136	l	3969	m	5929		

Proof: $(10a + b)^2 = 100(a^2) + 10(2ab) + b^2$

7.2 ALGEBRAIC SQUARING

This is just like squaring 2–figure numbers.

 Find $(2x + 3)^2$.

There are three Duplexes: D(2x) = $\mathbf{4x^2}$, D(2x+3) = $2\times2x\times3 = \mathbf{12x}$, D(3) = **9**.
So $(2x + 3)^2 = 4x^2 + 12x + 9$.

 Find $(x - 3y)^2$.

Similarly: D(x) = $\mathbf{x^2}$, D(x–3y) = $2\times x\times -3y = \mathbf{-6xy}$, D(–3y) = $\mathbf{9y^2}$.
So $(x - 3y)^2 = x^2 - 6xy + 9y^2$.

✎ **Practice C**   Square the following:

a $(3x + 4)$ b $(5y + 2)$ c $(2x - 1)$ d $(x + 7)$ e $(x - 5)$ f $(x + 2y)$

g $(3x + 5y)$ h $(2a + b)$ i $(2x - 3y)$ j $(x + y)$ k $(x - y)$ l $(x - 8y)$

| a | $9x^2+24x+16$ | b | $25y^2+20y+4$ | c | $4x^2-4x+1$ | | d | $x^2+14x+49$ | e | $x^2-10x+25$ | f | $x^2+4xy+4y^2$ |
| g | $9x^2+30xy+25y^2$ | h | $4a^2+4ab+b^2$ | i | $4x^2-12xy+9y^2$ | | j | $x^2+2xy+y^2$ | k | $x^2-2xy+y^2$ | l | $x^2-16xy+64y^2$ |

7.3 SQUARING LONGER NUMBERS

We can also find the duplex of 3-figure numbers or bigger.

For 3 figures D is **twice the product of the outer pair + the square of the middle digit,**

$$\text{e.g. } D(137) = 2\times1\times7 + 3^2 = \textbf{23};$$

for 4 figures D is **twice the product of the outer pair + twice the product of the inner pair.**

$$\text{e.g. } D(1034) = 2\times1\times4 + 2\times0\times3 = \textbf{8};$$

$D(10345) = 2\times1\times5 + 2\times0\times4 + 3^2 = \textbf{19};$
and so on.

✎ **Practice D**   Find the duplex of the following numbers:

a 234	b 282	c 717	d 304	e 270
f 1234	g 3032	h 7130	i 20121	j 32104

a	25	b	72	c	99	d	24	e	49
f	20	g	12	h	6	i	5	j	25

Just as for 2-figure numbers the square of any number is just the total of its duplexes.

  $341^2 = 116281$.

Here we have a 3-figure number:
D(3) = 9, D(34) = 24, D(341) = 22, D(41) = 8, D(1) = 1.

Mentally   9, 2 4 = 114

114, 2 2 = 1162

1162, 8, 1 = 116281.

6 $4332^2 = 18766224$.

D(4) = 16,   D(43) = 24,   D(433) = 33,   D(4332) = 34,
D(332) = 21,   D(32) = 12,   D(2) = 4.

Mentally: $16,2\underset{\smile}{4} = 184$

$18\underset{\smile}{4},33 = 1873$

$187\underset{\smile}{3},34 = 18764$

$1876\underset{\smile}{4},21 = 187661$

$18766\underset{\smile}{1},12 = 1876622$

$1876622,4 = 18766224$.

✏ **Practice E**   Square the following numbers:

| a 212 | b 131 | c 204 | d 513 | e 263 | f 264 |

| g 313 | h 217 | i 3103 | j 2132 | k 1414 | l 4144 |

m Find x given that $x23^2 = 388129$

n Find b, c and d given that $b15^2 = 17cccd$

a 44 944	b 17 161	c 41 616	d 263 169	e 69 169	f 69 696
g 97 969	h 47 089	i 9 628 609	j 4 545 424	k 1 999 396	l 17 172 736
m x=6	n b=4, c=2, d=5				

7.4 WRITTEN CALCULATIONS

7.4a LEFT TO RIGHT

In a similar way to Section 5.6 (writing left to right products) we can write down the answers step by step when squaring left to right.

   $43^2 = 1_68_449 = \mathbf{1849}$.

The steps are: D(4) = 16, put 1_6.
D(43) = 24, 24 + 60 = 84, put 8_4.
D(3) = 9, 9 + 40 = 49, put **49**.

8 $234^2 = 0_45_24_57_456 = \mathbf{54756}$.

$D(2) = 4$, put 0_4.
$D(23) = 12$, $12 + 40 = 52$, put 5_2.
$D(234) = 25$, $25 + 20 = 45$, put 4_5.
$D(34) = 24$, $24 + 50 = 74$, put 7_4.
$D(4) = 16$, $16 + 40 = 56$, put $\mathbf{56}$.

But note the carry to the left in the next example.

9 $191^2 = 0_12_8{}^16_34_881 = \mathbf{36481}$.

At the third step we get $D(191) = 83$, $83 + 80 = 163$, put ${}^16_3$.
The 1 in the 16 here is carried leftwards to give **36481**.

✎ **Practice F**   Square the numbers in Practice E in this way.

7.4b RIGHT TO LEFT

This is similar to multiplication from right to left (see Section 5.7).

10 $43^2 = 18_249 = \mathbf{1849}$.

The steps are: $D(3) = 9$, put 9:$\qquad\qquad\qquad 43^2 = \qquad 9$
$D(43) = 24$, put $_24$:$\qquad\qquad\qquad\qquad 43^2 = \quad{}_249$
$D(4) = 16$, $16 +$ carried $2 = 18$, put 18:$\qquad 43^2 = 18_249$

11 $234^2 = 5_14_27_25_16 = \mathbf{54756}$.

$D(4) = 16$:$\qquad\qquad\qquad\qquad\qquad 234^2 = \qquad\quad{}_16$
$D(34) = 24$, $24 + 1 = 25$:$\qquad\qquad 234^2 = \qquad{}_25_16$
$D(234) = 25$, $25 + 2 = 27$:$\qquad 234^2 = \qquad{}_27_25_16$
$D(23) = 12$, $12 + 2 = 14$:$\qquad 234^2 = \quad{}_14_27_25_16$
$D(2) = 4$, $4 + 1 = 5$:$\qquad\qquad 234^2 = 5_14_27_25_16$

12 $191^2 = 3_26_84_181 = \mathbf{36481}$.

$D(1) = 1$:$\qquad\qquad\qquad\qquad\qquad 191^2 = \qquad\quad 1$
$D(91) = 18$:$\qquad\qquad\qquad\qquad 191^2 = \qquad{}_181$
$D(191) = 83$, $83 + 1 = 84$:$\qquad 191^2 = \quad{}_84_181$
$D(19) = 18$, $18 + 8 = 26$:$\qquad 191^2 = \quad{}_26_84_181$
$D(1) = 1$, $1 + 2 = 3$:$\qquad\qquad 191^2 = 3_26_84_181$

An alternative method for 191^2 would be to remove the large digit, 9: $191^2 = 2\bar{1}1^2$.
And $2\bar{1}1^2 = 44\bar{5}\bar{2}1$ (no carries!) $= 36481$.

Practice G   Square the numbers in Practice E from right to left.

7.5 SQUARE ROOTS OF PERFECT SQUARES

For the square root of perfect squares it is worth noting the following facts:

> Square numbers can only end in 1, 4, 5, 6, 9, 0
> and they can only have digit sums of 1, 4, 7, 9.

It is therefore often easy to tell if a number is not a perfect square.

13   Find $\sqrt{6889}$.

First note that there are two groups of figures, 68'89, so we expect a 2-figure answer (we mark off pairs of digits from the right).

Next we use *The First by the First and the Last by the Last*. Looking at the 68 at the beginning we can see that since 68 is greater than 64 (8^2) and less than 81 (9^2) the first figure must be 8.

Or looking at it another way 6889 is between 6400 and 8100

$$6400 = 80^2$$
$$\mathbf{6889 = 8?^2}$$
$$8100 = 90^2$$

so $\sqrt{6889}$ must be between 80 and 90.
Now we look at the last figure of 6889, which is 9.
Any number ending with 3 will end with 9 when it is squared so the number we are looking for could be 83.

But any number ending in 7 will also end in 9 when it is squared so the number could also be 87.

So is the answer 83 or 87?
There are two easy ways of deciding. One is to use the digit sums.
If $87^2 = 6889$ then converting to digit sums we get $6^2 = 4$, which is not correct.
But $83^2 = 6889$ becomes $4 = 4$, so the answer must be **83**.

The other method is to recall that since $85^2 = 7225$ and 6889 is **below** this $\sqrt{6889}$ must be **below 85**. So it must be **83**.

> To find the square root of a perfect square we find the first figure by looking at the first figures of the given square, and we find two possible last figures by looking at the last figure. We then decide which is correct either by considering the digit sums or by considering the square of their mean.

 Find $\sqrt{5776}$.

The 57 at the beginning is between 49 and 64, so the first figure must be 7.

The 6 at the end tells us the square root ends in 4 or 6.
So the answer is 74 or 76.

$74^2 = 5776$ becomes $4 = 7$ which is not true in terms of digit sums, so 74 is not the answer.
$76^2 = 5776$ becomes $7 = 7$ so **76** is the answer.

Alternatively to choose between 74 and 76 we note that $75^2 = 5625$ and 5776 is greater than this so the square root must be greater than 75. So it must be **76**.

✎ **Practice H**   Find (mentally) the square root of:

a 2116	b 5329	c 1444	d 6724	e 3481	f 4489	g 8836
h 361	i 784	j 3721	k 2209	l 4225	m 9604	n 5929

a	46	b	73	c	38	d	82	e	59	f	67	g	94
h	19	i	28	j	61	k	47	l	65	m	98	n	77

 Find $\sqrt{31329}$.

If we mark off pairs of digits from the right here we get   3'13'29.
We have three groups, indicating that the answer is a 3-figure number.

However if you know all the square numbers up to 20^2 we can still get the answer by this method. We think of 31329 as 313'29.

Since 313 lies between 289 (17^2) and 324 (18^2) the first two figures must be 17.
And the last figure is 3 or 7, so 173 and 177 are the two possibilities.

The digit sum will then confirm **177** as the right one.

Alternatively you may argue that since 313 is closer to 324 than 289 it will be **177** rather than 173.

✎ **Practice I**   Find the square root of :

a 26896	b 32761	c 16129	d 24964	e 36864	f 18496
g 21025	h 29929	i 14161	j 11236		

---

a 164	b 181	c 127	d 158	e 192	f 136
g 145	h 173	i 119	j 106		

LESSON 8
APPLICATIONS OF TRIPLES

SUMMARY

This follows on from triple addition in Lesson 4 and shows how we subtract triples, which leads to more applications.

8.1 **Triple Subtraction**
8.2 **Triple Geometry** – working with triples rather than angles.
8.3 **Angle Between Two Lines**
8.4 **Half Angle** – obtaining a triple with half the angle of a given triple.
8.5 **Coordinate Geometry** – gradients. solving circle problems and finding the length of a perpendicular from a point onto a line.
8.6 **Complex Numbers** – products. quotients and square roots of complex numbers.

8.1 TRIPLE SUBTRACTION

If A) **4 3 5** and **B) 15 8 17** find a triple for **A–B**.

The diagram below shows how the angles are subtracted: the base of 15. 8. 17 is placed as usual on the hypotenuse of the 4. 3. 5 triangle. But its hypotenuse is below the base so that the angle B is subtracted from A.

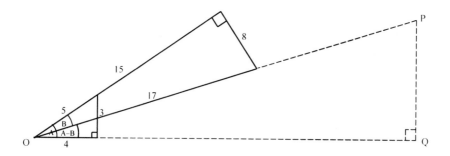

The vertical and crosswise pattern is exactly as before, the difference being that where before we subtracted we now add. and where before we added we now subtract:

A	4	3	5	
B	15	8	17	–
A–B	$(4 \times 15 + 3 \times 8)$,	$(3 \times 15 - 4 \times 8)$,	(5×17)	
=	84	13	85	

Alternatively we may think of triple subtraction as adding a triple with a negative height:

$$
\begin{array}{c|ccc}
A & 4 & 3 & 5 \\
B & 15 & -8 & 17 & + \\
\hline
A{-}B & 84 & 13 & 85 & \text{as above.}
\end{array}
$$

$$
\begin{array}{ccc}
3 & 4 & 5 \\
4 & 3 & 5 & - \\
\hline
24 & 7 & 25
\end{array}
$$

$$
\begin{array}{c|ccc}
A & 4 & 3 & 5 \\
B & 3 & 4 & 5 & - \\
\hline
A{-}B & 24 & -7 & 25
\end{array}
$$

Here we get a triple with a negative height. This is because B, the angle being subtracted, is larger than the angle A. See the diagram below.

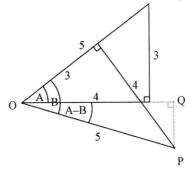

 If **A) –3 4 5** and **B) 12 5 13** find a triple for **2A–B**.

$$
\begin{array}{c|ccc}
A & -3 & 4 & 5 \\
2A & -7 & -24 & 25 \\
B & 12 & 5 & 13 & - \\
\hline
2A{-}B & -204 & -253 & 325
\end{array}
$$

Here 2A and 2A–B are both in the third quadrant.

✐ **Practice A**   Subtract the following triples:

a	b	c	d	e
7 24 25	4 3 5	12 5 13	12 5 13	3 –4 5
3 4 5 –	12 5 13 –	24 7 25 –	3 4 5 –	3 4 5 –

Given A)12,5,13 B)5, 12, 13 C)3,–4,5 find triples for:

f A–B	g B–C	h 2C–B	i A–B–C	j A–A

| a | 117, 44, 125 | b | 63, 16, 65 | c | 323, 36, 325 | d | 56, –33, 65 | e | –7,–24, 25 |
| f | 120,–119, 169 | g | –33, 56, 65 | h | –323,–36, 325 | i | 836, 123, 845 | j | 169, 0, 169 = 1,0,1 |

 Given A) 4 3 5 find a triple for 180°– A.

$$
\begin{array}{c|ccc}
180° & -1 & 0 & 1 \\
A & 4 & 3 & 5 \ - \\
\hline
180°–A & -4 & 3 & 5
\end{array}
$$

That is, we simply change the sign of the first element of a triple to obtain the **supplementary triple**.

 Given A) 3, 4, 5 find a triple for –A.

This means that A is measured clockwise rather than anti-clockwise.

Since 0 – A = –A we can get the required triple by subtracting the triple from A from the triple for 0°:

$$
\begin{array}{c|ccc}
0° & 1 & 0 & 1 \\
A & 3 & 4 & 5 \ - \\
\hline
-A & 3 & -4 & 5
\end{array}
$$

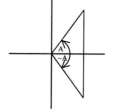

In general we change the sign of the middle element of a triple A to obtain the triple for –A. Geometrically the triangle is simply reflected in the horizontal axis.

 Rotate P(4,–5) clockwise through A) 4,3,5 about the origin.

Rotations were introduced in Lesson 4 where we added triples for anti-clockwise rotations. For clockwise rotations we **subtract** the triples.

$$
\begin{array}{cc}
4 & -5 \ - \\
4 & 3 \quad 5 \ - \\
\hline
1 & -32 \quad -
\end{array}
$$
  ∴ P'(0.2, –6.4).

✎ **Practice B**   Find the following triples:

a Given A) 12, 5, 13 find A–90°   **b** Given A) 15, 8, 17 find A–180°

c   Given A) 5, 12, 13 find triples for: i)   –A
                                                   ii) 45°– A
                                                   iii) 270°– 2A

d   Find a triple for –15°

e   Rotate (0,–3) clockwise about the origin by the triple 3, 4, 5

f   Through what angle (triple) must the point (10,3) be rotated about the origin so that it is in
    the direction OP where P is the point (5,4)?

---

a   5,–12, 13   b   –15,–8, 17
c i) 5, –12, 13   ii) 17, –7, 13 $\sqrt{2}$ iii) –120, 119, 169
d $\sqrt{3}+1, 1-\sqrt{3}, 2\sqrt{2}$ e   (–2.4,–1.8)   f   62, 25, -

8.2 TRIPLE GEOMETRY

We can solve triangles etc. by working with triples rather than angles.

8   **Two angles of a triangle are given by the triples 4, 3, 5 and 5, 12, 13.**
         Find the triple for the third angle.

         Given two angles of a triangle we would normally add them and take the result from
         180°.
         Here we do the same thing with the triples:

$$
\begin{array}{rrr}
4 & 3 & 5 \\
5 & 12 & 13 + \\
\hline
-16 & 63 & 65
\end{array}
$$

         We can subtract this result from the triple for 180° or use the short cut suggested in
         Example 5 to get **16, 63, 65** for the answer.

         Later we will see how to get this result more easily.

9   **Find a triple for angle CAD.**

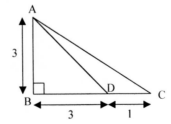

Since the required angle is the difference of the angles CAB and DAB we can write down triples for CAB and DAB and subtract them to get a triple for angle CAD.

CAB	3	4	5	
DAB	1	1	$\sqrt{2}$	−
CAD	7	1	$5\sqrt{2}$	

✎ **Practice C**

a Given that in triangle ABC, AB=AC and that a triple for B is B)12, 5, 13 show that the triple for angle BAC is −119, 120, 169.

b Find a triple for angle CAD:

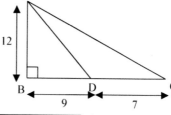

c Find a triple for angle x:

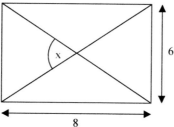

b 24, 7, 25   **c** 7, 24, 25

 10 Find the angle between the lines $3y = 4x - 12$ and $y = x + 10$.

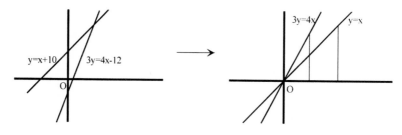

We are interested here only in the slope of the lines and so can disregard the absolute terms −12 and 10.

Then subtracting the line triples gives a triple for the angle between the two lines:

$$
\begin{array}{ccc}
3 & 4 & 5 \\
1 & 1 & \sqrt{2} \quad - \\
\hline
7 & 1 & 5\sqrt{2}
\end{array}
$$
which represents the required angle.

 Find the angle between y = 2x + 9 and 2y = −x − 4.

$$
\begin{array}{ccc}
1 & 2 & \sqrt{5} \\
2 & -1 & \sqrt{5} \quad - \\
\hline
0 & 5 & 5
\end{array}
$$
= 0, 1, 1

The lines are therefore perpendicular.

 Find the angle between y = 2x + 1 and 3y = x.

$$
\begin{array}{ccc}
1 & 2 & \sqrt{5} \\
3 & 1 & \sqrt{10} \quad - \\
\hline
5 & 5 & \sqrt{50}
\end{array}
$$
= 1, 1, $\sqrt{2}$

The angle is therefore 45°.

The angles between pairs of lines in this section have been left in triple form. Finding the angle in a given triple and a triple for a given angle is not dealt with here (see Reference 4).

✏ **Practice D**   Find the angle between the lines:

a y = 3x, y = 2x   **b** 2y = 3x, 3y = 4x   **c** 2y = 3x + 4, y = x + 3

d 2y = 3x, 5y = x   **e** 2y = 3x, 3y = 2x   **f** 3y = 2x, 2y + 3x = 0

---

a 7, 1, $\sqrt{50}$ **b** 18, 1, 5$\sqrt{13}$ **c** 5, 1, $\sqrt{26}$
d 45°   **e** 12, 5, 13   **f** 90°

8.4 HALF ANGLE

Here we see how to find triples containing half the angle in a given triple, and we consider
only the case where $0° < A < 180°$.

13   **Given A) 7   24   25 find a triple for ½A.**

½A) 7+25, 24, - = 32, 24, - = **4, 3, 5**

That is, we add the first and last elements of the triple to get the first element of the half-angle
triple and keep the middle element as the middle element of the half-angle triple.
The third element can be calculated from the first two.

Proof:

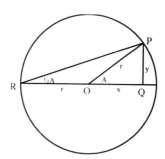

Given a triple A) x, y, r draw a circle centre O, radius r, as shown.
Produce QO to R and join RP.
Then the angle at R is ½A (a well-known circle theorem: the angle subtended at the centre is
twice that at the circumference) so that from ∆RPQ the triple for ½A is ½A) x+r, y, -.

Similarly if A is obtuse, so that x is negative:

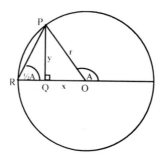

We still have ½A) x+r, y, -

14   If **A) 4, 3, 5** then ½A) 4+5, 3, - = **3, 1, $\sqrt{10}$** .

15   If **A) –3, 4, 5** then ½A) 2, 4, - = **1, 2, $\sqrt{5}$** .

In the diagram the angle A is given by the 3, 4, 5 triple.

Find a triple for the obtuse angle at C.

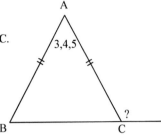

We could subtract 3,4,5 from the 180° triple, halve the result and then subtract from 180°.

	180°		−1	0	1	
	A		3	4	5	−
subtract 3,4,5 from the 180° triple	180°−A		−3	4	5	
halve the result	½(180°−A)		1	2	$\sqrt5$	= B = C
subtract from 180°	180°−C		−1	2	$\sqrt5$	Answer

Alternatively we can halve the isosceles triangle as shown, halve the 3,4,5 triple to get 2, 1, -, for the angle CAD,

find the complementary triple 1, 2, -, for the angle ACD

and then the supplementary triple **−1, 2, -.**

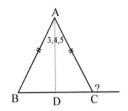

🖉 **Practice E**   Find the half angle triple for:

a 5,12,13   **b** 15,8,17   **c** 8,15,17   **d** 119,120,169   **e** −4,3,5

f −119,120,169   **g** −7,24,25

h Given A) 3,4,5 find triples for: i) ½A
                                              ii) ½A+A

i Find triples for: i) 15°   ii) 22½°   iii) 285°.

j Find a triple for angle x:

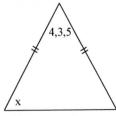

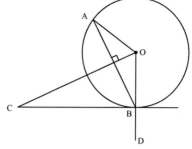

k In the diagram, CB is a tangent to the circle, angle AOB is given by the triple –3,4,5.

Find triples for angles OCB and ABD.

---

a 3, 2, $\sqrt{13}$	b 4, 1, $\sqrt{17}$	c 5, 3, $\sqrt{34}$	d 12, 5, 13	e 1, 3, $\sqrt{10}$
f 5, 12, 13	g 3, 4, 5			
h i) 2, 1, $\sqrt{5}$	ii) 2, 11, 5 $\sqrt{5}$	i i) $\sqrt{3}$ + 2, 1, - or $\sqrt{3}$ + 1, $\sqrt{3}$ - 1, 2$\sqrt{2}$		ii) $\sqrt{2}$ + 1, 1, -
iii) 1, $-\sqrt{3}$ – 2, -	j 1, 3, -	k 2, 1, -, -2, 1, -		

8.5 COORDINATE GEOMETRY

8.5a GRADIENTS

Triples are extremely useful in many areas of mathematics, including coordinate geometry which deals with forms within a 2 and 3-dimensional coordinate system.

This is, in part, because a triple can be used to describe different things, including an angle, a triangle, the position of a point and a gradient.

For example, the line $4y = 3x$ has a gradient of $\frac{3}{4}$ and a 4,3,5 triangle shows a slope with a gradient of $\frac{3}{4}$ if its base is extended to the right:

Similarly $12y = 5x$ will have a gradient of $\frac{5}{12}$ and so its gradient can be represented by the triple 12,5,13.

A triple can describe a point because the coordinates of a point define a right-angled triangle.

So (6,8) is described by the triple 6,8,10:

and (−3,2) by −3, 2, $\sqrt{13}$:

17   **Find the equations of the lines through (5,2) which make an angle of 45° to the line y = 2x + 3.**

There are two possibilities as the 45° could be added to or subtracted from the slope of the line:

line:	1	2	-			line:	1	2	-	
45°	1	1	-	+		45°	1	1	-	−
	−1	3	-				3	1	-	

∴ −y = 3x + c   ∴ 3y = x + c

and since the lines pass through the point (5,2) we get:

−y = 3x − 17 and 3y = x + 1.

8.5b LENGTH OF PERPENDICULAR

22   **Find the length of the perpendicular from the point P(5,2) onto the line 4y = 3x.**

This is the same as finding the distance of the point (5,2) from the line 4y = 3x.
We require the distance PQ in the diagram below.

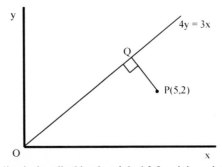

The slope of the line is described by the triple 4,3,5 and the point P can be described by the triple 5,2, $\sqrt{29}$.

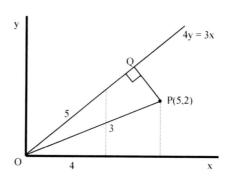

Drawing in the point triple and the gradient triple you can see that by subtracting these triples we get a triple for ΔOPQ:

line triple:	4	3	5
point triple:	5	2	$\sqrt{29}$ −
	26	7	$5\sqrt{29}$
divide by 5	$\frac{26}{5}$	$\frac{7}{5}$	$\sqrt{29}$ = ΔOPQ

Since OP = $\sqrt{29}$ we have to divide the third line through by 5 to make the triangle the right size.

$$\therefore PQ = \tfrac{7}{5} = 1.4.$$

Note: 1. we require only the middle element of the triple for ΔOPQ so we do not need to calculate the others,

2. subtracting the line triple from the point triple would give the same result but with the sign different, therefore we need not trouble ourselves about which triple to subtract from which.

23   **Find the distance of the point (−2,−5) from the line 5y + 12x = 0.**

Think of the equation of the line as 5y = −12x to get the line triple: 5,−12,13.

5	−12	13
−2	−5	-
-	49	-

$\therefore$ Distance = $\frac{49}{13}$.

24 **Find the distance of (6,3) from 3y = 4x + 2.**

Here the line does not pass through the origin.
But we observe that the point (1,2) lies on the line and transpose the origin to there.
Then find the distance of (5,1) from 3y = 4x:

3	4	5	
5	1	-	–
-	17	-	

∴ Distance = $\frac{17}{5}$ = **3.4**.

No adjustment is required due to the transposition of the origin.

 25 **Find the distance of 3x – 2y = 5 from the origin.**

We can transpose the origin to the point (1,–1), which is on the line and then find the
distance of (–1,1) from 3x – 2y = 0:

2	3	$\sqrt{13}$	
–1	1	-	–
-	–5	-	

∴ Distance = $\dfrac{5}{\sqrt{13}}$.

✎ **Practice F**   Find the length of the perpendicular from:

a (–3,2) onto 3y = 4x   **b** (0,4) onto 24y = 7x   **c** (9,10) onto 3y = 4x + 3

d (3,5) onto 6y + 8x = 3   **e** (1,1) onto 12y = 5x – 13   **f** (4,–5) onto y = 3x – 4

g (6,2½) onto 4y = 3x   **h** (4,5) onto y = 2x + 3

i   Find the shortest distance of the line y = 3x from the circle $(x – 4)^2 + (y – 3)^2 = 4$.

a	3.6	b	3.84	c	1.8
d	5.1	e	$\frac{20}{13}$	f	$\frac{13}{\sqrt{10}}$
g	1.6	h	$\frac{6}{\sqrt{5}}$		
i	$\frac{9}{\sqrt{10}}-2$				

8.5c CIRCLE PROBLEMS

18 **Find the coordinates of the points of contact of the tangents to the circle $(x - 3)^2 + (y - 4)^2 = 9$ which pass through the origin.**

The centre of the circle is at (3,4) and the radius is 3.

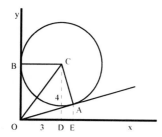

So OC = 5

and OA = OB = 4.

For A we obtain ΔOEA by subtracting ΔOAC from ΔODC:

3	4	5	
4	3	5	–
angle AOE 24	7	25	

∴ as OA = 4 we need to have the hypotenuse of the triple just found equal to 4 and so we multiply by $\frac{4}{25}$ i.e. $\frac{96}{25} \cdot \frac{28}{25} \cdot 4$.

∴ $A\left(\frac{96}{25}, \frac{28}{25}\right)$ And B is clearly at **(0,4)**.

19 **Find the equation of the circle, centre (3,4), to which the line $y = 2x$ is tangential.**

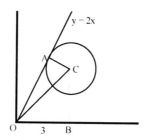

We need the radius of the circle, AC.
Since the (triple) sum of the two triangles shown has a gradient of 2 we can find ΔOAC by triple subtraction:

$$
\begin{array}{ccc}
1 & 2 & \sqrt{5} \\
3 & 4 & 5 \\
\hline
\text{angle AOC} \quad 11 & 2 & 5\sqrt{5}
\end{array}
\quad - \quad = \quad \tfrac{11}{\sqrt{5}}, \tfrac{2}{\sqrt{5}}, 5, \ \text{since OC} = 5.
$$

$\therefore$ AC = $\frac{2}{\sqrt{5}}$ and the equation of the circle is $(x-3)^2 + (y-4)^2 = \frac{4}{5}$.

 20 **Find the equation of a circle of radius 4 which touches the x-axis and the line 4y = 3x.**

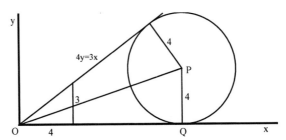

The line triple is 4,3,5 and so the half angle triple is 3,1, -.
$\therefore$ as OP bisects the angle formed by the two tangents $\triangle$OPQ is represented by the triple 3, 1, -.
But since PQ=4 the coordinates of P are (12,4).
The equation of the circle is then $(x - 12)^2 + (y - 4)^2 = 4^2$.

 21 **Find the coordinates of the centre of a circle, radius 6, which touches the lines 3y = 4x and 12y = 5x.**

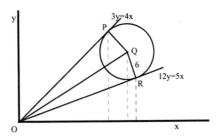

By subtracting the triples for the two given lines we get a triple for angle POR.
The half angle triple then gives us a triple for angle QOR.
We can then add this to the triple for 12y = 5x to get a triple for angle QOx.

So: 3   4   5
          12   5   13   –
          _____
          56   33   65   triple for PÔR

Halving this we get: 11, 3, - as a triple for QÔR.
And since QR = 6, OR = 22.

∴   22   6   OQ
         15   5   13   +
         _____
         234   182 13OQ = 18, 14, OQ.

The coordinates of Q are therefore **(18,14)**.

✐ Practice G

a Find the equations of the lines through the point (3,1) which make an angle of 45° to the
line y = 3x + 1

b Find the equation of the circle, centre (2,5), to which the line y = 3x is tangential.

c Find the equation of the upper tangent from the origin to the circle:
$(x – 24)^2 + (y – 7)^2 = 15^2$.

---

a   y=-2x+7, 2y=x-1   b $(x-2)^2 + (y-5)^2 = 0.1$ c   3y = 4x

8.5d EQUATION OF A LINE

The following method for finding the equation of a straight line through two given points is a
slightly modified version of that in the book "Vedic Mathematics" (Reference 1).

 Find the equation of the line through (6,5) and (4,1).

                6   5
                4   1
           _____
           $(6 – 4)y = (5 – 1)x + (6×1 – 5×4)$

∴ 2y = 4x – 14

The coefficient of y is found by subtracting the x-coordinates,
the coefficient of x is found by subtracting the y-coordinates

and the third term is the determinant: $\begin{vmatrix} 6 & 5 \\ 4 & 1 \end{vmatrix}$ i.e. 6×1 – 5×4 = –14.

∴ **y = 2x – 7**

27   Find the equation of the line through (–1,2) and (3,–5).

$$
\begin{array}{cc}
3 & -5 \\
\underline{-1} & \underline{2} \\
4y \;\;=\;\; & -7x + 1
\end{array}
$$

✒ **Practice H**   Find the equation of the line through:

a (7,3), (2,1)   **b** (8,–1), (2,–5)   **c** (–1,7), (–5,4)

d (–3,0), (1,6)   **e** (0,7), (–7,0)   **f** (0,–3), (–1,–2)

| a $5y = 2x + 1$ | b $3y = 2x – 19$ | c $4y = 3x + 31$ |
| d $2y = 3x + 9$ | e $y = x + 7$ | f $y = –x – 3$ |

This easy application of the Vedic formula *Vertically and Crosswise* can be used for solving other problems. For example, in statistics we may need to find a median value in a grouped data distribution and have to use linear interpolation to find it. Or we may need to use linear interpolation to estimate a zero of a function.

28   Given the points (17,12) and (10,7) find the value of x corresponding to y = 10.

We get the equation of the line joining the given points.
This is $7y = 5x – 1$.
And when y = 10 we have **x = 14.2**.

29   Show that $f(x) = x^3 – 2$ has a root between x = 1 and x = 2 and use linear interpolation to get a more accurate value for the root.

We find $f(1) = –1$, $f(2) = 6$, (the change of sign shows there is a root between x = 1 and x = 2),
so using a similar diagram to the one above:

This gives $y = 7x – 8$ for the line and putting y = 0
we get $x = \tfrac{8}{7}$.

In this case though, where y = 0, the answer can be found more easily.
We simply apply *Vertically and Crosswise* to the four known values:

$$ x = \frac{1\times6-(-1)\times2}{6-(-1)} = \frac{8}{7}. $$

That is, we cross-multiply and subtract for the numerator and subtract vertically in the y-column for the denominator.

8.6 COMPLEX NUMBERS

Multiplying complex numbers is similar to adding triples and dividing complex numbers is similar to subtracting triples. This is of course not surprising as the product of two complex numbers involves adding their arguments and the quotient involves subtracting them.

30   Find $(4 + 3i)(12 + 5i)$.

$$\begin{array}{rcr} 4 & + & 3i \\ 12 & + & 5i \\ \hline \end{array}$$
$$(4 \times 12 - 3 \times 5) + (3 \times 12 + 4 \times 5)i = \mathbf{33 + 56i}.$$

That is, we multiply vertically and subtract, then multiply crosswise and add.

31   Find $\dfrac{4+3i}{12+5i}$.

$$\begin{array}{rcr} 4 & + & 3i \\ 12 & + & 5i \\ \hline \end{array}$$
$$[(48 + 15) + (36 - 20)i] \div 13^2 = \frac{\mathbf{63 + 16i}}{\mathbf{169}}.$$

For division we must also divide by the square of the third element of the denominator triple, i.e. $12 + 5i \rightarrow 12, 5, 13$, so divide by 13^2.

This is far easier than the usual division method which involves multiplying top and bottom of the fraction by the complex conjugate of the denominator.

In the case of the square root of a complex number the difference is even more striking.

32   Find $\sqrt{3+4i}$.

We know that when the square root of a complex number is taken the argument gets halved and the modulus gets "square-rooted".

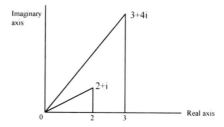

The complex number 3+4i relates to the triple 3,4,5 whose half angle triple is 2,1,-. The numbers 2, 1 are the coefficients of the answer: $\sqrt{3+4i} = \pm(2+i)$.

Since the modulus of 3+4i is 5 we require the modulus of the square root to be $\sqrt{5}$ and the modulus of 2+i is indeed $\sqrt{5}$.

Similarly, $\sqrt{8+6i} = \pm(3+i)$.

$\sqrt{5+12i} = \pm(3+2i)$.

$\sqrt{3-4i} = \pm(2-i)$.

 33 Find $\sqrt{6+8i}$.

The half angle triple for 6,8,10 is 2,1,- but here the modulus of 2+i is $\sqrt{5}$ and $\sqrt{10}$ is required.
We must therefore give the answer as $\pm\sqrt{2}(2+i)$.

 34 Find $\sqrt{4+3i}$.

Similarly the half angle triple for 4,3,5 is 3,1,$\sqrt{10}$ but 3+i has a modulus of $\sqrt{10}$, when $\sqrt{5}$ is required: we must therefore divide by $\sqrt{2}$:

$$\sqrt{4+3i} = \pm\frac{3+i}{\sqrt{2}}.$$

We simply find the half angle triple, compare the moduli and add an appropriate factor if necessary.

Examination questions invariably ask for the square root of a complex number where the complex number given has coefficients which are the first two elements of a perfect triple. If this is not so the arithmetic gets quite 'complex'. The reader is invited to find $\sqrt{2+i}$ by the usual method and also by the triple method above.

For other applications of triples see Reference 4.

✎ **Practice I**   Find:

a $(2 + 3i)(1 + i)$ b $(3 - i)(2 + 3i)$ c $\dfrac{2+3i}{1+i}$ d $\dfrac{3-i}{2+3i}$

e $\sqrt{15+8i}$ f $\sqrt{5+12i}$ g $\sqrt{12+5i}$ h $\sqrt{8+15i}$ i $\sqrt{i}$

---

a $-1 + 5i$ b $9 + 7i$ c $(5 + i)/2$ d $(3 - 11i)/13$

e $\pm(4+i)$ f $\pm(3+2i)$ g $\pm\frac{(5+i)}{\sqrt{2}}$ h $\pm\frac{(5+3i)}{\sqrt{2}}$ i $\pm\frac{(1+i)}{\sqrt{2}}$

LESSON 9
DIVISIBILITY

SUMMARY

This lesson offers a simple procedure, called 'osculation', for testing for divisibility of numbers by prime numbers.

9.1 **Elementary Parts** – small divisors are not dealt with in this book.
9.2 **The Ekadhika** – a useful term, used for the tests that follow.
9.3 **Osculation** – the Vedic divisibility process.
9.4 **Testing Longer Numbers** – extension of osculation technique to numbers with many digits.
9.5 **Other Divisors** – testing for the factors of a potential divisor.
9.6 **The Negative Osculator** – a parallel osculator method involving divisors ending in 1.
9.7 **Osculating with Groups of Digits** – osculating 2, 3 or more digits at a time.

9.1 ELEMENTARY PARTS

We can omit the earlier parts of this topic (as they are well-known) except to mention that *Only the Last Terms* is used to test for divisibility by 2, 4, 8, 5, 10. To test for divisibility by 3 and 9 we use *By Addition*.

So suppose we already know how to tell if a number is divisible by 2, 3, 4, 5, 6, 8, 9, 10 and numbers like 6 and 15 which can be expressed as a product of two or more numbers which are relatively prime.

Next we see how to test for divisibility by larger numbers, and especially prime numbers.

9.2 THE EKADHIKA

You will recall that the **Ekadhika** is the number "one more" than the one before. In this section the Ekadhika is the number *One More Than the One Before* when the number ends in a 9 or a series of 9s.

So for example for **19** the Ekadhika is **2** because the one before the 9 is 1 and one more than 1 is **2**.

For **69** the Ekadhika is **7**.

And for **13** the Ekadhika is **4** because **to obtain a 9 at the end we must multiply 13 by 3**, which gives 39, for which the Ekadhika is **4**.

Similarly, for **27**, to get a 9 at the end we multiply 27 by 7 which gives 189. So the Ekadhika for 27 is **19** (one more than 18 is 19).

✎ **Practice A**   Find the Ekadhika for each of the following numbers:

a 29	b 89	c 109	d 23	e 43	f 7	g 17	h 21

a 3	b 9	c 11	d 7	e 13	f 5	g 12	h 19

9.3 OSCULATION

There are two types of osculators: the positive osculator and the negative osculator.
The positive osculator is just the Ekadhika. We will deal with the negative osculator later.

A simple example will illustrate the osculation procedure, which follows the sub-Sutra *By Osculation.*.

 Find out if **91** is divisible by **7**.

The Ekadhika for 7 is **5, so we osculate the 91 with 5**.

> We osculate a number by multiplying its last figure by the osculator and adding the result to the previous figure.

This means we multiply the 1 in 91 by the osculator, 5, and add the result to the 9.

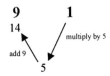

We get **14** as the result.
Since 14 is clearly divisible by 7 we can say that 91 is also divisible by 7.

The result we get from osculation (14 above) can also be osculated: in fact we can continue to osculate as many times as we like.

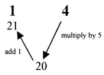

If we osculate **14** with 5 we get $4×5 + 1 = 21$ (also clearly a multiple of 7).

If we osculate this result, **21**, we get $1×5 + 2 = 7$.

If we osculate 7 (think of **07**) we get $7×5 + 0 = 35$.

If you continue this osculation process you will see that only multiples of 7 are produced!

We find that osculating any multiple of 7 with the osculator, 5, always produces a multiple of 7. And osculating any number which is not a multiple of 7 will never produce a multiple of 7.

✳ Osculate 16 (which is not a multiple of 7) with the osculator, 5, and continue to osculate until you have produced at least 8 results. None of your results will be a multiple of 7.

Answers: 16, 31, 8, 40, 4, 20, 2, 10, 1, 5, 25, 27 . . .

The explanation for this is given at the end of this section.

   Test **78** for divisibility by **13**.

First we find the Ekadhika for 13, which is 4 (E=4).

Then osculate 78 with this 4: $8×4 + 7 = 39$.
Since 39 is clearly a multiple of 13 we can say that 78 is divisible by 13.

If we did not recognise 39 as a multiple of 13 we could continue to osculate:
For 39: $9×4 + 3 = 39$.
Here the 39 gets repeated and this also indicates divisibility.
Repetition indicates divisibility.

※ **5**   Test **86** for divisibility by **13**.

We osculate 86 with **4**: $6\times4 + 8 = 32$.
This is not a multiple of 13 so 86 is not divisible by 13.

But we can continue osculating if we do not see that 32 is not a multiple of 13.
Osculating the 32 we get $2\times4 + 3 = 11$.
Clearly 11 is not a multiple of 13, so 86 is not divisible by 13.

✎ **Practice B**   Test the following for divisibility by 7:

a 63   **b** 84   **c** 53   **d** 98

Test for divisibility by 13:

e 91   **f** 52   **g** 86   **h** 65

Test for divisibility by 19:

i 57   **j** 95   **k** 76   **l** 114 (multiply 4 by the osculator
                                                                  and add on 11)

Test for divisibility by 29:

m 87   **n** 116   **o** 57   **p** 58

Test for divisibility by 17:

q 85   **r** 56   **s** 51   **t** 102

a	yes	b	yes	c	no	d	yes
e	yes	f	yes	g	no	h	yes
i	yes	j	yes	k	yes	l	yes
m	yes	n	yes	o	no	p	yes
q	yes	r	no	s	yes	t	yes

EXPLANATION

First note the following two facts:
1. addition or subtraction of zeros to or from the end of a number do not affect the divisibility or non-divisibility of that number by the potential divisor;
2. addition or subtraction of the divisor or multiples of the divisor do not affect the divisibility or non-divisibility of a number.

So if we want to know if 247 is divisible by 19, which is the same as $2\bar{1}$, we add $2\bar{1}$ as many times as are needed to bring the 7 in 247 to zero, which means adding it 7 times.
This means we are adding $\bar{1}$ seven times to the 7 in 247 and adding 2 seven times to the 4 in 247.

This gives $2/_18/0$ and the zero can be dropped off to give $2/_18$.
We can then either repeat this process with the 18 (adding $2\bar{1}$ 18 times) or else we can carry the subscript 1 over to the left and remove the 8 by adding $2\bar{1}$ eight times.
In the latter case we add $16/\bar{8}$ to 3/8 to get 19/0 and dropping the zero leaves 19.

9.4 TESTING LONGER NUMBERS

If the number we are testing is a long number the osculation procedure is simply extended.

 Is **247** divisible by 19?

The Ekadhika is **2**.
We multiply the 7 by 2 and add on the next figure, the 4:

$$\begin{array}{ccc} 2 & 4 & 7 \\ & & 18 \end{array}$$

$7\times2 + 4 = 18$. We put this under the 4 as shown.

We then multiply this 18 by 2 and add the 2 at the left of 247:

$$\begin{array}{ccc} 2 & 4 & 7 \\ 38 & 18 \end{array}$$

$18\times2 + 2 = 38$ which is two 19s so **247 is divisible by 19.**

There is a useful short-cut however which prevents the numbers on the bottom line from getting too big.

Suppose the first stage is completed, so that we have:

$$\begin{array}{ccc} 2 & 4 & 7 \\ & 18 & \end{array}$$

Instead of multiplying 18 by 2 and adding the 2 on, we can suppose that the 1 in the 18 is carried over to join the 2. So we multiply only the 8 by 2 and add the 1 next to it *and* the 2.

So $8\times2 + 1 + 2 = 19$:

$$\begin{array}{ccc} 2 & 4 & 7 \\ 19 & 18 & \end{array}$$

This is much easier and the 19 shows again that 247 is divisible by 19.

> *And we were agreeably astonished and intensely gratified to find that exceedingly tough mathematical problems (which the mathematically most advanced present day Western scientific world had spent huge lots of time, energy and money on and which even now it solves with the utmost difficulty and after vast labour and involving large numbers of difficult, tedious and cumbersome "steps" of working) can be easily and readily solved with the help of these ultra-easy Vedic Sutras (or mathematical aphorisms) contained in the Parishishta (the Appendix-portion) of the ATHARVAVEDA in a few simple steps and by methods which can be conscientiously described as mere "mental arithmetic".*
> From "Vedic Mathematics", Page xv.

Is **4617** divisible by **19**?

The Ekadhika is still **2**.
We multiply the 7 by 2 and add on the 1:   **4 6 1 7**
                                                                                        15

Then multiply the 5 by 2 and add on the 1 and the 6:   **4 6 1 7**
                                                                                    17 15

Then multiply the 7 by 2 and add on the 1 and the 4:   **4 6 1 7**
                                                                                19 17 15

We end up with 19 and so **4617 is divisible by 19**.

✎ **Practice C**   Test the following numbers for divisibility by 19:

a 2774   **b** 589   **c** 323   **d** 4313   **e** 779   **f** 4503

g 14003   **h** 1995   **i** 10203   **j** 30201   **k** 234555

a	yes	b	yes	c	yes	d	yes	e	yes	f	yes
g	yes	h	yes	i	yes	j	no	k	yes		

The Ekadhika is 2 for all these. Testing for divisibility for other numbers than 19 means using a different Ekadhika.

 Is **13455** divisible by **23**?

The Ekadhika for 23 is **7**.
We simply osculate as before using this 7: **1 3 4 5 5**
                                                                        69 59 8   40

We have 69 at the end which is clearly three 23s, so **yes: 13455 is divisible by 23**.

✎ **Practice D**   Test the following numbers for divisibility by the number shown:

a 41963 by 29   **b** 4802 by 49   **c** 4173 by 13   **d** 2254 by 23   **e** 10404 by 17

f 1003 by 59   **g** 4171 by 43   **h** 5432 by 7   **i** 4321 by 109

a	yes	b	yes	c	yes	d	yes	e	yes
f	yes	g	yes	h	yes	i	no		

9.5 OTHER DIVISORS

Is **6308** divisible by **38**?

We see that $38 = 2 \times 19$ so we have to test for divisibility by **2 and 19**.
The number is clearly divisible by 2 (because the last figure is even) so we only have to test for 19:

$$\begin{matrix} 6 & 3 & 0 & 8 \\ 19 & 16 & 16 & \end{matrix}$$

6308 is also divisible by 19 so **it is divisible by 38**.

Is **5572** divisible by **21**?

Since $21 = 3 \times 7$ we must test for 3 and 7.
It is not divisible by 3 (digit sum is 1) so we need go no further:
5572 is not divisible by 21.

Is **1764** divisible by **28**?

We must test for 4 and 7 since $28 = 4 \times 7$ (note that 4 and 7 are relatively prime, we do not use $28 = 2 \times 14$ as 2 and 14 are not relatively prime).
The last two figures of 1764 indicate that it is divisible by 4 so we test for 7 next.

The osculator is 5:
$$\begin{matrix} 1 & 7 & 6 & 4 \\ 49 & 39 & 26 & \end{matrix}$$

and we see that the test for 7 is passed.
So **1764 is divisible by 28**.

In testing for divisibility by a number we look at the factors of that number first and start with the easiest factors.

✎ **Practice E**   Test the following numbers for divisibility by the number shown:

a 3538 by 58   b 1254 by 38   c 21645 by 65

d 1771 by 46   e 767 by 95   f 5985 by 95

g 37932 by 58   h 334455 by 39   i 305448 by 52

a	yes	b	yes	c	yes
d	no	e	no	f	yes
g	yes	h	no	i	yes

If we want to test for divisibility by **31** we would have to multiply it by 9 to get a 9 in the last place. This would give 279 and an Ekadhika of **28**, which is too large to osculate with easily. So we need an alternative method here and this is where we use the negative osculator.

9.6 THE NEGATIVE OSCULATOR

The negative osculator for 31 is **3**, we just drop the 1.

The negative osculator for 41 is **4**. And so on.

To get the negative osculator for 17 we need to get a 1 at the end of the number and this can be done by multiplying 17 by 3. This gives 51 so the negative osculator for 17 is **5**.

✎ **Practice F**   Obtain the negative osculator for:

a 61	b 91	c 101	d 11	e 27	f 37
g 7	h 13	i 23	j 19		

---

a 6   b 9   c 10   d 1   e 8   f 11
g 2   h 9   i 16   j 17

Is **3813** divisible by **31**?

We can use the negative osculator here, which is **3**.
The osculation process is slightly different for the negative osculator.
We begin by putting a bar over every other figure in 3813, starting with the second figure from the right:

$$\overline{3} \quad 8 \quad \overline{1} \quad 3$$

We then osculate as normal except that **any carry figure is counted as negative**.

$$\overline{3} \quad 8 \quad \overline{1} \quad 3$$
$$0 \quad 32 \quad 8$$

$3 \times 3 + \overline{1} = \textbf{8},$
$8 \times 3 + 8 = \textbf{32},$
$2 \times 3 + \overline{3} + \overline{3} = \textbf{0}.$

This zero indicates that **3813 is divisible by 31**.

Test **a** 367164 and **b** 6454 for divisibility by 7?

Multiplying the 7 by 3 gives 21, so we can use a negative osculator of **2**.

a We put a bar on every other figure and osculate as above:

$$\overline{3} \quad 6 \quad \overline{7} \quad 1 \quad \overline{6} \quad 4$$
$$0 \quad\; 12 \quad 3 \quad\; 5 \quad\; 2$$

b Similarly:

$$\overline{6} \quad 4 \quad \overline{5} \quad 4$$
$$\overline{7} \quad 10 \quad 3$$

Since $\overline{7}$ is a multiple of 7 we find that **both these numbers are divisible by 7**.

 Is **11594** divisible by **62**?

Since $62 = 31\times2$ we need to test for 31 and 2.
The number is certainly divisible by 2 so we test for 31 by osculating with 3:

$$1 \quad \overline{1} \quad 5 \quad \overline{9} \quad 4$$
$$0 \quad\; 10 \quad 14 \quad 3$$

The number is divisible by 2 and 31 and is therefore **divisible by 62**.

Similarly, asked if the above number is divisible by 63, since $63 = 9\times7$ we would check for divisibility by 9 and then (if it passed this test) test for 7 by either using a positive osculator of 5 or a negative osculator of 2.

[We would not use $63 = 3\times21$ because we would be checking for divisibility by 3 twice and not testing for divisibility by 9. **The factors we split 63 into must be relatively prime.**]

✐ **Practice G**   Test the following for divisibility by the given number:

a 2914 by 31	**b** 9576 by 21	**c** 6039 by 61	**d** 20022 by 71
e 73472 by 41	**f** 63909 by 81	**g** 1728 by 91	**h** 7072 by 17
i 14715 by 27	**j** 7071 by 61	**k** 178467 by 31	**l** 45787 by 7
m 2394 by 42	**n** 4838 by 82	**o** 17949 by 93	**p** 9658 by 11

a yes	b yes	c yes	d yes
e yes	f yes	g no	h yes
i yes	j no	k yes	l yes
m yes	n yes	o yes	p yes

An interesting and useful result is that if you are testing for divisibility by a number, D, and its positive and negative osculators are P and Q respectively, then P + Q = D. So if we know P we can find Q and vice versa.

9.7 OSCULATING WITH GROUPS OF DIGITS

If we are testing for divisibility by, say, 299 which ends in two nines we can osculate two digits at a time.

For 299 we write $P_2 = 3$ meaning that the positive osculator is 3 and we osculate with pairs of digits.

Similarly testing for 60001 we use the negative osculator, Q, with groups of four digits so we write $Q_4 = 6$.

16   Is **80132** divisible by **299**?

Here we have $P_2 = 3$, so:

$$\begin{array}{ccc} 8 & 01 & 32 \\ 299 & 97 & \end{array}$$

We split the given number into pairs of digits starting from the right, then osculate with 3. So $32 \times 3 + 01 = \textbf{97}$
Then $97 \times 3 + 8 = \textbf{299}$.
Therefore **80132 is divisible by 299**.

17   Is **1625325** divisible by **5001**?

Here $Q_3 = 5$, so:

$$\begin{array}{ccc} 1 & \overline{625} & 325 \\ 0 & 1000 & \end{array}$$

Split into groups of three.
$325 \times 5 - 625 = 1000$.
The 1 in this 1000, counts as $\bar{1}$ as it is to be carried, so $000 \times 5 + 1 + \bar{1} = \textbf{0}$.

So **165325 is divisible by 5001**.

> *"The symbology has its deep significance and high practical utility in our determining of the divisibility (or otherwise) of a certain given number (however big) by a certain given divisor (however large) inasmuch as it throws light on (1) the number of digits to be taken in each group and (2) the actual osculator itself in each individual case before us.".*
> From "Vedic Mathematics", Page 288.

Is **358211** divisible by **701**?

Here $Q_2 = 7$, so:

$$35 \quad \overline{82} \quad 11$$
$$ \quad 0 \quad \overline{5}$$

$11 \times 7 - 82 = \overline{5}$.
$\overline{5} \times 7 + 35 = 0$.

So 358211 is divisible by 701.

✏ **Practice H**   Test the following for divisibility by the given number:

a 647546 by 199   b 3304662 by 299   c 2784607 by 1999

d 264385741 by 1999   e 1821849 by 499   f 12256985 by 701

g 41221372 by 1001   h 359061579 by 999

---

a yes   b no   c yes   d yes   e yes   f yes   g no   h yes

To test for divisibility of numbers which do not end in nine (or nines) or end in 1 (or a series of zeros ending in 1) we take a suitable multiple of the number we are testing for, which does have one of these characteristics.

  Obtain a suitable osculator for **857**.

Since $857 \times 7 = 5999$ we can use $\mathbf{P_3 = 6}$.

20 Obtain a suitable osculator for **43**.

Since $43 \times 7 = 301$, $\mathbf{Q_2 = 3}$.
Or, since $43 \times 93 = 3999$ we can use $\mathbf{P_3 = 4}$.

We also have $\mathbf{P_1 = 13}$ if we wish, as $43 \times 3 = 129$.

We need a systematic procedure for finding a suitable multiple of the number we are testing for divisibility of. This is provided by the reverse *Vertically and Crosswise* multiplication technique.

21 Find a suitable osculator for **647**.

If we look for a suitable positive osculator, we know its last figure must be 7 (as 7×7 ends in 9), and 7×647 = 4529 which is not suitable.

$$
\begin{array}{r}
6\ 4\ 7 \\
7 \times \\
\hline
_4 9
\end{array}
$$

$$
\begin{array}{r}
6\ 4\ 7 \\
1\ 7 \\
\hline
1\ 0\ 9\ 9\ 9
\end{array}
$$

In this sum we need another 9 next to the 9 already there. Since we have 4×7 + carried 4 = 32 we need to add a number ending in 7. This means that 1 will do, and since the full product is then 10999 we find $P_3 = 11$ is a suitable osculator.

This process for finding a suitable P or Q can be extended to any number of figures. Note also that as $P_n + Q_n = D$, $Q_3 = 636$.

 22 Is **1737351** divisible by **231**?

Clearly 231 = 3 × 77 and as we can see the given number is divisible by 3 (from its digit sum) we just need to test for 77.

Now 77 × 13 = 1001 so we can use $Q_3 = 1$ as an osculator:

$$
\begin{array}{ccc}
1 & \overline{737} & 351 \\[4pt]
\overline{385} & \overline{386} &
\end{array}
$$

Since $\overline{385}$ is a multiple of 77, **1737351 is divisible by 231**.

🖋 **Practice I**   Test the following for divisibility by the given number:

a 738567 by 137   b 11610529 by 229   c 5007968 by 566

d 168133371 by 267   e 290735742 by 353   f 77208453 by 1263

---

a (Q_4=1) yes   b (P_4=3) yes   c (P_3=15) yes
d (Q_2=8) yes   e (Q_3=6) yes   f (P_3=8) yes (1263=3×421)

For further details on divisibility see References 1 and 3.

LESSON 10
STRAIGHT DIVISION

SUMMARY
This lesson shows the Vedic one-line method by which any number or polynomial expression can be divided by any other number or polynomial expression.
10.1 Single Figure on the Flag – one-line division by 2-figure numbers.
10.2 Short Division Digression – choosing the remainder you want.
10.3 Longer Numbers – dividing numbers of any size.
10.4 Decimalising the Remainder
10.5 Negative Flag Digits – using bar numbers to simplify the work.
10.6 Larger Divisors
10.7 Algebraic Division

10.1 SINGLE FIGURE ON THE FLAG

Straight division is the general division method by which any numbers of any size can be divided in one line. Bharati Krsna, the man who rediscovered the Vedic system, called this "the crowning gem of Vedic Mathematics".
It comes under the *Vertically and Crosswise* Sutra.

 Suppose we want to **divide 209 by 52**.

We need to know how many 52s there are in 209.
Looking at the first figures we see that since 5 goes into 20 four times we can expect four 52s in 209.

We now take four 52s from 209 to see what is left.
Taking four 50s from 209 leaves 9 and we need to take four 2s away as well.
This leaves a remainder of 1.

We can set the sum out like this:

$$
\begin{array}{c|cc|c}
2 & 2 & 0 & 9 \\
5 & & & {}^{0} \\
\hline
& & 4 & 1
\end{array}
$$

The **divisor, 52,** is written with the 2 raised up. *On the Flag,* and a vertical line is drawn one figure from the right-hand end to separate the answer, 4, from the remainder, 1.

The steps are:

A. 5 into 20 goes 4 remainder 0, as shown.
B. Answer digit 4 multiplied by the flagged 2 gives 8, and this 8 taken from 9 leaves the remainder of 1, as shown.

 Divide 321 by 63.

We set the sum out:

$$3 \begin{array}{c|cc} & 3\ 2 & 1 \\ & & ^2 \\ 6 & & \\ \hline & 5 & 6 \end{array} = 5 \text{ remainder } 6$$

6 into 32 goes 5 remainder 2, as shown,
and answer, 5, multiplied by the flagged 3 gives 15, which we take from the 21 to leave the remainder of 6.

What we are doing here is subtracting five 60s from 321, which leaves 21 and then subtracting five 3s from the 21. That means we have subtracted five 63s and 6 is left.

In the following exercise set the sums out as shown above.

✐ **Practice A**   Divide the following:

a $103 \div 43$ **b** $234 \div 54$ **c** $74 \div 23$ **d** $504 \div 72$

e $444 \div 63$ **f** $543 \div 82$ **g** $567 \div 93$

a 2r17	b 4r18	c 3r5	d 7r0
e 7r3	f 6r51	g 6r9	

10.2 SHORT DIVISION DIGRESSION

Suppose we want to divide 3 into 10.
The answer is clearly 3 remainder 1: $3\underline{)\ 1\ 0}$
                                              $3 \text{ rem } 1$

But other answers are possible: $3\underline{)\ 1\ 0}$ or $3\underline{)\ 1\ 0}$ or even $3\underline{)\ 1\ 0}$
                                          $2 \text{ rem } 4$ $1 \text{ rem } 7$ $4 \text{ rem } \overline{2}$

Since all of these are correct we can select the one which is best for a particular sum.

✎ **Practice B**   Copy each of the following sums and replace the question mark with the correct number:

a 5)2 1   **b** 7)5 1   **c** 4)3 0   **d** 3)2 2
      3 rem ?   6 rem ?   6 rem ?   ? rem 4

e 5)4 2   **f** 6)3 9   **g** 5)2 4   **h** 7)2 6
      6 rem ?   4 rem ?   5 rem ?   4 rem ?

---

a 6   **b** 9   **c** 6   **d** 6̄
e 12   **f** 15   **g** 1̄   **h** 2̄

  503 ÷ 72.

If we proceed as before:

$$2\,|5\ \ 0\,|3$$
$$7^1$$
$$\overline{7}$$

We find we have to take 14 from 13, which means the answer is 7 rem 1̄.

If a negative remainder is not acceptable however we can say that 7 into 50 in the sum above is not 7 rem 1, but 6 remainder 8:

$$2\,|5\ \ 0\,|3$$
$$7^8$$
$$\overline{6\,|71}$$

Then we find we can take 12 from 83 to get the positive remainder 71.

This reducing of the answer figure by 1 or 2 is sometimes necessary if negative numbers are to be avoided. But it worth noting that when the answer figure is reduced by 1 the remainder is increased by the first figure of the divisor: so in the answer above the 7 rem 1 is replaced by 6 rem 8: the remainder is increased by 7, the first figure of 72.

Continuing the above example with the first method we would get:

$$2\,|5\ \ 0\,|3$$
$$7^1$$
$$\overline{7\,|\bar{1}}\ = 6 \text{ rem } 71.$$

The 7 we get in the answer represents seven 72s, so we take one of these (leaving 6 of them) and add it to the negative remainder to get 72 + 1̄ = 71 for the remainder.

Notice that when the answer digit is reduced by 1, the remainder is increased by the divisor.

📏 **Practice C**   Divide the following:

a 97 ÷ 28   **b** 184 ÷ 47   **c** 210 ÷ 53   **d** 373 ÷ 63   **e** 353 ÷ 52

f 333 ÷ 44   **g** 267 ÷ 37   **h** 357 ÷ 59   **i** 353 ÷ 59

---

a	3r13	b	3r43	c	3r51	d	5r58	e	6r41
f	7r25	g	7r8	h	6r3	i	5r58		

10.3 LONGER NUMBERS

4   17496 ÷ 72.

The procedure is just the same as before and goes in cycles.

We set the sum out in the usual way:

$$
\begin{array}{c|cccc}
2 & 1 & 7 & 4 & 9 & 6 \\
7 & & & & & \\
\hline
& & & & & \\
\end{array}
$$

Then we divide 7 into 17 and put down 2 remainder 3.
Note the diagonal of numbers: 2, 3, 4.

$$
\begin{array}{c|cccc}
2 & 1 & 7 & 4 & 9 & 6 \\
7 & & _3 & & & \\
\hline
& 2 & & & & \\
\end{array}
$$

Next we multiply the answer figure by the flag figure:
2×2=4, take this from the 34 to get 30, and then divide
by 7 again, to get 4 remainder 2, as shown:

$$
\begin{array}{c|cccc}
2 & 1 & 7 & 4 & 9 & 6 \\
7 & & _3 & _2 & & \\
\hline
& 2 & 4 & & & \\
\end{array}
$$

Then we repeat: multiply the last answer figure by the
flag to get 8, take this from 29 to get 21, then 7 into 21
goes 3 remainder 0, as shown:

$$
\begin{array}{c|cccc}
2 & 1 & 7 & 4 & 9 & 6 \\
7 & & _3 & _2 & _0 & \\
\hline
& 2 & 4 & 3 & 0 & \\
\end{array}
$$

Finally we again multiply the last answer figure by the flag to get 6 and take this
from the 6 to get a remainder of 0.

It is important to note that we proceed in cycles as shown in the diagrams above.
Each cycle is completed as each diagonal goes down.

> Each cycle consists of:
> **A.** multiplying the last answer figure by the flag,
> **B.** taking this from the number indicated by the top two figures of the diagonal,
> **C.** dividing the result by the first figure of the divisor and putting down the answer and remainder.

That is (divide),   multiply, subtract, divide;
                    multiply, subtract, divide;
                    . . .

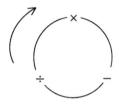

 5   **50607 ÷ 123.= 411 rem 54.**

Although the divisor has three digits here dividing by 12 is not a problem and so we can use the same procedure:

$$
\begin{array}{c|c c c c|c}
3 & 5 & 0 & 6 & 0 & 7 \\
12 & & {}^2 & {}^2 & & {}^5 \\
\hline
 & & 4 & 1 & 1 & 54 \\
\end{array}
$$

✏ **Practice D** Divide the following (the remainder is zero for the first four sums, so you will know if it is correct):

a 19902 ÷ 62   **b** 44749 ÷ 73   **c** 1936 ÷ 88   **d** 4032 ÷ 72

e 4154 ÷ 92   **f** 23824 ÷ 51   **g** 92054 ÷ 63   **h** 142857 ÷ 61

i 12233 ÷ 53   **j** 9018 ÷ 71   **k** 8910 ÷ 72   **l** 23658 ÷ 112

m 40000000 ÷ 61   **n** 14018 ÷ 64   **o** 4712 ÷ 45   **p** 22222 ÷ 76

q 651258 ÷ 82   **r** 301291 ÷ 56   **s** 511717 ÷ 73   **t** 360293 ÷ 46

a	321	b	613	c	22	d	56
e	45r14	f	467r7	g	1461r11	h	2341r56
i	230r43	j	127r1	k	123r54	l	211r26
m	655737r43	n	219r2	o	104r32	p	292r30
q	7942r14	r	5380r11	s	7009r60	t	7832r21

MULTIPLICATION REVERSED

Straight division can also be demonstrated by reversing the vertically and crosswise multiplication method. Given 4032÷72 for example:

$$
\begin{array}{c}
\text{p q}\\
\underline{7\ 2}\\
4\ 0\ 3\ 2
\end{array}
$$

We need the values of p and q so that the number pq multiplied by 72 gives 4032.
We see p must be 5 because p multiplied by 7 must account for the 40 in 4032 (or most of it).
And since 5×7=35 there is a remainder of 5:

$$
\begin{array}{c}
5\quad \text{q}\\
\underline{7\quad 2}\\
4\ 0\ _5 3\ 2
\end{array}
$$

We are left with 532 to be accounted for by the crosswise multiplication and the vertical product on the right. Considering the crosswise part we see we have 5×2=10 and we can take this off the 53 in 532 to leave 43: to be produced by the other part of the crosswise product, 7×q. This tells us that q must be 6 and there is a remainder of 1 from the 53:

$$
\begin{array}{c}
5\quad 6\\
\underline{7\quad 2}\\
4\ 0\ _5 3\ _1 2
\end{array}
$$

The 12 now in the right-hand place is then fully accounted for by the vertical product on the right, so there is no remainder.

All divisions, both arithmetic and algebraic, can be done in this way, as a reversal of the multiplication process, and the *On the Flag* method in this lesson can be derived from it.

10.4 DECIMALISING THE REMAINDER

We can continue the division when the remainder is reached and give the answer to as many decimal places as required.

 Find **40342 ÷ 73** to 5 decimal places.

$$
\begin{array}{c|l}
3 & 4\ 0\ 3\ 4\ 2\ .0\ 0\ 0\ 0\ 0\\
7 & \ \ \ 5\ 3\ 5\ 4\ 1\ 1\ 3\ 6\ 2\\
\hline
 & 5\ 5\ 2\ .6\ 3\ 0\ 1\ 3\ 7
\end{array}
$$

To give an answer correct to 5 decimal places we should find 6 figures after the point in case we need to round up. So we put a decimal point and six zeros after 40342.

The decimal point in the answer goes where the vertical line went before, one figure to the left of the last figure of the number being divided.
We proceed as usual: multiply by the flag, subtract, divide by 7 for each cycle.

So the answer is **552.63014** to 5 decimal places.

7   Find **23.1 ÷ 83** to 3 decimal places.

The answer is clearly less than 1 because 23 is less than **83**.

$$
\begin{array}{r|l}
3 & 2\ 3\,.\,1\ \ 0\ \ 0\ \ 0 \\
8 & \ 7\ \ 9\ \ 5\ \ 2 \\
\hline
 & 0\,.\,2\ \ 7\ \ 8\ \ 3
\end{array}
$$

As before the decimal point goes one figure to the left in the **answer, which is 0.278.**

✐ Practice E   Find to 2 decimal places:

a   40342 ÷ 73   **b**   371426 ÷ 81   **c**   888 ÷ 61   **d**   17 ÷ 72

e   89179 ÷ 53   **f**   209029 ÷ 85   **g**   22.22 ÷ 36   **h**   104077 ÷ 59

a	552.63	b	4585.51	c	14.56	d	0.24
e	1682.62	f	2459.16	g	0.62	h	1764.02

10.5 NEGATIVE FLAG DIGITS

When the flag number is large we often need to reduce more frequently. It is possible to avoid these reductions however by using negative flag digits.

 8   **97 ÷ 28.**

If we proceed as usual we get:

$$
\begin{array}{r|l|l}
8 & 9 & 7 \\
2 & & {}^{3} \\
\hline
 & 3 & 13
\end{array}
$$

We have to reduce the answer digit from 4 to 3 so that the remainder is big enough.

These reductions occur more frequently when the flag number is large (8 here). This can be avoided however by re-writing 28 as $3\bar{2}$.

$$
\begin{array}{r|l|l}
\bar{2} & 9 & 7 \\
3 & & {}^{0} \\
\hline
 & 3 & 13
\end{array}
$$

3 into 9 goes 3 remainder 0.

We then multiply the $\bar{2}$ by 3 to get $\bar{6}$ and this is to be subtracted from 7.

But subtracting a negative number means adding it so we get $7 - \bar{6} = 13$ for the remainder.

This is much easier and it means that:

> **whenever we use a bar number on the flag we add the product at each step instead of subtracting it.**

✏ **Practice F**   Divide the following, giving answer and remainder:

a $373 \div 58$ **b** $357 \div 48$ **c** $300 \div 59$ **d** $321 \div 47$

e $505 \div 78$ **f** $543 \div 68$

Find to 2 decimal places: **g** $777 \div 47$ **h** $83.222 \div 58$ **i** $13 \div 79$

a	6r25	b 7r21	c 5r5	d 6r39
e	6r37	f 7r67		
g	16.53	h 1.43	i 0.16	

Two other variations may be noted.

     $277 \div 38$.

We write 38 as $4\bar{2}$.

$$\begin{array}{c|ccc} \bar{2}|2 & 7 & 7 \\ 4 & & & {}^3 \\ \hline & & 6 & 49 \end{array}$$

We get 6 remainder 49.

Since we are trying to find how many 38s there are in 277 we cannot allow a remainder greater than 38. There is clearly another 38 in the remainder so the answer, 6, must be increased to 7, and the remainder reduced to 11.

So the answer is **7 remainder 11**.

     Find **545.45 ÷ 29** to 2 decimal places.

$$\begin{array}{c|cccccc} \bar{1}|5 & 4 & 5 .4 & 5 & 0 \\ & {}^2 & {}^1 & {}^2 & {}^1 & {}^1 \\ 3 & & & & & \\ \hline & 1 & 8 .7 & {}_1 0 & 8 \end{array}$$

In the third cycle we find we get 31 to divide by 3, and this gives a 2-figure answer.
We simply put the 2-figure answer down (10 remainder 1) and carry on.
The 1 in this 10 is then carried back to the 7 to give 18.808.
So the answer is **18.81** to 2 D.P.

✳ It is possible to avoid this 10 in the answer by having a negative remainder in the previous cycle. You may like to do the sum this way. You should get 18.808 just the same.

✎ **Practice G**   Divide the following, giving answer and remainder:

a 234 ÷ 39   **b** 345 ÷ 49   **c** 555 ÷ 67   **d** 24454 ÷ 37

e 999 ÷ 48   **f** 917499 ÷ 67   **g** 32243 ÷ 48   **h** 24464 ÷ 37

i 81201 ÷ 27   **j** 135791 ÷ 28

a	6r0	b	7r2	c	8r19	d	660r34
e	20r39	f	13694r1	g	671r35	h	661r7
i	3007r12	j	4849r19				

Another choice you have is in restructuring the dividend.

For example you may want to remove the large digits in the last question of the last exercise by writing **135791** as **136 $\overline{21}$ 1**.

This is another way of avoiding the 2-figure numbers which can come up in the answer:

$$\begin{array}{r} \overline{2}|1\ 3\ 6\ \overline{2}\ \overline{1}|\ 1 \\ {}_{1}\ {}_{0}\ {}_{2}|0 \\ \hline 4\ 8\ 4\ 9|19 \end{array}$$

In the following exercise use whatever method you think is best.

✎ **Practice H**   Divide the following, giving answer and remainder:

a 234 ÷ 52   **b** 545 ÷ 83   **c** 343 ÷ 58   **d** 222 ÷ 29

e 141 ÷ 17   **f** 777 ÷ 46   **g** 1344672 ÷ 63   **h** 19792 ÷ 92

i 12585 ÷ 83   **j** 1111 ÷ 19

Divide the following giving answers to 2 decimal places:

k 108 ÷ 31   **l** 4050 ÷ 73   **m** 9876 ÷ 94   **n** 25.52 ÷ 38

o 78 ÷ 49   **p** 6.7 ÷ 88   **q** 19 ÷ 62   **r** 62 ÷ 19

a	4r26	b	6r47	c	5r53	d	7r19
e	8r5	f	16r41	g	21344r0	h	215r12
i	151r52	j	58r9				
k	3.48	l	55.48	m	105.06	n	0.67
o	1.59	p	0.08	q	0.31	r	3.26

10.6 LARGER DIVISORS

Dividing by 3-figure, 4-figure, etc. numbers is an easy extension of the above technique which involves putting all but the first 1 or 2 figures on the flag.

12   **Divide 2250255 by 721.**

We set the sum out with two figures on the flag:

$$
\begin{array}{r|l}
21 & 2\ 2\ 5\ 0\ 2\ 5\ 5 \\
7\quad\ \ & \qquad\ \ _1 \\
\hline
& \boxed{3\qquad\ \ .}
\end{array}
$$

Since there are 2 figures on the flag the decimal point goes 2 figures in from the right, as shown.
Then we divide 7 into 22 and put down 3 remainder 1, as shown above.

Next we multiply the answer figure, 3, by the first flag figure, 2, to get 6.
This is deducted from the 15 to give 9 which is divided by 7 to get 1 remainder 2.

$$
\begin{array}{r|l}
21 & 2\ 2\ 5\ 0\ 2\ 5\ 5 \\
7\quad\ \ & \qquad\ _{1\ \ 2} \\
\hline
& \boxed{3\ 1\qquad\ .}
\end{array}
$$

We now cross-multiply the flag digits, 21, with the last two answer figures, 31, to get 5:

$$
\begin{array}{cc}
2 & 1 \\
 & \times \qquad 2 \times 1 + 1 \times 3 = 5 \\
3 & 1
\end{array}
$$

This 5 is then deducted from the 20 in the next diagonal to give 15 which is then divided by 7 to give 2 remainder 1.

At every stage from now on we cross-multiply the two flag digits with the last two answer digits to get the number to be deducted.

$$
\begin{array}{r|l}
21 & 2\ 2\ 5\ 0\ 2\ 5\ 5 \\
7\quad\ \ & \quad\ _{1\ 2\ 1\ 0\ 1} \\
\hline
& \boxed{3\ 1\ 2\ 1\ .0}
\end{array}
$$

Having got the first three answer figures we cross-multiply 21 with 12 to get 5:

$$
\begin{array}{cc}
2 & 1 \\
 & \times \qquad 2 \times 2 + 1 \times 1 = 5 \\
1 & 2
\end{array}
$$

Remember, the first deduction is the first answer figure multiplied by the first flag number. After that we always cross-multiply the flag digits by the last two answer figures.

✐ **Practice I**   Divide the following until you have five figures in the answer:

a 111010 ÷ 725   b 17078 ÷ 812   c 20006 ÷ 623

d 30405 ÷ 721   e 23654 ÷ 713

| a | 153.11 | b | 21.032 | c | 32.112 |
| d | 42.170 | e | 33.175 | | |

As before we sometimes have to reduce a figure or go into negative numbers. And sometimes we may find it convenient to introduce a bar number into the divisor.

For example in dividing **1251413 by 519** we would write 519 as 52$\bar{1}$ as this avoids large flag digits and helps to keep the subtractions small.

$$
\begin{array}{c|l}
2\ \bar{1} & 1\ 2\ 5\ 1\ 4\ 1\ 3\ .0\ 0 \\
& 2\ \bar{1}\ 0\ \bar{1}\ 0\ 0\ 2 \\
5 & \\
\hline
& 2\ 4\ 1\ 1\ .2\ 0\ 0
\end{array}
$$

✐ **Practice J**   Divide the following until you have five figures in the answer:

a 253545 ÷ 821   b 34567 ÷ 612   c 23456 ÷ 621

d 13531 ÷ 629   e 7777 ÷ 493   f 6789 ÷ 1089

| a | 308.82 | b | 56.482 | c | 37.771 |
| d | 21.512 | e | 15.775 | f | 6.2341 |

"We go on, at last, to the long-promised Vedic process of STRAIGHT (AT SIGHT) DIVISION which is a simple and easy application of the URDHVA-TIRYAK Sutra which is capable of immediate application to all cases and which we have repeatedly been describing as the 'CROWNING GEM of all' for the very simple reason that over and above the universality of its application, it is the most supreme and superlative manifestation of the Vedic ideal of the at-sight mental-one-line method of mathematical computation."
From "Vedic Mathematics", Page 240.

5678943 ÷ 112345 = 50.55 to 4 significant figures.

Using 11 as a suitable divisor we put 2345 *on the flag.*

$$
\begin{array}{c|l}
2\ 3\ 4\ 5 & 5\ 6\ 7\ 8\ 9\ 4\ 3 \\
 & {}^{1}\ {}^{7}\ {}^{8}\ {}^{4}\ {}^{5} \\
11 & \\
\hline
 & 5\ 0.5\ 5\ \bar{1}
\end{array}
$$

The method is the same as before, only the quantities subtracted at each step need to be specified:

1. 2×5 = 10,
2. 2×0 + 3×5 = 15,
3. 2×5 + 3×0 + 4×5 = 30,
4. 2×5 + 3×5 + 4×0 + 5×5 = 50.

10.7 ALGEBRAIC DIVISION

The same technique for dividing numbers can be applied to dividing algebraic expressions.

 Find **(3x² + 10x + 13) ÷ (x + 2).**

$$
\begin{array}{r}
x + 2\ \overline{)\ 3x^2 + 10x + 13} \\
\mathbf{3x\ +\ 4\ rem\ 5}
\end{array}
$$

We divide the first term of the dividend by the first term of the divisor: $3x^2 ÷ x = \mathbf{3x}$ and put this down.

The coefficient of this 3x i.e. 3 is then multiplied by the +2 in the divisor and the result subtracted in the next column: $3 × 2 = 6$, and $10 – 6 = \mathbf{4}$, which we put down.

We then multiply this 4 by the +2 in the divisor and subtract the result from the 13: $4 × 2 = 8$, $13 – 8 = \mathbf{5}$.
The explanation for this is similar to that given for numerical division on Page 138.

Find **(x³ – 5x² + 7x – 1) ÷ (x – 3).**

$$
\begin{array}{r}
x - 3\ \overline{)\ x^3 - 5x^2 + 7x\ - 1} \\
\mathbf{x^2 - 2x\ + 1\ rem\ 2}
\end{array}
$$

Similarly each figure brought down into the answer is multiplied by –3 and the result is subtracted in the next column.

17   Find $(x^3 + 6x^2 + 13x + 13) \div (x^2 + 2x + 3)$.

$$x^2 + 2x + 3 \overline{)x^3 + 6x^2 + 13x + 13}$$
$$\underline{x + 4 \quad rem\ 2x + 1}$$

Here we have two coefficients after the first term, +2 and +3.
$x^3 \div x^2 = x$ which goes into the answer.
Its coefficient, 1, then multiplies the +2 and the result is subtracted from the 6 in the divisor: $6 - 2 = 4$.
Now we have the coefficients 1 and 4 in the answer line and we cross-multiply them with the +2 , +3 coefficients in the divisor: $2 \times 4 + 3 \times 1 = 11$. This is then subtracted from the 13 in the dividend to give $2x$ as the first part of the remainder.

Finally, we multiply the 4 in the answer line with the +3 in the divisor to get 12, which we take from the 13 in the dividend to get 1 as the last part of the remainder.

18   Find $(6x^2 + 17x + 15) \div (2x + 3)$.

$$2x + 3 \overline{)6x^2 + 17x + 15}$$
$$\underline{3x + 4 \quad rem\ 3}$$

Dividing here by $2x + 3$ we proceed as before, but divide each answer figure by 2 before putting it down.
That is: $6x^2 \div 2x = 3x$.
$17 - 3 \times 3 = 8,\ 8 \div 2 = 4$.
$15 - 4 \times 3 = 3$ (the remainder is not divided).

✎ **Practice K**   Divide:

a $x + 5 \overline{)3x^2 + 20x + 30}$ b $x - 3 \overline{)2x^2 + x - 30}$

c $x^2 - 2x - 1 \overline{)x^3 + 2x^2 + x + 1}$ d $x^2 + 2x - 3 \overline{)2x^3 + 2x^2 + x + 1}$

e $2x - 4 \overline{)2x^3 + 2x^2 - 6x + 9}$ f $3x + 2 \overline{)3x^2 + 5x - 1}$

---

a	3x+5	R5		b	2x+7	R −9
c	x+4	R10x+5		d	2x−2	R 11x−5
e	x²+3x+3	R21		f	x+1	R−3

Some more variations follow.

A fractional divisor:

 $(x^2 + 2x + 3) \div (\frac{x}{2} + 3) = 2x - 8$ **remainder 27.**

$$\frac{x}{2} + 3 \,) \, x^2 + 2x \;\; + \; 3$$
$$ x + 6 \;\; \underline{}$$
$$ 2 \times \;\; x \; - \, 4 \;\; \text{rem 27}$$
$$ \underline{2x - 8 \;\; \text{rem 27}}$$

We double the divisor here, divide, and double the quotient at the end.

 $\dfrac{x-2}{x-3} = 1 + \dfrac{1}{x-3}.$

$$x - 3 \,) \, x \; - \; 2$$
$$ \underline{1 \; \text{rem 1}}$$

First $x \div x = 1$. Then this $1 \times -3 = -3$ is subtracted from the -2 to give the remainder of 1.

Dividing the remainder:

 $(x^2 + 2x + 4) \div (x + 3) = x - 1 + 7x^{-1} - 21x^{-2} + 63x^{-3} \dots$

$$x + 3 \,) \, x^2 + 2x + \; 4$$
$$ \underline{x \; - \; 1 \; + \; 7x^{-1} - 21x^{-2} + 63x^{-3} \dots}$$

We simply continue to multiply the last answer coefficient by 3 and subtract the result in the next column.
And the remainder is $-\dfrac{189}{x^3}$.

$\dfrac{1}{1+x} = 1 - x + x^2 - x^3 \dots$

$$1 + x \,) \, 1$$
$$ \underline{1 - x + x^2 - x^3 \dots}$$

The usual restrictions apply:
in this case $-1 < x < 1$.

$1 \div 1 = 1$. Then multiply this answer coefficient by $+1$ (the coefficient of x in the divisor) to get 1 which we subtract in the next column.

23   $$\frac{1}{x+1} = \frac{1}{x} - \frac{1}{x^2} + \frac{1}{x^3} - \frac{1}{x^4} \cdots$$

$$x + 1 \,) \, \underline{1} \\ \qquad \frac{1}{x} - \frac{1}{x^2} + \frac{1}{x^3} - \frac{1}{x^4} \cdots$$

✎ **Practice L**

Give answer and remainder:

a $\frac{x}{2} + 5)x^3 + 3x^2 + 4x + 5$ 　　 b $\frac{x}{3} - 4)x^2 - 3x + 4$ 　　 c $\frac{x}{2} + \frac{1}{3})3x^2 + 3x + 4$

d $\frac{x+4}{x-3}$ 　　　　 e $\frac{x-5}{x+2}$ 　　　　 f $\frac{2x+7}{x+4}$

Find the first four terms (by dividing the remainder):

g $x + 2)2x^2 + 3x + 4$ 　　 h $x - 3)x - 5$ 　　 i $x^2 + 2x - 3)x^3 + 3x^2 + 4x + 5$

j $\frac{2}{1+2x}$ 　　　　 k $\frac{2}{x+3}$ 　　　　 l $\frac{1}{x^2+2x+3}$

---

a $2x^2-14x+148$ R–735	b $3x+27$ R112	c $6x+2$ R$3\frac{1}{3}$
d 1 R7 or $1+\frac{7}{x-3}$	e 1 R–7 or $2-\frac{7}{x+2}$	f 2 R–1 or $2-\frac{1}{x+4}$
g $2x-1 + \frac{6}{x} - \frac{12}{x^2}$	h $1 - \frac{2}{x} - \frac{6}{x^2} - \frac{18}{x^3}$	i $x+1+\frac{5}{x} - \frac{2}{x^2}$
j $2-4x+8x^2-16x^3$	k $\frac{2}{x} - \frac{6}{x^2} + \frac{18}{x^3} - \frac{54}{x^4}$	l $\frac{1}{x^2} - \frac{2}{x^3} + \frac{1}{x^4} + \frac{4}{x^5}$

✦ 24   **Find the value of $3x^4 - 5x^3 + 0.3x + 3$ when $x = 2$.**

We frequently need to evaluate polynomial expressions like this, when using the remainder theorem for example.

The coefficients in the quartic are: 3, –5, 0, 0.3, 3.

We simply multiply the first of these by 2 (since we require the value when x=2), and add on the next coefficient. We then multiply the result by 2 and add on the next coefficient and so on until the end.

$$\begin{array}{ccccc} 3 & -5 & 0 & 0.3 & 3 \\ \hline 3 & 1 & 2 & 4.3 & 11.6 \end{array}$$

So the answer is 11.6.

This is a good example of the one-line method: the Vedic method is done with the attention following one line, whereas with the conventional method the attention is moving back and forth.

LESSON 11
SQUARE ROOT

SUMMARY

This lesson covers the general method of one-line square roots, of both numbers and polynomials.

11.1 Squaring – revision.
11.2 Square Root of a Perfect square – where the square root is a 2 or 3-figure number.
11.3 General Square Roots
11.4 Changing the Divisor – choosing a small or large divisor.
11.5 Algebraic Square Roots – square root of polynomials.

11.1 SQUARING

The general method of finding the square root of a number is just the reverse of the squaring process so we begin this lesson by revising squaring (see Lesson 7).

We square a number by combining the Duplexes contained in the number.

1 Find 5431^2.

The Duplexes are:
$D(5)=25$, $D(54)=40$, $D(543)=46$, $D(5431)=34$, $D(431)=17$, $D(31)=6$, $D(1)=1$.

Working from left to right we get $2_59_04_69_45_7761$ (see Section 7.4a).

✐ Practice A   Square the following numbers, from left to right:

a 23	b 34	c 54	d 61	e 421	f 124	g 423

h 818	i 4321	j 6032	k 5234

a	529	b	1156	c	2916	d	3721	e	177241	f	15376	g	178929
h	669124	i	18671041	j	36385024	k	27394756						

11.2 SQUARE ROOT OF A PERFECT SQUARE

11.2a PREAMBLE

If we are given a number which we are to find the square root of there are two important facts we can immediately get from the number:

      1) the number of figures in the square root before the decimal point,
      2) the first figure of the square root.

 Suppose we want the **square root of 543200**.

We mark off pairs of digits from the right (in fact from the decimal point): 54'32'00. Since there are 3 groups of digits formed there will be 3 figures in the square root before the decimal point.

Since the group on the left is 54 this tells us that the first figure will be **7** because **the first square number below 54 is 49** $(=7^2)$.

Using these two results together we can say that since the answer starts with 7 and has 3 figures before the decimal point, $\sqrt{543200} \approx$ **700**.

 Find an approximate value for $\sqrt{543.2}$.

Split the number into pairs starting at the decimal point: 5'43.2.
There are 2 groups (the single digit, 5, counts as a group as 5 = 05) so there will be 2 figures in the answer before the point.

The group at the left is 5 and the first square number below 5 is 4, which is 2^2.
So the first figure of the square root is **2**.

So the square root begins with 2 and has 2 figures before the point.
Therefore $\sqrt{543.2} \approx$ **20**.

11.2b TWO-FIGURE ANSWER

 Find the **square root of 1849**.

Marking off two figures from the right, 18'49, we expect two figures before the decimal point and the first figure of the answer is 4.

We set the sum up like this:

```
            1  8  4  9
      8)         2
      ─────────────────
                4
```

Since $4^2 = 16$ and 18 is 2 more than this we have a remainder of 2 which we place as shown. **Note the 24 formed diagonally by this 2 and the 4 above it.**
The answer goes on the bottom line.

We also put **twice the first figure**, which is 8, as a divisor at the left as shown.

Next we divide the 24 by the divisor 8.
This gives 3 remainder 0, placed as shown below:

```
            1  8  4  9
      8)         2  0
      ─────────────────
                4  3
```

We now see 09 and we deduct from this the Duplex of the last answer figure:
$D(3) = 9$ and $09 - 9 = 0$. This means the answer is exactly **43**.

 Find $\sqrt{1369}$.

Again we expect 2 figures before the point and the first figure will be 3.

```
            1  3  6  9
      6)         4
      ─────────────────
                3
```

Since $3^2 = 9$ we have a remainder of 4 placed as shown above. Also we again put twice the first figure, 6, as a divisor on the left.
Note the 46 in the diagonal of figures.

Next we divide the divisor, 6, into 46 and put down 7 remainder 4:

```
            1  3  6  9
      6)         4  4
      ─────────────────
                3  7
```

Finally we see 49 in the second diagonal and we take the Duplex of the last answer figure, $D(7) = 49$, from this to get 0.

So the answer is exactly **37**.

> **A.** We first set up the initial sum including the first figure of the answer, the remainder and twice the first figure placed as a divisor on the left.
>
> **B.** We then divide the figures shown in the diagonal by the divisor and put down the answer and remainder.
>
> **C.** Finally check the answer is exact by subtracting the Duplex of the last answer figure from the second diagonal.

In an exactly similar way we can find the square root of a polynomial which is an exact square.

✎ **Practice B**   Find the square root of the following, using the method shown:

a 3136	b 3969	c 5184	d 3721	e 6889	f 1296
g 2304	h 4624	i 1521	j 3844	k 8649	

a	56	b	63	c	72	d	61	e	83	f	36
g	48	h	68	i	39	j	62	k	93		

REVERSING SQUARING

Considering the square root of 1849, the first figure is clearly 4, and there is a remainder of 2, as $4^2 = 16$ and we have 18 in the first two places.

So we could write: $\sqrt{18_,49} = 4p$. where 4p is the 2-figure answer, and the remainder, 2, is written as a subscript.
Squaring the 4 (which represents 40) therefore accounts for 1600 of 1849 and so 249 are left (as you can see under the square root above).

Now the duplex of 4p must account for the 24 in $_249$. or most of it. So twice the product of 4 and p must be 24 or nearly 24. Therefore p must be 3.

This shows why we use twice the first figure as a divisor. since to solve $2\times(4\times p) = 24$ we can divide 24 by 8: we will always be dividing by twice the first digit.

Square roots could be taught this way initially if understanding the steps is important. or of course it can be explained this way afterwards.

> *"People who have practical knowledge of the application of the Sutras need not go in or the theory side of it at all. The actual work can be done. Tremendous time is saved. It is a saving not merely of time and energy and money, but more than all, I feel, it is saving the child from tears that very often accompany the study of mathematics.".*
> From "Vedic Metaphysics", Page 170.

11.2c THREE-FIGURE ANSWER

6   Find the **square root of 293764**.

We first mark off pairs of figures from the right: 29'37'64.
This shows us that we expect 3 figures before the decimal point,
and that the answer begins with a 5.

We set up the sum as before:
      2 9 3 7 6 4

10)   4
_____
      5 .

We have a remainder of 4 from the 29 and twice the first figure is 10.
Since we know there are 3 figures before the point we can insert the decimal point as
shown.

We get the next figure of the answer by dividing 10 into the 43.
This gives 4 remainder 3 which we write down as shown below:

      2 9 3 7 6 4

10)   4   3
_____
      5 4 .

Next, before we divide 10 into the 37 in the second diagonal we subtract the duplex
of the 4 (in the answer) from it. The duplex of 4 is 16.
37 – 16 = 21 and 21 ÷ 10 = 2 remainder 1, which we write down as shown below:

      2 9 3 7 6 4

10)   4   3   1
_____
      5 4 2.

Next, before dividing 10 into the 16 in the third diagonal we deduct the duplex of the
42 in the answer. D(42)=16, 16–16=0 and 0÷10=0 rem 0:

      2 9 3 7 6 4

10)   4   3   1   0
_____
      5 4 2 . 0

Finally we deduct the duplex of the last answer figure, 2, from the 04 in the fourth
diagonal. This leaves 0 and so the answer is exactly **542**.

The method is a continuation of the shorter sums done before.

We set out the initial sum as before and divide into the first diagonal as before.
The next three steps involve deducting the Duplex of **a** the 2nd answer figure,
  b the 2nd and 3rd answer figures,
  c the 3rd answer figure
from the last diagonal before dividing by the divisor.

✎ **Practice C**   Find the square root of:

a 186624   **b** 264196   **c** 400689   **d** 318096

e 119025   **f** 524176   **g** 59049   **h** 197136

i 519841   **j** 375769   **k** 53361

a	432	b	514	c	633	d	564
e	345	f	724	g	243	h	444
i	721	j	613	k	231		

REVERSING SQUARING

Again, thinking back to how we square a 3-figure number we can reverse the procedure to obtain the square root of, say, 293764.

We know the answer will have three figures and will start with 5. There will therefore be a remainder of 4 ($29 - 25 = 4$):

$29_43764 = (5pq)^2$, where p and q are the remaining unknown digits.

Now we know that the duplex of 5p = $D(5p) = 2\times(5\times p)$ must equal 43 ($_43$ under the square root above) or most of it. Therefore p = 4, and 3 are remaining. In fact we can just divide 43 by 10 (twice the first digit).

So we now have: $29_43_3764 = (54q)^2$.

Next we have our eye on the 37 ($_37$).
This must be accounted for by the duplex of 54q = $D(54q) = 2\times(5\times q) + 4^2$.
So to solve $2\times(5\times q) + 16 = 37$ we take the duplex of the 4 in (54q) from 37 and divide the result by 10 (twice the first digit again). This tells us that q must be 2 with 1 remaining:

$29_43_37_164 = (542)^2$.

Now we see that the remaining two duplexes of 542 account for the remaining digits:
$D(42) = 16$, and $D(2) = 4$.

This explains the method given above and leads into the general square rooting method in which we use twice the first digit as a divisor repeatedly and reduce the dividend at each step by the duplex of all the answer figures after the first one.

11.3 GENERAL SQUARE ROOTS

Next we consider the general case where the square root does not terminate but has an infinite number of figures after the decimal point.
This is just an extension of the method above.

7   Find the first 5 figures and an approximate answer for the **square root of 38**.

There is clearly 1 figure before the point and it is a 6.
There is also a remainder of 2.
Then $20 \div 12 = 1$ rem 8:

$$
\begin{array}{r}
3\ 8.0\ 0\ 0\ 0\ 0 \\
12)\quad 2\ \ 8 \quad\quad\quad \\
\hline
6\ .\ 1 \quad\quad\quad\quad
\end{array}
$$

From now on **we deduct the Duplex of all the figures <u>after the first</u>** (the 6) **from the diagonal figures** and then divide by 12.

So $D(1)=1$, $80-1=79$, $79 \div 12 = 6$ rem 7:

$$
\begin{array}{r}
3\ 8.0\ 0\ 0\ 0\ 0 \\
12)\quad 2\ \ 8\ \ 7 \quad\quad \\
\hline
6\ .\ 1\ \ 6 \quad\quad\quad
\end{array}
$$

Then $D(16)=12$, $70-12=58$, $58 \div 12 = 4$ rem 10:

$$
\begin{array}{r}
3\ 8.0\ 0\ 0\ 0\ 0 \\
12)\quad 2\ \ 8\ \ 7\ \ 10 \quad \\
\hline
6\ .\ 1\ \ 6\ \ 4 \quad\quad
\end{array}
$$

Then $D(164)=44$, $100-44=56$, $56 \div 12 = 4$ rem 8:

$$
\begin{array}{r}
3\ 8.0\ 0\ 0\ 0\ 0 \\
12)\quad 2\ \ 8\ \ 7\ \ 10\ \ 8 \\
\hline
6\ .\ 1\ \ 6\ \ 4\ \ 4 \quad
\end{array}
$$

So $\sqrt{38} \approx$ **6.1644**.

8   Find the first seven figures of $\sqrt{10330130}$.

The procedure is just the same.
10'33'01'30 shows there are 4 figures before the point and the first one is 3:

$$
\begin{array}{r}
1\ 0\ 3\ 3\ 0\ 1\ 3\ 0.0 \\
6)\quad\quad 1 \quad\quad\quad\quad\quad \\
\hline
3 \quad\quad\quad . \quad\quad\quad\quad
\end{array}
$$

There is a remainder of 1 and the divisor is 6.

The full sum to seven figures is shown below:

```
        1  0  3  3  0  1  3  0 . 0
    6)        1  1  3  2  4  5  2
    ─────────────────────────────
        3  2  1  4 . 0  5  2
```

The Duplexes to be found at each step are D(2), D(21), D(214), D(2140), D(21405).

✎ **Practice D**   Find to 5 significant figures the square root of:

a 27.2727   **b** 38.83   **c** 2929   **d** 11.23

e 3737   **f** 123356   **g** 707172   **h** 5000

i Find the first 9 figures of the square root of 26.123456789

j Find the first 8 figures of the square root of 17

a 5.2223	**b** 6.2314	**c** 54.120	**d** 3.3511
e 61.131	**f** 351.22	**g** 840.94	**h** 70.711
i 5.11111111	**j** 4.1231056		

As in the case of division sums it is sometimes necessary to alter an answer figure or to use bar numbers.

 Find the **square root of 19.2**.

Initially we have:
```
        1  9 . 2  0  0
    8)        3
    ───────────────────
        4 .
```

The next step is 32÷8 = 4 rem 0.
But this would mean subtracting 16 from 0 in the next step:
```
        1  9 . 2  0  0
    8)        3  0
    ───────────────────
        4 . 4
```

Method 1: Anticipating this happening we can avoid the negative numbers by saying 32÷8=3 rem 8 (see the second diagonal below) rather than 4 rem 0.

```
        1  9 . 2  0  0  0
    8)        3  8  7  14
    ───────────────────────
        4 . 3  8  1
```

Method 2:   Alternatively we can accept the negative digits:

$$
\begin{array}{r}
\mathbf{1}\ \mathbf{9}\ .\ \mathbf{2}\ \ \mathbf{0}\ \ \mathbf{0}\ \ \mathbf{0}\ \ \mathbf{0} \\
8)\quad\quad 3\ \ 0\ \ 0\ \ 0\ \ 4 \\
\hline
4\ .\ 4\ \ \overline{2}\ \ 2\ \ \overline{3} \quad\quad = \mathbf{4.3817}
\end{array}
$$

After $32 \div 8 = 4$ rem 0 in the second diagonal we have:

$D(4) = 16$, $0-16 = \overline{16}$, $\overline{16} \div 8 = \overline{2}$ rem 0.

Then $D(4\,\overline{2}) = \overline{16}$, $0-\overline{16} = 16$, $16 \div 8 = 2$ rem 0.

And $D(4\,\overline{2}\,2) = 20$, $0-20 = \overline{20}$, $\overline{20} \div 8 = \overline{3}$ rem 4 (or $\overline{2}$ rem $\overline{4}$).

Sometimes it is convenient to introduce a bar number right at the beginning of a calculation, when the given number is just below a perfect square.

 Find the first 5 figures of $\sqrt{34}$.

If we begin like this:

$$
\begin{array}{r}
\mathbf{3}\ \ \mathbf{4}\ .\ \mathbf{0}\ \ \mathbf{0}\ \ \mathbf{0} \\
10)\quad\quad 9\ \ 10 \\
\hline
\mathbf{5}\ .\ \mathbf{8}
\end{array}
$$

the large 8 here leads to large Duplex values and therefore frequent reduction of answer figures.

Alternatively, since 34 is close to 36, a perfect square, we could put 6 for the first figure and a remainder of $\overline{2}$:

$$
\begin{array}{r}
\mathbf{3}\ \ \mathbf{4}\ .\ \mathbf{0}\ \ \mathbf{0}\ \ \mathbf{0}\ \ \mathbf{0}\ \ \mathbf{0} \\
12)\quad\quad \overline{2}\ \ 4\ \ 0\ \ 0\ \ \overline{5} \\
\hline
\mathbf{6}\ .\ \overline{\mathbf{2}}\ \ \mathbf{3}\ \ \mathbf{1}\ \ \mathbf{0} \quad\quad = \mathbf{5.8310}
\end{array}
$$

✎ **Practice E** Find the first 4 figures in the square root of the following numbers (do at least the first 4 sums by both methods and remove any bar numbers from your answer). For the last four use the method of Example 10 above.

a 27	b 39.6	c 1930	d 11.5
e 575	f 53	g 5	h 2
i 35	j 24	k 3	l 8.321

a	5.196	b	6.292	c	43.93	d	3.391
e	23.97	f	7.280	g	2.236	h	1.414
i	5.916	j	4.899	k	1.732	l	2.884

11.4 CHANGING THE DIVISOR

Because the first figure of a square root can take any whole value from 1 to 9, the divisor ranges from 2 to 18 inclusive.

Having 2 as a divisor can mean having to decide carefully about each answer digit so that the dividend at each step is kept manageable. Having 14, 16 or 18 as a divisor means mental division by these numbers.

11 Find $\sqrt{112.9}$.

$$
\begin{array}{l}
\quad\; 1\; 1\; 2.9\; 0\; 0 \\
2)\quad {}^{0}1\;{}^{1}0\;{}^{0}3\;{}^{3}4 \\
\hline
\quad 1\; 0\;.6\; 3\; \overline{5} \qquad = \textbf{10.625}
\end{array}
$$

$$
\begin{array}{l}
\quad\;\; 1\; 1\; 2.9\; 0\; 0\; 0 \\
20)\quad\quad {}^{12}9\;{}^{9}14\;{}^{16} \\
\hline
\quad\;\; 1\; 0\;.6\; 2\; 5
\end{array}
$$

In the first method above we divide by 2 and we need to think carefully about the appropriate answer figure and remainder at each step.

This can be alleviated however, as shown on the right, by looking at the first three figures in the number, 112, instead of only the first. That way we get 10 as the 'first figure', 20 as a divisor, and 12 as the remainder. This 10 is not involved in the duplex subtractions. Dividing by 20 is quite easy and there will be no reductions to consider.

12 Find $\sqrt{87.37}$.

$$
\begin{array}{l}
\quad\; 8\; 7.3\; 7\; 0\; 0 \\
18)\quad\; {}^{6}9\;{}^{9}16\;{}^{10} \\
\hline
\quad\;\; 9\;.3\; 4\; 7
\end{array}
$$

$$
\begin{array}{l}
\quad\; 8\; 7.3\; 7\; 0\; 0 \\
20)\quad {}^{\overline{13}}13\;{}^{8}\overline{4} \\
\hline
\quad 10\;.7\; 4\; 7
\end{array}
$$

The first method is straightforward except that we have to divide by 18 at each step. But if we take 10 as the first figure and a remainder of $\overline{13}$ we can arrange to have 20 as a divisor.

Another option is to divide the given number by 4, take the square root (which gives a divisor of 8 or 10) and multiply by 2 at the end.

It is worth experimenting to find the preferred method.

HEURISTIC PROOF

In finding a square root we are solving an equation of the form $x^2 = N$.
Suppose $x = a.bcde....$, that is, $x = a + 10^{-1}b + 10^{-2}c + 10^{-1}d + ...$ where a, b, c, d etc. take the integral values 0, 1, 2, 3, 4, 5, 6, 7, 8 or 9.

Then we have $(a.bcde....)^2 = N$.
Expanding the left-hand side in duplexes from left to right:

$$(a^2) + (2ab) + (2ac + b^2) + (2ad + 2bc) + (2ae + 2bd + c^2) + ... = N.$$

Here the brackets show successive duplexes and we assume each is a power of ten below the one before. N has to be exhausted by these bracketed quantities.

Notice that the first term in each bracket after the first is twice the first digit, a, multiplied by b, c, d, e etc., and that the other terms in those brackets are the successive duplexes of the answer digits ignoring the first answer digit, a.

This shows the method because we take the square of the first digit from N and the remainder (multiplied by 10) is then divided by 2a to give b.
Then from the remainder (multiplied by 10) we subtract b^2 and divide again by 2a to get c.
And so on.

Finding the square root of a number is equivalent to solving the equation $x^2 = c$. However this method can be extended to the solution of equations of the form $ax^2 + bx = c$ and to higher order polynomial equations: see Lesson 14 and Reference 5.

11.5 ALGEBRAIC SQUARE ROOTS

Having this numerical method for finding square roots of numbers, we can use exactly the same process to find square roots of polynomial expressions.

$$\sqrt{x+1} = \sqrt{x} + \frac{1}{2\sqrt{x}} - \frac{1}{8x\sqrt{x}} \cdots$$

$$2\sqrt{x} \underline{\begin{array}{c} x + 1 \\ \overline{\sqrt{x} + \frac{1}{2\sqrt{x}} - \frac{1}{8x\sqrt{x}}} \end{array}}$$

Put down the square root of the first term, and put double this up as a divisor.
Then divide the 1 in x+1 by this divisor:

$$1 \div 2\sqrt{x} = \frac{1}{2\sqrt{x}}.$$

Next we subtract the duplex of $\frac{1}{2\sqrt{x}}$ in the next column and divide the result by the divisor: so square $\frac{1}{2\sqrt{x}}$, subtract it from zero, and divide by $2\sqrt{x}$ again.

In fact, since the powers of x decrease by 1 each time we could work with just the coefficients and a divisor of 2. See next example.

  14 $\sqrt{1+x} = 1 + \frac{1}{2}x - \frac{1}{8}x^2 + \frac{1}{16}x^3 \ldots$

$$1 + x$$
$$2)\overline{}$$
$$1 + \frac{1}{2}x - \frac{1}{8}x^2 + \frac{1}{16}x^3 \ldots$$

$\sqrt{1} = 1$, put it down. Put up the divisor, 2.
Then 1 (i.e. 1x) $\div 2 = \frac{1}{2}$, put it down.
$0 - \frac{1}{4} = -\frac{1}{4}, -\frac{1}{4} \div 2 = -\frac{1}{8}$, put it down.
$\frac{1}{2} \times (-\frac{1}{8}) \times 2 = -\frac{1}{8}, 0 - -\frac{1}{8} = \frac{1}{8},$
$\frac{1}{8} \div 2 = \frac{1}{16}$, put it down.

  15 $\sqrt{3 - 2x + x^2 + 2x^3} = \sqrt{3} - \frac{x}{\sqrt{3}} + \frac{x^2}{3\sqrt{3}} + \frac{10x^3}{9\sqrt{3}} \ldots$

$$3 - 2x + x^2 + 2x^3$$
$$2\sqrt{3})\overline{}$$
$$\sqrt{3} - \frac{x}{\sqrt{3}} + \frac{x^2}{3\sqrt{3}} + \frac{10x^3}{9\sqrt{3}} \ldots$$

  16 $\sqrt{4x^2 + 12x + 9} = 2x + 3.$

$$4x^2 + 12x + 9$$
$$4x)\overline{}$$
$$2x + 3 \quad \text{exactly}$$

✐ **Practice F**

Find the square root to 4 terms:

a $4 - 3x$

b $1 + 3x + 4x^2$

c $1 + x + x^2 + x^3$

d $x^2 + 3x + 2$

e $16x^4 + 96x^3 + 216x^2 + 216x + 81$

---

a $2 - \frac{3x}{4} - \frac{9x^2}{64} - \frac{27x^3}{512}$ **b** $1 + \frac{3x}{2} + \frac{7x^2}{8} - \frac{21x^3}{16}$ **c** $1 + \frac{x}{2} + \frac{3x^2}{8} + \frac{5x^3}{16}$

d $x + \frac{3}{2} - \frac{1}{8x} + \frac{3}{16x^2}$ **e** $4x^2 + 12x + 9$

LESSON 12
TRIPLE TRIGONOMETRY

SUMMARY
This lesson shows how the triple methods studied earlier can be used for solving various trigonometric problems, including proofs and solution of equations.

12.1 Compound Angles
12.2 Inverse Functions
12.3 The General Triple – and its use in proofs etc.
12.4 Trigonometric Equations

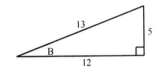

12.1 COMPOUND ANGLES

1   If $\sin A = \frac{3}{5}$ and $\cos B = \frac{12}{13}$, where both A and B are acute angles, find $\tan(A + B)$.

We have:

The third element of each triple is obtained from Pythagoras' Theorem.

Adding these triples:

A	4	3	5
B	12	5	13
A+B	33	56	65

$+$ i.e.

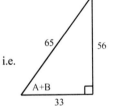

$\therefore \tan(A + B) = \dfrac{56}{33}$

2   If $\cos A = \frac{2}{3}$ and $\sin B = \frac{5}{6}$ find $\sin(A + B)$.

A	2	$\pm\sqrt5$	3
B	$\pm\sqrt{11}$	5	6
A+B	–	$\pm\sqrt{55}+10$	18

$+$

$\therefore \sin(A + B) = \dfrac{\pm\sqrt{55}+10}{18}$.

There is no need to find the first element of the triple for A+B.

3 If $\cos A = \frac{7}{25}$ and $\sin B = \frac{4}{5}$, where A is acute and B is obtuse, find $\cos(A-B)$.

	7	24	25
A	7	24	25
B	−3	4	5	−
A−B	75	-	125

$\therefore \cos(A-B) = \frac{75}{125} = \dfrac{3}{5}$.

For obtuse angles the first element is negative and the second positive.

4 Given $\sin A = \frac{3}{5}$ and that A is acute, find $\tan(90^\circ - A)$.

90°	0	1	1
A	4	3	5	−
90°− A	3	4	5

$\therefore \tan(90^\circ - A) = \dfrac{4}{3}$.

5 Given A) −2, −3, $\sqrt{13}$ find $\cot(-A)$.

0°	1	0	1
A	−2	−3	-	−
−A	−2	3	-

$\therefore \cot(-A) = -\dfrac{2}{3}$.

6 If $\tan A = \frac{24}{7}$ and A is acute, find $\sec(A-30°)$.

A	7	24	25
30°	$\sqrt{3}$	1	2	−
A − 30°	$7\sqrt{3}+34$	-	50

$\therefore \sec(A-30°) = \dfrac{50}{7\sqrt{3}+24}$.

7 If $\cot A = \frac{4}{3}$ find $\cos 2A$ and $\tan\frac{1}{2}A$ (A is acute).

A	4	3	5
2A	7	24	25
½A	9	3	-

$\therefore \cos 2A = \dfrac{7}{25}$ and $\tan\frac{1}{2}A = \dfrac{1}{3}$.

✐ **Practice A**   If $\sin A = \frac{4}{5}$ and $\cos B = \frac{12}{13}$ (A and B both acute) find:

a $\sin(A+B)$ b $\operatorname{cosec}(B-A)$ c $\tan 2A$ d $\cot(B+45°)$ e $2\tan\tfrac{1}{2}B$

If $\tan A = \frac{5}{12}$ and $\sin B = \frac{15}{17}$ find:

f $\tan(A+B)$ if A is acute and B obtuse   **g** $\cos 3A$ if A is in the third quadrant

h $\sin \frac{1}{2}A$ if A is acute   **i** $\sin \frac{1}{2}A$ if A is in the third quadrant

j $\sec(60° - \frac{1}{2}B)$ if B is acute

a	$\frac{63}{65}$	**b**	$-\frac{65}{33}$	**c**	$-\frac{24}{7}$	**d**	$\frac{7}{17}$	**e**	$\frac{2}{5}$
f	$-\frac{140}{171}$	**g**	$-\frac{828}{2197}$	**h**	$\frac{1}{\sqrt{26}}$	**i**	$-\frac{5}{\sqrt{26}}$	**j**	$\frac{2\sqrt{34}}{5+3\sqrt{3}}$

12.2 INVERSE FUNCTIONS

Evaluate $\tan^{-1}\frac{1}{2} + \tan^{-1}\frac{1}{3}$.

(I.e. the angle whose tangent is $\frac{1}{2}$ plus the angle whose tangent is $\frac{1}{3}$.)

We have: where $A = \tan^{-1}\frac{1}{2}$
                                                          and $B = \tan^{-1}\frac{1}{3}$

∴

A	2	1	-
B	3	1	-
A+B	5	5	-

$= 1, 1, \sqrt{2}$

So $\tan^{-1}\frac{1}{2} + \tan^{-1}\frac{1}{3} = \dfrac{\pi}{4}$ radians.

Show that $2\tan^{-1}2 + \tan^{-1}3 = \pi + \tan^{-1}\frac{1}{3}$.

Let the angles be A, B and C respectively
so we have to prove that $2A + B = \pi + C$.

Then

A	1	2	-
2A	-3	4	-
B	1	3	-
2A+B	-15	-5	-
=	-3	-1	-

But

π	-1	0	1
C	3	1	-
π+C	-3	-1	-

∴ $2\tan^{-1}2 + \tan^{-1}3 = \pi + \tan^{-1}\frac{1}{3}$.

It is worth noting here that sin. cos. tan. cosec. sec. cot are avoided by this triple method. Students find this use of these "part-words" confusing: the triple notation is much more straightforward and clear.

Conventional trigonometry also relies on a mass of complex formulae which the student has to remember or look up. These are not needed in the triple method.

12.3 THE GENERAL TRIPLE

Since dividing a triple through by any positive number does not change the angle:

$$A) x \qquad y \qquad 1$$

can be considered a general triple.

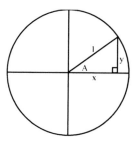

Then $\cos A = x$ $\qquad$ $\sin A = y$ $\qquad$ $\tan A = \frac{y}{x}$ $\qquad$ $\cot A = \frac{x}{y}$ $\qquad$ $\sec A = \frac{1}{x}$ $\qquad$ $\csc A = \frac{1}{y}$

These can be neatly represented on a single diagram:

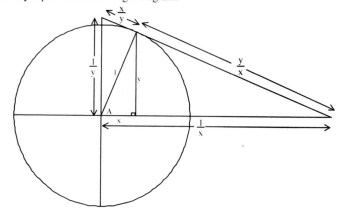

Or, alternatively:

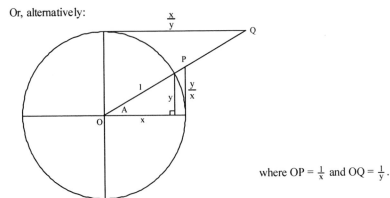

where OP = $\frac{1}{x}$ and OQ = $\frac{1}{y}$.

So we know that $x^2 + y^2 = 1$. And the triple for the general double angle is also frequently in use:

A	x	y	r
2A	$(x^2 - y^2)$,	$(2xy)$,	(r^2)

  10 Prove that **tanA + cotA ≡ secA cosec A** .

That is: prove $\frac{y}{x} + \frac{x}{y} = \frac{1}{x} \times \frac{1}{y}$

But $\frac{y}{x} + \frac{x}{y} = \frac{y^2 + x^2}{xy} = \frac{1}{xy}$ as $x^2 + y^2 = 1$

∴ $\frac{y}{x} + \frac{x}{y} = \frac{1}{x} \times \frac{1}{y}$ Q.E.D.

  11 Prove that **$\sin^2 A \, \mathrm{cosec}(90^\circ - A) \equiv \cot^2(90^\circ - A)\cos A$** .

We need a triple for $90^\circ - A$:

90°	0	1	1	
A	x	y	1	−
90°−A	y	x	1	

So we have to show that $y^2 \times \frac{1}{x} = \frac{y^2}{x^2} \times x$.

Which it clearly is, so Q.E.D.

Prove $\frac{\sin 2A}{1+\cos 2A} \equiv \tan A$.

Using the triples

A	x	y	r
2A	(x^2-y^2),	$(2xy)$,	(r^2)

we need to prove that $\frac{2xy}{1+x^2-y^2} = \frac{y}{x}$

But $1-y^2 = x^2$ $\therefore$ $\frac{2xy}{1+x^2-y^2} = \frac{2xy}{2x^2} = \frac{y}{x}$ Q.E.D.

 Express $\sqrt{\frac{1-\sin 2A}{1+\sin 2A}}$ in terms of $\tan A$.

$$\sqrt{\frac{1-\sin 2A}{1+\sin 2A}} = \sqrt{\frac{1-2xy}{1+2xy}} = \sqrt{\frac{x^2+y^2-2xy}{x^2+y^2+2xy}} = \frac{x-y}{x+y} = \frac{1-\frac{y}{x}}{1+\frac{y}{x}} = \frac{1-\tan A}{1+\tan A}$$

 Simplify $\tan^{-1}x + \tan^{-1}\left(\frac{1-x}{1+x}\right)$.

We have

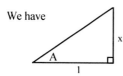 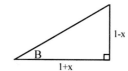

We are given the addition of two angles so we can add their triples:

A	1	x	-
B	1+x	1-x	-
A+B	1+x − (1−x)	x(1+x) + 1−x	-
=	$1 + x^2$	$1 + x^2$	-

Since the first and second elements of the result are equal this triple must be 1, 1, $\sqrt{2}$ (we could divide the triple through by 1+x²). The angle in this triple must therefore be 45° or $\frac{\pi}{4}$ radians.

So $\tan^{-1}x + \tan^{-1}\left(\frac{1-x}{1+x}\right) = \frac{\pi}{4}$.

 Show that $\sin(2\tan^{-1}x) = \frac{2x}{x^2+1}$..

Let $\tan^{-1}x = A$:

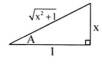

Then | A | 1 | x | $\sqrt{x^2+1}$ |
and | 2A | - | 2x | x^2+1 |

So $\sin(2\tan^{-1}x) = \sin 2A = \frac{2x}{x^2+1}$.   Q.E.D.

16   Prove that $\tan A + \tan B = \frac{\sin(A+B)}{\cos A \cos B}$.

Let A) x   y   1
    B) X   Y   1

$$
\begin{array}{ccc}
x & y & 1 \\
X & Y & 1 \\
\hline
xX-yY & yX+xY & 1
\end{array} +
$$

Then $\frac{\sin(A+B)}{\cos A \cos B} = \frac{yX+xY}{xX} = \frac{y}{x} + \frac{Y}{X} = \tan A + \tan B$.   Q.E.D.

✏ Practice B

a Evaluate $\tan^{-1}\frac{1}{2} + \tan^{-1}\frac{1}{5} + \tan^{-1}\frac{1}{8}$

Prove   **b** $2\tan^{-1}\frac{1}{2} = \tan^{-1}\frac{4}{3}$ **c** $(\operatorname{cosec}^2 A - 1)\sin^2 A = \cos^2 A$

d $\tan A(1 + \cos 2A) = \sin 2A$ **e** $\sin 2A = \frac{2\tan A}{1+\tan^2 A}$

f $\sin(120° - A) = \sin(60° + A)$ **g** $\frac{\sin A}{1+\cos A} = \tan\frac{1}{2}A$

h $3\tan^{-1}2 - \pi = \tan^{-1}\frac{2}{11}$

i If $\tan(A+B) = \frac{1}{2}$ and $\tan(A-B) = \frac{1}{3}$ find $\tan 2A$ and A.

---

a $\frac{\pi}{4}$ i   1, $\frac{\pi}{8}$

12.4 TRIGONOMETRIC EQUATIONS

12.4a SIMPLE EQUATIONS

17   Express in triple form: **a** $\sin A = \frac{1}{2}$ **b** $\cos B = \frac{1}{2}$ **c** $\tan C = \sqrt{3}$

a If $\sin A = \frac{1}{2}$ then A) - , 1, 2,   and so A) $\pm\sqrt{3}$, 1, 2 are the triples.

b Similarly, if $\cos B = \frac{1}{2}$ then B) 1, $\pm\sqrt{3}$, 2.

c $\operatorname{Tan} C = \sqrt{3} = \frac{\sqrt{3}}{1}$ so C) ± 1, $\pm\sqrt{3}$, 2 (two triples).

18 Solve $\cos 2A - \sin 2A = 1$.

With the usual substitutions we have $x^2 - y^2 - 2xy = 1$.

$$\therefore -y^2 - 2xy = y^2 \quad \therefore -2xy = 2y^2 \quad \therefore y = 0 \text{ or } \tfrac{y}{x} = -1.$$

y=0 gives	±1	0	1
and $\tfrac{y}{x}=-1$ gives	−1	1	$\sqrt{2}$
and	1	−1	$\sqrt{2}$

four solutions in all.

✐ **Practice C**

Solve the following equations giving the answers as triples:

a $\sin A(\sin A + \cos A) = 1$ **b** $1 - \sin A = 2\cos^2 A$

c $\tan 2A = 4\tan A$.   **d** $\tan^{-1}\tfrac{1}{2} - \tan^{-1}\tfrac{1}{3} = \sin^{-1} x$

---

a $0,\pm 1,1$; $1,1,\sqrt{2}$; $-1,-1,\sqrt{2}$ **b** $\pm\sqrt{3},-1,2$; $0,1,1$

c $1,0,1$; $\pm\sqrt{2},\pm 1,\sqrt{3}$ **(4 solutions)**   **d** $\tfrac{\sqrt{2}}{10}$

12.4b A SPECIAL TYPE

The type of trigonometric equation solved below with triple arithmetic is one that students find very difficult. The appropriate formula has to be selected and applied and a calculator has to be used a number of times. But using triples the answer is very easy and quick. They are solved *By Addition and Subtraction* of triples.

 19 Solve $10\cos A + 5\sin A = 11$.

This converts to $10x + 5y = 11$.
From the coefficients on the left of this equation we construct the triple:

B)10,   5,   -.

Now consider the following subtraction sum:

	x	y	1
A			
B	10	5	$\sqrt{125}$ —
A–B	11		

The two vertical products formed when beginning this subtraction sum give $10x + 5y$ and since we know that this is 11 we can put this down in the first column of the answer.

Also we know the last element of the answer: $\sqrt{125}$. We can therefore fill in the middle element, which must be 2.

So A–B) 11, 2, $\sqrt{125}$.

We can now add the second and third rows and since we are adding the angles B and A–B the result must be a triple for A, which is what we require:

$$
\begin{array}{r|lll}
A & x & y & 1 \\ \hline
B & 10 & 5 & \sqrt{125} \quad - \\
A-B & 11 & 2 & \sqrt{125} \quad + \\ \hline
A & 100 & 75 & 125 = 4,3,5
\end{array}
$$

which is an answer.

Now in evaluating the middle element of the triple for A–B the result could have been –2 as well as 2. But adding the triples with 2 changed to –2 will give the same result as subtracting the original triples:

$$
\begin{array}{r|lll}
A & x & y & 1 \\ \hline
B & 10 & 5 & \sqrt{125} \quad - \\
A-B & 11 & 2 & \sqrt{125} \quad - \\ \hline
A & 120 & 35 & 125 = 24,7,25
\end{array}
$$

which is the other solution.

Alternatively of course 2 and –2 can be used as the middle element of A–B and only triple addition need then be used.

There are variations of this method but the one shown above is the most efficient.

20   Solve $4\cos A - 7\sin A = 8$.

This becomes $4x - 7y = 8$.

The coefficients 4, –7 are inserted as the first elements of B and 8 is then the first entry for A–B:

$$
\begin{array}{r:lll}
A & x & y & 1 \\ \hline
B & 4 & -7 & \sqrt{65} \; - \\
A-B & 8 & \pm 1 & \sqrt{65} \; - \\ \hline
A & 39 & -52 & 65 = \quad 3, -4, 5 \\
A & 25 & -60 & 65 = \quad 5, -12, 13
\end{array}
$$

The method is just the same. We add and then subtract in the third row to get the two answers.

This example shows the whole working and is far easier than the conventional method for solving this type of equation.

It is worth noting that the third element of the triple for B gives the maximum and minimum values of the expression on the left-hand side of the equation: $\pm\sqrt{65}$ in the example above.

✎ **Practice D**   Solve the following equations:

a $10\cos A - 5\sin A = 11$ **b** $2\cos A + 3\sin A = 3$ **c** $4\cos A + 7\sin A = 8$

---

a 24, –7, 25; 4, –3, 5   b   0, 1, 1;   12, 5, 13   c   5, 12, 13;   3, 4, 5

For further variations and examples of triple trigonometry see Reference 4.

LESSON 13
COMBINED OPERATIONS

SUMMARY

This lesson shows how to combine algebraic or arithmetic expressions and give the result term by term or digit by digit from the left. Lessons 17, 18 follow on from this.

13.1 Algebraic – algebraic products in one line.

13.2 Arithmetic – finding sums of products etc. including mean and variance.

13.3 Pythagoras' Theorem – finding the square root of the sum of two squares in one line.

13.1 ALGEBRAIC

 Expand and simplify: $(x + 3)(x + 4) + (x - 7)(x + 5)$.

There is no need to do a lot of intermediate paper work when we can write the answer straight down.

There will clearly be two x^2 terms, one from each product, so we have $2x^2$.
There will also be 7x from the first product and –2x from the second, giving **5x**.
And we also get +12 and –35, making **–23**.

So $(x + 3)(x + 4) + (x - 7)(x + 5) = 2x^2 + 5x - 23$.

 Expand and simplify: $(2x - 3)^2 - (3x - 2)(x + 5)$.

We have $4x^2 - 3x^2 = x^2$.
Then $-12x - 13x = -25x$.
And $9 - - 10 = 19$.

So $(2x - 3)^2 - (3x - 2)(x + 5) = x^2 - 25x + 19$.

With a little practice it becomes easy.

 Expand: $(2x + 3y + 4)(x - 3y + 5)$.

Here we can use the *Vertically and Crosswise* pattern from left to right to easily get the product term by term.

$$
\begin{array}{ccccccc}
2x & + & 3y & + & 4 \\
x & - & 3y & + & 5 \\
\hline
2x^2 - 3xy - 9y^2 & + & 14x + 3y + 20
\end{array}
$$

✏ **Practice A**   Expand and simplify the following:

a $(x + 2)(x + 3) + (x + 1)(x + 5)$ **b** $(2x - 3)(x + 4) + (x - 1)(x + 3)$

c $(2x - 3)(x - 4) + (3x + 1)(x + 3)$ **d** $(2x + 3)(3x + 1) + (x + 3)(x + 4) + 5x + 6$

e $(x + 3)^2 + (x + 2)(x + 5)$ **f** $(x + 4)^2 + (x + 2)^2$

g $(5x + 2)^2 + (2x + 1)^2$ **h** $(5x + 2)^2 - (2x + 1)^2$

i $(x - 2)^2 + (2x - 1)^2$ **j** $(2x + 3)^2 + (x - 2)^2 + (x - 5)^2$

k $2x + (x + 1)^2 - 3$ **l** $(x + 2y + 3)(2x + y + 1)$

---

a	$2x^2 + 11x + 11$	b	$3x^2 + 7x - 15$
c	$5x^2 - x + 15$	d	$7x^2 + 23x + 21$
e	$2x^2 + 13x + 19$	f	$2x^2 + 12x + 20$
g	$29x^2 + 24x + 5$	h	$21x^2 + 16x + 3$
i	$5x^2 - 8x + 5$	j	$6x^2 - 2x + 38$
k	$x^2 + 4x - 2$	l	$2x^2 + 5xy + 2y^2 + 7x + 5y + 3$

4   Expand and simplify: $(x + 2)(x + 3)(x + 4)$.

Here we expect a cubic (with an x^3-term, x^2-terms, x-terms and the final independent term).

Multiplying three brackets means **we multiply one term from each of the three brackets** in all possible ways.

Multiplying the first term in each bracket gives $x \times x \times x = x^3$.

The x^2-term is formed by multiplying the x terms from two brackets and the independent term in the third. There are three ways of doing this, shown in bold below:

$(x + 2)(x + 3)(x + 4)$ $(x + 2)(x + 3)(x + 4)$ $(x + 2)(x + 3)(x + 4)$
gives $x \times x \times 4 = 4x^2$ gives $x \times x \times 2 = 2x^2$ gives $x \times x \times 3 = 3x^2$

So we find $9x^2$ altogether.

For the x-term of the answer we multiply an x-term in one bracket by the independent terms in the other two brackets:

$(x + 2)(x + 3)(x + 4)$ $(x + 2)(x + 3)(x + 4)$ $(x + 2)(x + 3)(x + 4)$
gives $3 \times 4 \times x = 12x$ gives $2 \times 4 \times x = 8x$ gives $2 \times 3 \times x = 6x$

So we find $26x$ altogether.

The independent term of the answer is just the product of the three independent terms:
$2 \times 3 \times 4 = 24$.

So our answer is $(x + 2)(x + 3)(x + 4) = x^3 + 9x^2 + 26x + 24$.

5   Expand and simplify: $(2x + 3)^3$.

We can apply the process shown above, by writing
$(2x + 3)^3$ as $(2x + 3)(2x + 3)(2x + 3)$ or we can use the expansion of $(a + b)^3$:

$$(a + b)^3 = a^3 + 3a^2b + 3ab^2 + b^3$$

This means we cube the first term $(2x)^3$, which is $8x^3$,
then find 3 times the first term squared times the second term: $3 \times (2x)^2 \times 3 = 36x^2$,
then 3 times the first term times the second term squared: $3 \times (2x) \times (3)^2 = 54x$,
and finally cube the second term: $(3)^3 = 27$.

So the answer is $(2x + 3)^3 = 8x^3 + 36x^2 + 54x + 27$.

Practice B   Use any one-line method to expand the following:

a $(x + 1)(x + 2)(x + 3)$ b $(x + 2)(x + 4)(x + 6)$

c $(2x + 1)(3x + 1)(x + 3)$ d $(x + 2)(x + 3)(x - 4)$

e $(x + 1)(3x - 1)(x - 3)$ f $(x + 1)(x + 3)(x + 5) - (x + 2)(x + 4)$

g $(x + 2)^3$ h $(2x + 1)^3$ i $(2x + 5)^3$

a $x^3 + 6x^2 + 11x + 6$	b $x^3 + 12x^2 + 44x + 48$	
c $6x^3 + 23x^2 + 16x + 3$	d $x^3 + x^2 - 14x - 24$	
e $3x^3 - 7x^2 - 7x + 3$	f $x^3 + 8x^2 + 17x + 7$	
g $x^3 + 6x^2 + 12x + 8$	h $8x^3 + 12x^2 + 6x + 1$	i $8x^3 + 60x^2 + 150x + 125$

13.2 ARITHMETIC

In the case of arithmetic calculations we have increased flexibility as we can choose when and how to introduce the vinculum, whether to work from left to right or right to left etc. The Sutra in use is *Vertically and Crosswise*.

The ability to work from left to right means that we can combine calculations and find sums of products, sums of squares etc. in one line. And if we want only the first 3 or 4 figures of an answer we save ourselves a lot of work by finding only those figures. In fact for some calculations there is no last figure to work from: for example there is no last figure for the square root of 2. We need to find these from left to right.

13.2a SUMS OF PRODUCTS

Here we assume the left to right methods in Lessons 1, 5 and 7 have already been covered.

$(53 × 6) + (72 × 4) = 6_{\bar{2}}0\ 6.$

To find the most significant figure (the left-most figure) we multiply the 5 by the 6 and the 7 by the 4 and add the two results: 30 + 28 = 58, but the large digit (8) here suggests we put $6\bar{2}$, as shown.

We then multiply the 3 by 6 and the 2 by 4 to get 26.
To this we add the $\bar{2}$, as $\overline{20}$, to get 06, which we put down.

Had we put down 5_8 as the first result instead of $6_{\bar{2}}$ we would have had 26 again for the next step, and when these were combined we would get 26 + 80 = 106, giving
5 ^{1}0 6 = 606.

$(293 × 4) + (709 × 6) = (3\bar{1}3 × 4) + (7\bar{1}\bar{1} × 6) = 5_4\ 4_2\ 2\ 6 = \textbf{5426}.$
We can use the vinculum here to change 293 to $3\bar{1}3$ and 709 to $7\bar{1}\bar{1}$.
It is probably better not to change the 7 into $\bar{1}3$ as it is easier to deal with two 3-figure numbers rather than one 3-figure and one 4-figure number.

Multiplying the left-most digits then gives 12+42 = 54, which we put down.
The next pair of products gives $\bar{4}$ +6 = 2 and combining this with the carried 4 (as 40) gives 42, which we put down.

The last pair of products gives $12+\bar{6}$ = 6 and adding the carry we get 26 which we put down.

It is worth noting that it is often best not to introduce too many vinculums. We want the positive and negative parts to cancel in the calculation, as far as possible, and so we need to leave some positive digits to help with this.

$(6345 × 4) + (257 × 3) + (67 × 8) = 2_4\ 6_{\bar{2}}\ 6_{\bar{1}}\ 8\ 7 = \textbf{26687}.$

Here we have three products.
We begin by finding the number of thousands and for this we only need to look at the first product: 6 × 4 = 24, we put down 2_4.
Next, for hundreds we have 3 × 4 in the first product and also 2 × 3 in the second. This gives 18 altogether and with the carry 4 we get 58 which we write as $6_{\bar{2}}$.

Now for the tens we bring in all three products: $4 \times 4 + 5 \times 3 + 6 \times 8 = 79$.
To this we add the carried $\overline{20}$ to get 59, which we write as $6_{\bar{1}}$.

Lastly for the units we have $20+21+56 = 97$. The carry makes this 87 which we put down.

 (62 × 6) – (38 × 4) $= 2_4\, 2\ 0 = \textbf{220}$.

Here we have to subtract the products.
The two products on the left are 36, 12 and subtracting gives 24 which we put down.

The other products give $12 - 32 = -20$, and to this we add the carry: $-20 + 40 = 20$, which we put down.

✎ **Practice C**

a $(62 \times 6) + (38 \times 4)$ b $(43 \times 5) + (36 \times 3)$

c $(33 \times 4) + (35 \times 3) + (42 \times 6)$ d $(72 \times 4) - (34 \times 6)$

e $(83 \times 4) - (44 \times 6)$ f $(443 \times 4) + (345 \times 6)$

g $(513 \times 5) + (215 \times 4)$ h $(536 \times 6) + (405 \times 4) + (721 \times 3)$

i $(333 \times 7) + (34 \times 6)$ j $(4532 \times 4) + (34 \times 6)$

k $(7124 \times 6) + (192 \times 7)$

a	524	b	323
c	489	d	84
e	68	f	3842
g	3425	h	6999
i	2535	j	18332
k	44088		

 (36 × 49) + (62 × 42) $= (36 \times 5\bar{1}) + (62 \times 42) = 4_{\bar{1}}\, 3_{\bar{7}}\, 6\ 8 = \textbf{4368}$.

First remove the 9 in 49.
Then the first product in each part is 3×5 and 6×4.
This gives 39 for the hundreds which we put down as $4_{\bar{1}}$.

Next we take the crosswise step in each part and add them: $(30+\bar{3}) + (8+12) = 47$.
With the carry this becomes 37 which we put down.

Finally for the units we get $\bar{6} + 4 = \bar{2}$.
Adding 70 to this gives 68 which we put down.

11 $57^2 + 73^2 = 7_4 \; {}^15_2 \; 7 \; 8 = \mathbf{8578}$.

Taking the duplex of the left-most digit in each number first we get:
$D(5) + D(7) = 25+49 = 74$. which we put down.

Then the next duplex: $D(57) + D(73) = 70+42 = 112$.
To this we add the carried 4 to get 152, as shown.
The 2-figure number we put down (15) means that the 1 will have to be carried leftwards (to the 7).

Next $D(7) + D(3) = 58$. And $58 + 20 = 78$ which we put down.

Finally take the 1 in 15 over to the 7 to get 8578.

Other ways of doing this calculation are:

a) to put $8_{\bar{6}}$ down at the outset instead of 7_4. This gives $8_{\bar{6}} \, 5_2 \, 7 \; 8$.

b) to change 57^2 to $63^{\,\bar{2}}$. This gives $8_5 \, 5_6 \, 7 \; 8$.

12 $(34321 \times 62) + 413^2 = 2_{\bar{5}} \, 2_6 \, 9_4 \, 8_3 \, 4_6 \, 7 \; 1 = \mathbf{2298471}$.

The first result in the bracket is $3 \times 6 = 18$. and this is actually followed by five zeros. The first result from 413^2 will be 16 followed by four zeros.

This means that the square does not come in until the second step.

So first we get 18, written as $2_{\bar{5}}$.

Next imagine 62 under 34:   3 4 3 2 1   (moving multiplier method)
                              6 2

Then crosswise gives $3 \times 2 + 4 \times 6 = 30$. And to this we add the first duplex from 413^2, which we saw above was 16.
This gives 46 and we have a carry which makes this 26 which we put down.

The next crosswise step   3 4 3 2 1
                              6 2

gives 26 and the next duplex is $D(41) = 8$. Adding these gives 34.
With the carry this now gives 94, put down 9_4.

Next we get $(3 \times 2) + (2 \times 6) + D(413) = 18 + 25 = 43$.
Adding the carry we get 8_3.

Then $10 + D(13) = 16$. And $16 + \text{carry} = 46$.
Finally $2 + D(3) = 11$. And $11 + 60 = 71$.

So we see that the method is quite straightforward: we combine all products of the highest order of magnitude first, then all those of the next order, and so on. We make full use of the vinculum, where appropriate, either changing the given numbers into vinculum form or changing results obtained during the calculation.

It is also wise to have an eye on the next stage of the calculation when deciding how to express the result of a particular stage.

✐ **Practice D**

a $(34 \times 44) + (53 \times 63)$ b $(48 \times 42) + (72 \times 82)$ c $(81 \times 26) + (54 \times 48)$

d $47^2 + 63^2$ e $53^2 + 72^2$ f $76^2 + 44^2$

g $42^2 + 83^2 + 56^2$ h $29^2 + 37^2 + 68^2$ i $52^2 + 63^2 + 28^2 + 34^2$

j $84^2 - 56^2$ k $49^2 + 53^2 - 66^2$ l $(76 \times 54) - (32 \times 24)$

m $(61 \times 53) - (54 \times 43)$ n $(66 \times 32) + (57 \times 75)$ o $(444 \times 32) + (617 \times 8)$

p $(64 \times 34) + 48^2$ q $(4343 \times 32) + (56 \times 44)$ r $(479 \times 32) + 732^2$

Find to 3 S.F.

s $(3749 \times 27) + (187 \times 75)$ t $7359^2 + 427^2$ u $(888.34 \times 73) - 187^2$

a	4835	b	7920	c	4698
d	6178	e	7993	f	7712
g	11789	h	6834	i	8613
j	3920	k	854	l	3336
m	911	n	6387	o	19144
p	4480	q	141440	r	551152
s	115000	t	54300000	u	29900

13.2b ADDITION AND DIVISION

We begin with the division of a sum of numbers. This is useful when finding means of sets of numbers.

$(77 + 93 + 68 + 43) \div 8 = 3_2\ 5_1 = \textbf{35 rem 1}$.

We add the tens figures in the bracket and divide this total by 8: $26 \div 8 = 3$ rem 2, we put 3_2 as shown, and carry the 2 forward.

Adding the units in the bracket we get 21 and adding the carried 2 (as 20) we get 41, then $41 \div 8 = 5_1$ as shown.

The answer is 35 remainder 1, but if we continued the division the carried 1 becomes 10, $10 \div 8 = 1_2$. So we have $3_2\ 5_1\ .1_2$ and so on until we have 35.125.

Or, once we get 35 rem 1, since the remainder must be divided by 8 we have $35\frac{1}{8}$ for the answer.

$(17049 + 3535 + 43434) \div 13 = 4_{11}\ 9_2\ 2_4\ 4_6 = 4924$ rem 6

Adding the figures in the ten thousands place we get only 5 so we could begin by adding the thousands: there are 63 thousands altogether.
$63 \div 13 = 4$ rem 11, we put 4_{11}.

Totalling the hundreds we get 9, $9+110 = 119$, $119 \div 13 = 9_2$.

In the tens: $10 + 20 = 30$, $30 \div 13 = 2_4$

And in the units: $18 + 40 = 58$, $58 \div 13 = 4$ rem 6.

$(53.84 + 97.4 + 8.631) \div 11 = 1_3\ 4_4\ .\ 5_3\ 3_4\ 3_8 = 14.534$ to 3 D.P.

The decimal point is inserted when we come to it.
In the tens we have 14, $14 \div 11 = 1_3$.

In the units: $18 + 30 = 48$, $48 \div 11 = 4_4$.

In the tenths: $18 + 40 = 58$, $58 \div 11 = 5_3$.

In the hundredths: $7 + 30 = 37$, $37 \div 11 = 3_4$.

In the thousandths: $1 + 40 = 41$, $41 \div 11 = 3_8$.

Since this 8 is to be divided by 11 it is clearly over one half and so the previous digit (the 3) is increased by one to give an answer to 3 decimal places.

✒ Practice E

a $(86 + 47 + 91 + 38) \div 7$

b $(444 + 789 + 369 + 41) \div 6$

c $(735 + 816 + 357) \div 7$

d $(9.6 + 9.8 + 9.6 + 9.4) \div 17$ (to 2 d.p.)

e $(9743 + 364 + 8645) \div 6$

f $(3579 + 579 + 79 + 9) \div 4$

g $(7.309 + 19.43 + 3.212) \div 7$ (to 3 d.p.)

h $(512512 + 667788 + 987654) \div 8$

i $(313.13 + 94.8 + 86.4 + 777.1) \div 8$ (to 2 d.p.)

j $(5544 + 3456.7 + 838) \div 6$ (to 1 d.p.)

These answers include some carry figures, but as there are many ways to arrive at the answer these may be different yours. This also applies to subsequent answers in this lesson.

a $3_3 7$ r3   b $2_7 0_3$ r5   c $2_4 7_0 2$ r4   d $2_2.2_1 0_6$ to 2 d.p.

e $3_{\bar{1}} 1_0 2_2 5$ r2   f $10_0 5_1{}^1 1_2 = 1061.5$ g $4_1.2_5 7_5 9$ to 3 d.p.   h $2_4 7_{\bar{1}} 0_6 9_6 9_2 4$ r2

i $1_2 5_5 8_6.9_2 3_{\bar{1}}$ to 2 d.p.   j $1_6 3_4 9_4.8_{\bar{1}}$ to 1 d.p.

13.2c STRAIGHT DIVISION

(16) $(654 + 735 + 478) \div 83 = 2_1 2_3 .5_1 0_5 \bar{6}_5 \ldots = \textbf{22.494}$ to 3 D.P.

Here we use *On the Flag* for the division.
Totalling the hundreds we get $6 + 7 + 4 = 17$, then $17 \div 8 = 2_1$.

The tens total to 15, and $15 + 10$ (the carried 1) = 25. Then deducting the product of the flag digit and the last quotient digit $25 - 3 \times 2 = 19$, $19 \div 8 = 2_3$.

The units total is 17, $17 + 30 = 47$, $47 - 3 \times 2 = 41^*$, $41 \div 8 = 5_1$.

Then we just continue the straight division: 10 (the carry) $- 3 \times 5 = \bar{5}$, $\bar{5} \div 8 = 0_{\bar{5}}$. Etc.

Using the usual method, when we make the units calculation we know that the decimal point goes one place to the left of this (as we have one flag digit).

*If an integral answer was required this 41 would be the remainder.
That is: 22 remainder 41.

✎ **Practice F**   Evaluate giving quotient and remainder.

a $(386 + 445 + 787) \div 62$ b $(55 + 73 + 84 + 63) \div 71$

c $(8338 + 766 + 7456) \div 52$ d $(343 + 767 + 456) \div 59$

e $(1333 + 1443 + 2429) \div 68$ f $(5544 + 7384 + 9231) \div 48$

a $2_2 6_0$ r6   b 3_5 r62

c $3_0 1_3 8_2$ r24   d $2_2 6_1$ r32

e $0_4 7_2 6_1$ r37   f $4_1 5_3{}^1 1_0$ r31 = 461 r31

13.2d MEAN AND MEAN DEVIATION

We find the mean of a set of n numbers by adding them and dividing the result by n.

 Find the mean of **17, 34, 53, 81, 36, 31**.

We need: $(17 + 34 + 53 + 81 + 36 + 31) \div 6 = 4_i 2$ (if we say $23 \div 4 = 4$ rem $\bar{1}$).

We can write $\bar{x} = 42$ where we use the symbol $\bar{x}$ to denote the mean.

The mean, $\bar{x}$, of a set of numbers gives a value that represents the set, a sort of average of the numbers.
Another characteristic of a set of numbers is how spread out they are around the mean value and it is important to have ways of measuring this spread.

One way is to find their mean deviation from the mean.
This means we find how far each of the numbers is from the mean (the deviation) and find the mean of these deviations by adding them and dividing by the number of numbers.

Then a set of numbers that are close to the mean will give a smaller mean deviation than a set which is more spread out.

Another useful option we have is to reduce all the given values by a suitable number, find the mean of the new set and add the number back on.

 Find the mean deviation of **17, 34, 53, 81, 36, 31**.

This is the same set of numbers as in the previous example in which the mean was found to be 42.

To find the mean deviation we subtract the mean from each of the numbers to get:

$$-25, -8, 11, 39, -6, -11. \qquad \text{- - - (1)}$$

We now simply ignore the minuses and find the mean of the numbers.

Mean deviation $= (25 + 8 + 11 + 39 + 6 + 11) \div 6 = 100 \div 6 = \mathbf{16\frac{2}{3}}$.

There is an easier way to do this because if you add the numbers in (1) above you will get a total of zero. In fact this will always happen because that is what the mean is, it makes the total deviation zero.

This means the total of the positive numbers will always equal the total of the negative numbers. So we only need to find one total and double it. That is, in this example we can add the 11 and 39 to get 50 and double this to 100, which we then divide by 6.

Alternatively, we could add all the negative numbers (ignoring the minuses) and still get 50. But in this example there are only two positive numbers so it is better to use them.

To find the mean deviation, then, first find the mean.
Then decide which of the numbers are above and below the mean.
Add the deviation from the mean of all the numbers above or below the mean and double.
Divide by the number of numbers.

 Find the mean deviation of **30, 40, 43, 48, 49**.

The mean is 42 again.

There are two numbers below the mean and three above it, so we look at the deviations of 30 and 40 from the mean and add them. This gives $12 + 2 = 14$.

We now double 14 and divide by 5, the number of numbers: $28 \div 5 = \textbf{5.6}$.

Comparing the mean deviations in these two examples we see that 5.6 is less than $16\frac{2}{3}$, reflecting the fact that the second set of numbers are less spread out than the first set (even though they have the same mean).

✒ **Practice G**   Find the mean and mean deviation of:

a 20, 30, 40, 50   b 7, 16, 31   c 5, 7, 8, 12, 13   d 23, 31, 42, 55, 64

---

a $10\,(\overline{x}=35)$ b $8\frac{2}{3}\,(\overline{x}=18)$ c $\frac{14}{5}\,(\overline{x}=9)$ d 13.2 $(\overline{x}=43)$

13.2e DIVIDING SUMS OF PRODUCTS

 $(32\times8 + 41\times4) \div 9 = 4_4\,6_6 = \textbf{46 rem 6}$.

Here we must multiply the **tens** digits and add: $3\times8 + 4\times4 = 40$; then $40\div9 = 4_4$.

And multiplying and summing the **units**: $2\times8 + 1\times4 = 20$; $20+40$ (carried) $= 60$, $60\div9 = 6_6$.

Of course the answer can also be given as $46\frac{6}{9} = 46\frac{2}{3}$ or as $46.\dot{6}$.

21 $(777 \times 7 + 898 \times 6) \div 8 = \left(1\overline{223} \times 7 + 1\overline{102} \times 6\right) \div 8 = 1_5 3_0 5_6 3_3 = \textbf{1353.375}.$

Here we may bring in the vinculum.
The steps are similar to those in the previous example.

 Practice H

a $(53 \times 4 + 44 \times 6) \div 8$ **b** $(234 \times 3 + 414 \times 4) \div 7$ **c** $(717 \times 3 + 535 \times 6) \div 7$

d $(66 \times 6 + 34 \times 3) \div 8$ **e** $(235 \times 6 + 838 \times 4) \div 7$ **f** $(76.17 \times 5 + 438.2 \times 6) \div 8$

g $(3949 \times 5 + 289 \times 6) \div 7$ **h** $(86 \times 6 - 42 \times 4) \div 9$ **i** $(235 \times 6 + 838 \times 4) \div 13$

---

a $5_1 9$ r4   b $3_1 3_2 6$ r6   c $7_2 6_{\bar{1}} 5$ r6

d $5_5 {}^1 2$ r2 = 62 r2   e $6_2 7_1 {}^1 0$ r2 = 680 r2   f $3_0 6_5 {}^1 6_0 . 2_1 5_5$ = 376.26 to 2 d.p.

g $2_1 9_4 {}^1 5_3 {}^1 8$ r3 = 3068 r3   h $3_5 8$ r6   i $3_5 6_2 6$ r4

22 $(43^2 + 71^2 + 35^2) \div 6 = 12_2 \, {}^1 4_4 \, {}^1 2_3 = \textbf{1352.5}.$

Here we take the duplex of the tens figure of each of the three numbers being squared, add them and divide by 6. And then proceed to the next duplex.

$4^2 + 7^2 + 3^2 = 74, \ 74 \div 6 = 12_2.$

$2 \times (4 \times 3 + 7 \times 1 + 3 \times 5) = 68, \ 68 + 20 = 88, \ 88 \div 6 = 14_4.$

$3^2 + 1^2 + 5^2 = 35, \ 35 + 40 = 75, \ 75 \div 6 = 12_3.$

The tens in these last two results must be carried back (**leftwards**) to get the final answer.

These 2-figure results are a bit cumbersome and can be eliminated by arranging to have the duplex totals reduced through putting down a negative carry digit.

$(43^2 + 71^2 + 35^2) \div 6 = 13_{\bar{4}} 5_{\bar{2}} 2_3 = \textbf{1352.5}$ again.

When we get the initial duplex total of 74 and divide by 6 we deliberately put down $13_{\bar{4}}$ so that the negative carry will reduce the next total. And so on.

$(303^2 + 42^2 + 33^2) \div 9 = 1_0 0_5 \bar{5}_2 \bar{2}_4 2 = 10518$.

Here we begin by taking the first two duplexes of 303: $D(3) = 9$, $9 \div 9 = 1_0$.
Then $D(30) = 0$, $0+0 = 0$, $0 \div 9 = 0_0$.

[These two can also be taken together: the two duplex results give 90, $90 \div 9 = 10_0$.]

Now we can bring in the other two squares also: $D(303) + D(4) + D(3) = 43$,
$43 + 0 = 43$, $43 \div 9 = 5_{\bar{2}}$.

Then $2(0 + 8 + 9) = 34$, $34 - 20 = 14$, $14 \div 9 = 2_{\bar{4}}$.

Finally, $9 + 4 + 9 = 22$, $22 - 40 = \overline{18}$, $-18 \div 9 = \overline{2}$.

We also have the option of using the vinculum to rewrite the numbers being squared.

✏ Practice I

a $(14^2 + 28^2 + 52^2) \div 8$ b $(32^2 + 43^2 + 54^2 + 73^2) \div 9$

c $(69^2 + 47^2 + 44^2) \div 7$ d $(31^2 + 41^2 + 49^2 + 59^2) \div 14$

e $(123^2 + 231^2 + 432^2) \div 7$ f $(512^2 + 52^2 + 38^2) \div 8$

---

a $3_6 {}^1 5_0 {}^1 0$ r4 = 460 r4   b $11_0 {}^1 3_1 5$ r3 = 1235 r3
c $12_3 6_2 {}^1 2$ r2 = 1272 r2   d $6_2 1_{\bar{2}} 2$ r12 = 608 r12
e $3_0 6_{\bar{2}} 4_0 4_2 4$ r6   f $3_1 2_4 {}^1 2_6 8_4 6$ r4 = 33286 r4

Dividing sums of squares can be useful when finding variances in statistics.

13.2f VARIANCE

Find the variance of **42, 68, 51, 83**.

The variance is given by $\sigma^2 = \dfrac{\sum (x - \bar{x})^2}{n}$ or by $\sigma^2 = \dfrac{\sum x^2}{n} - \bar{x}^2$.

Let us assume we know the mean, 61: calculated as shown previously. And we will write $7\bar{2}$ for 68.

We will use the second formula above, which means squaring, adding, dividing by n and subtracting a square.

To square the given numbers we first square the first (left-hand) digit. We then add these, divide by 4 and subtract the square of the first digit of the mean, $\bar{x}$.

So, first: add the first duplexes of the given numbers to get 154, divide this by 4 to get: 38_2 (where the subscript, 2, is a remainder). From this we take the first duplex of the mean, 36, and so we have: 2_2.

Next add the next duplex of each number to get 46, add the carried 2 above to get 66, divide by 4 to get 16_2 and subtract from this 16 the next duplex of $\bar{x}$ (12), so that we now have: $2_2 4_2$.

Now add the next duplexes of the numbers to get 18, add the carried 2 to get 38, divide by 4 to get 9_2 and subtract the next duplex of $\bar{x}$ (1) to get: $2_2 4_2 8_2$.

We have now exhausted all the duplexes so we now just divide he remainder by 4 to get an exact answer of **248.5**.

The steps may be listed as follows:

Find $\bar{x}$.

$\left\{\begin{array}{l} \text{Sum the duplexes} \\ \text{Add any carry} \\ \text{Divide by n} \\ \text{Subtract the corresponding duplex of the mean} \\ \text{Combine with result of previous step} \end{array}\right\}$ repeat until all duplexes are exhausted

When the duplexes are exhausted divide any remainder by n

25 Find the variance of **69, 72, 93**.

The mean is found to be $\bar{x} = 78$.
Adding the left-most duplexes we get 179 (treating 69 as $7\bar{1}$).
Dividing by 3 we have 59_2.
Subtracting the first duplex of the mean we get 10_2.

The next set of duplexes total 68 and adding the carried 20 we have 88.
Dividing this by 3 gives 29_1,
Subtracting the next duplex of the mean gives $\overline{83}_1$.
Combining this with 10 from before we now have 17_1 (the $\bar{8}$ carries back to the 10).

The last duplexes total 14, and with the carry becomes 24,
Divide by 3: 8_0.
Subtract the last duplex of the mean to get: $\overline{56}_0$.
Combining this with the 17 from before gives **114** exactly.

We have the option also to reduce all the values if we wish as the variance is unchanged if all values are reduced by the same number. So the above example would have been easier if all the numbers were reduced by 70.

Practice J   Find the mean and variance of the following sets of numbers:

a 3, 5, 6, 6   b 21, 31, 32, 44   c 12, 13, 15, 18, 22   d 33, 41, 52, 62

---

a   1.5 ($\bar{x} = 5$, steps are: 1_2)   b   66.5 ($\bar{x} = 32$, steps are: $0_2, 6_2, 66_2$)
c   13.2 ($\bar{x} = 16$, steps are: $1_1, 4_0, 13_1$)   d   120.5 ($\bar{x} = 47$, steps are: $5_2, 16_2, 120_2$)

13.3 PYTHAGORAS' THEOREM

In finding the hypotenuse of a right-angled triangle whose other sides are, say, 4 and 5, we need to find $\sqrt{4^2 + 5^2} = \sqrt{41}$. This just involves finding a square root, though, which has been covered in Lesson 14.

In finding $\sqrt{317^2 + 421^2}$ however we can proceed digit by digit by first finding the total of the duplexes of 3 and 4 and the first digit of the square root of the result, and then proceed to the next order down and so on.

We must of course assume that the reader is familiar with the method of squaring from left to right and square root.

26   Find $\sqrt{317^2 + 421^2}$ to 4 significant figures.

We will take the duplexes of the two numbers from left to right, add them up, and then take the square root:

Writing the duplexes out we have: 9/6/43/14/49 + 16/16/12/4/1*
                                                    = 25/22/55/18/50.

Then for the square root we have:

$$
\begin{array}{c}
25/22/55/18/50 \\
10) \quad \underline{0 \quad 2 \quad 1 \quad 0 \quad 1} \\
5 \quad 2 \quad 7 . \; 0 \quad 0 \ldots
\end{array}
$$
          The answer is **527.0**.

The first figure is clearly 5 rem 0; then 10 into 22 is 2 rem 2.

Then $75 - 2^2 = 71$, 10 into 71 is 7 rem 1.
Then $28 - 28 = 0$, 10 into 0 is 0 rem 0.
Then $50 - 49 = 1$, 10 into 1 is 0 rem 1.
Etc.

*Note that although we have calculated all the duplexes here, before finding the square root, in practice we need only find each duplex as we need it, add it to the other duplex, and obtain the next figure of the square root. See the next example.

27   Find $\sqrt{53.6^2 + 732^2}$ to 4 significant figures.

$$49/42/62/42/73/36$$
$$14) \quad \underline{0 \quad 0 \quad \bar{3} \quad 2 \quad \bar{1}}$$
$$7 \quad 3 \quad 4 \;.\; \bar{1} \quad 6 \ldots$$

53.6 will not contribute to either of the first two duplexes from 732, so we begin with $D(7) = 49$, the square root is 7, there is no remainder, and the divisor is 14.

The next duplex is $D(73) = 42$, 14 into 42 is 3 rem 0.
Then $D(5) + D(732) = 62$, $62 - D(3) = 53$, 14 into 53 is 4 rem $\bar{3}$.
[the D(3) here comes from the second answer digit.]
Then $D(53) + D(32) = 42$, $42 + \overline{30} = 12$, $12 - D(34) = \overline{12}$, 14 into $\overline{12}$ is $\bar{1}$ rem 2.
Then $D(536) + D(2) = 73$, $73 + 20 = 93$, $93 - D(34\bar{1}) = 83$, 14 into 83 is 6 rem $\bar{1}$.
So the answer is **734.0**.

There is no question of attempting this using conventional methods without a calculator or tables. Two long multiplications would be required, then an addition and finally a square root.

28    $\sqrt{69^2 - 43^2} = \mathbf{53.96}$ to 4 significant figures.

Here we will write 69 as $7\bar{1}$ and subtract the duplexes.
We will also abbreviate the working further.

$$\sqrt{7\bar{1}^2 - 43^2} = 5_8 4_2 . 0_{\bar{4}} \bar{4}_0 3_2 \ldots$$

First $7^2 - 4^2 = 33$, so the first figure is 5, the
first remainder is 8 and the divisor will be 10:

$$10)\underline{\qquad\qquad}$$
$$5_8\underline{\qquad\qquad}$$

Then the duplexes are: $2(\bar{7} - 12) = -38$, and
$80 - 38 = 42$ and $42 \div 10 = 4_2$:

$$10)\underline{\qquad\qquad}$$
$$5_8 4_2 .\underline{\qquad\qquad}$$

Next: duplexes, $\left(\bar{1}\right)^2 - 3^2 = -8; \ 20 - 8 = 12,$

$12 - 4^2 = -4, \ -4 \div 10 = 0_{\bar{4}}:$

$$\underline{\begin{array}{r} 10) \\ \hline 5_8 4_2 . 0_{\bar{4}} \end{array}}$$

Now we continue just as in the usual square rooting method, as there are no more duplexes to bring in: $D(40) = 0, \ \overline{40} - 0 = \overline{40}, \ \overline{40} \div 10 = \bar{4}_0$ and so on.

$$\underline{\begin{array}{r} 10) \\ \hline 5_8 4_2 . 0_{\bar{4}} \bar{4}_0 3_2 \ldots \end{array}}$$

✎ **Practice K**   Evaluate the following, to 4 S.F.

a $\sqrt{33^2 + 41^2}$ b $\sqrt{23^2 + 34^2}$ c $\sqrt{81^2 + 21^2}$

d $\sqrt{81^2 - 21^2}$ e $\sqrt{302^2 + 411^2}$ f $\sqrt{512^2 + 33^2}$

g $\sqrt{613^2 - 321^2}$

---

a $5_0 2_6 . 6_6 3_6$ b 41.05   c 83.68
d 78.23   e 510.0   f 513.1
g 522.2

We can now calculate trigonometric functions from their series expansions but we leave this until Lesson 17 where those series are derived.

LESSON 14
SOLUTION OF POLYNOMIAL EQUATIONS

SUMMARY

Here we see two methods of solution, one of which uses derivatives, to find real roots.

14.1 Quadratic Equations

14.2 Higher Order equations – cubics and quintics.

Solution of quadratic equations has been covered in Lesson 6. The method shown here is effectively an extension of the square root procedure shown in Lesson 11 and, for solution $x>1$, is based on the work of Dr Jeremy Pickles (see Reference 5, Chapter 12).

14.1 QUADRATIC EQUATIONS

14.1a x > 1

In fact, finding the square root of a number, n, is equivalent to solving the quadratic equation: $x^2 = n$. The solution of $x^2 + mx = n$ involves only a change at the beginning of the calculation.

In solving $x^2 = n$, we use 2a, where a is the first figure of x, as a divisor. Note that 2a is the derivative of x^2 where $x = a$.

Similarly, in solving $x^2 + mx = n$, the derivative of $x^2 + mx$ is $(2x+m)$ and so $(2a+m)$ is used as a divisor.

  Solve $x^2 + x = 13$.

In solving $x^2 + x = 13$ --- (1)

we get **2x + 1** when we differentiate the left-hand side and this tells us that we use: $2a + 1 = $ **twice the first figure + 1** as a divisor.

You will see that the first figure of the answer to equation (1) is **3** because if $x = 3$ we get $3^2 + 3 = 12$ for the left-hand side of equation, which is close to the 13 on the right-hand side.

This 12 leaves a **remainder of 1** from the 13 on the right side.

We now get our divisor by putting $x = 3$ in 2x+1. This gives **7**.

And we set up the initial chart:

$$
\begin{array}{r}
1\,3\,.\,0\,0\,0 \\
7)\ \underline{\quad 1 \quad\quad\quad} \\
3\,.\quad\quad\quad
\end{array}
$$

The rest of the calculation is identical to finding a square root: $10 \div 7 = 1$ rem 3 etc. as in Lesson 11.

The answer to 7 figures is shown below:

$$
\begin{array}{r}
1\,3\,.\,0\ 0\,0\ 0\,0\ 0\,0 \\
7)\ \underline{\quad 1\ 3\ 1\ 2\ 4\ 5\ 5} \\
\underline{3\,.\,1\ 4\,0\ 0\,5\ 5}
\end{array}
$$

Since the sum of the roots of a quadratic $x^2 + mx = n$ is $-m$ the other root is available by taking the above root from -1 (and in general from $-m$).
This gives $x = 3.140055$ and $x = -4.140055$ to 6 D.P.

PROOF

To solve $x^2 + mx = n$, where $D_1 = (2x+m)$.
Let $x = a/b/c/d...$ in which $a/b/c/d...$ are the decimal digits in the answer, the different powers of ten being separated by an oblique line, $x = a + 10^{-1}b + 10^{-2}c + ...$ and a is the units digit of x.

The first digit of the answer being a then $D_1(a) = 2a + m$. This is the divisor used in the above calculation.

Then $x^2 + mx = (a/b/c/d...)^2 + m(a/b/c/d...)$

$\qquad = a^2 + ma / 2ab + mb / 2ac + b^2 + mc / 2ad + 2bc + md / ...$ (taking duplexes)

$\qquad = a^2 + ma / b(2a+m) / c(2a+m) + b^2 / d(2a+m) + 2bc / ...$ $\qquad$ - - - (2)

$\qquad = n$

We want to find the value of x that exhausts n when $x^2 + mx$ is subtracted from it. That is, when the successive terms on the right-hand side of (2) are subtracted from it.

In (2) above we note:
a) That the first part, $a^2 + ma$, is the value of the LHS of the given equation with $x = a$.
b) And also $(2a+m)$ is contained in each succeeding part, multiplied by b, c, d etc.
c) The remaining parts of (2), (in bold) are the successive duplexes of b/c/d...

This means that, having found a and what remains of n, we divide the remainder by $(2a+m)$ to get b and a remainder.
Then subtract b^2 and divide by $(2a+m)$ to get c and a remainder.
Then subtract 2bc and divide by $(2a+m)$ to get d and a remainder.
And so on.

② Solve $x^2 - 7x + 2 = 0$.

Then $x^2 - 7x = \bar{2}$, $D_1 = 2x - 7$, the first digit of x is 7 and so $2 \times 7 - 7 = 7$ is the divisor.

$$
\begin{array}{r}
\bar{2}.\,0\ \ 00\ \ 00\ \ 000 \\
7)\quad \underline{\bar{2}\ 1\ 1\ 3\ 1\ \bar{2}\ 1\ 5} \\
7.\bar{3}\ 0\ 1\ 5\ 6\ 2\ 1
\end{array}
$$

So $x = 6.7015621$ and $x = 0.2984379$ to 7 D.P.

The second root of the equation in Example 2 is also found in Practice C by a different method. Similarly **i** in Practice A below is the same equation as **d** in Practice C.

✎ Practice A   Solve:

a $x^2 + 3x = 19$ **b** $x^2 + 2x = 100$ **c** $x^2 + 6x = 17$

d $x^2 + 3x = 45$ **e** $x^2 - 3x = 5$ **f** $x^2 - 2x = 1$

g $x^2 - 3x = 4.6$ **h** $x^2 - 5x + 5 = 0$ **i** $x^2 - 4x + 2 = 0$

Note, there are many possible routes to the answer. Only one is shown below.

a
$$
\begin{array}{r}
19.0\ 0\ 0\ 0\ 0 \\
9)\quad \underline{1\ \ 1\ \ 0\ \ \bar{2}\ \ \bar{3}} \\
3.1\ 1\ 0\ \bar{2}
\end{array}
$$
$x = 3.1098, -6.1098$

b
$$
\begin{array}{r}
100.0\ 0\ 0\ 0\ 0\ 0\ 0\ 0 \\
20)\quad \underline{1\ 10\ 0\ 0\ \bar{5}\ \overline{10}\ 10\ 0} \\
9.0\ 5\ 0\ \bar{1}\ \bar{2}\ \bar{5}\ 6
\end{array}
$$
$x = 9.0498756, -11.0498756$

c
$$
\begin{array}{r}
17.0\ 0\ 0\ 0\ 0 \\
10)\quad \underline{1\ \ 0\ \ \bar{1}\ \ 0\ \ 2} \\
2.1\ 0\ \bar{1}\ 0
\end{array}
$$
$x = 2.0990, -8.0990$

d
$$
\begin{array}{r}
45.0\ 0\ 0\ 0\ 0 \\
13)\quad \underline{5\ \ 11\ \ 10\ \ 6\ \ 0} \\
5.3\ 7\ 4\ \bar{1}
\end{array}
$$
$x = 5.3739, -8.3739$

e
$$
\begin{array}{r}
5.0\ 0\ 0\ 0\ 0\ 0 \\
5)\quad \underline{1\ 0\ 1\ 4\ 1\ 0} \\
4.2\ \bar{1}\ 2\ 6\ \bar{2}
\end{array}
$$
$x = 4.19258, -1.19258$

f
$$
\begin{array}{r}
1.0\ 0\ 0\ 0\ 0 \\
2)\quad \underline{1\ 2\ 2\ 4\ 3} \\
2.4\ 1\ 4\ 2
\end{array}
$$
$x = 2.4142, -0.4142$

g
$$
\begin{array}{r}
4.6\ 0\ 0\ 0\ 0\ 0\ 0\ 0 \\
5)\quad \underline{1\ 4\ 3\ 5\ 7\ 7\ 7} \\
4.1\ 1\ 7\ 2\ 5\ 0\ 5
\end{array}
$$
$x = 4.1172505, -1.1172505$

h
$$
\begin{array}{r}
\bar{5}.0\ 0\ 0\ 0\ 0\ 0\ 0\ 0 \\
3)\quad \underline{\bar{1}\ 2\ \bar{2}\ 2\ 0\ \bar{1}\ \bar{2}\ 0} \\
4.\bar{4}\ 2\ \bar{2}\ 0\ 3\ 4\ 0
\end{array}
$$
$x = 3.6180340, 1.3819660$

i
$$
\begin{array}{r}
\bar{2}.0\ 0\ 0\ 0\ 0\ 0\ 0\ 0 \\
2)\quad \underline{1\ 2\ 2\ 4\ 3\ 4\ 6\ 6} \\
3.4\ 1\ 4\ 2\ 1\ 3\ 6
\end{array}
$$
$x = 3.4142136, 0.5857864$

"In the Vedic mathematics Sutras, CALCULUS comes in at a very early stage."
From "Vedic Mathematics", Page 157.

3   Solve $2x^2 + 3x = 16$.

The initial coefficient, **2**, involves a slight change to the procedure.

Every duplex is doubled before it is subtracted. Otherwise the method is the same.

The first figure is found to be 2 and there is a remainder of 2.
$D_1 = 4x + 3 = 11$ when x = 2.

$$
\begin{array}{r}
16\,.0 \quad 0 \quad 0 \quad 0 \quad 0 \quad 0 \\
11)\;\; {}^{2}\;\; {}^{\bar{2}}\;\; {}^{\bar{6}}\;\; {}^{0}\;\; {}^{2}\;\; {}^{5} \\
\hline
2\,.2 \;\; \bar{2} \;\; \bar{4} \;\; 2 \;\; \bar{3}
\end{array}
$$

$20 \div 11 = 2$ rem $\bar{2}$, put down second diagonal.
We now subtract **twice** the duplex of 2 (in the tenths place of the answer) from $\overline{20}$ to get $\overline{28}$ and then $\overline{28} \div 11 = \bar{2}$ rem $\bar{6}$, which we put down.
Then we take twice the duplex of $2\bar{2}$ from $\overline{60}$ to get $\overline{44}$, and $\overline{44} \div 11 = \bar{4}$ rem 0.
Etc.

The earlier proof can be modified to justify this.

To solve $kx^2 + mx = n$, where $D_1 = 2kx+m$.

The first digit of the answer being a then the value of D_1 at a is 2ka + m.

Then $kx^2 + mx \quad = k(a/b/c/d...)^2 + m(a/b/c/d...)$

$\qquad\qquad = ka^2 + ma / 2kab + mb / 2kac + kb^2 + mc / ...$

$\qquad\qquad = ka^2 + ma / b(2ka+m) / c(2ka+m) + kb^2 / ... \qquad\qquad - - - (3)$

$\qquad\qquad = n$

$(ka^2 + ma)$ is the LHS of the given equation with x = a and (2ka + m) is its first derivative with x = a. All remaining terms are the duplexes of bcd... multiplied by k.

🖉 **Practice B**

a $2x^2 - 3x = 37$ **b** $3x^2 + 2x = 35$ **c** $3x^2 - 2x = 10$

a	37.0 0 0 0 0 0	b	35.0 0 0 0 0 0	c	10.0 0 0 0 0
17)	${}^{2}\;{}^{3}\;{}^{11}\;{}^{4}\;{}^{\bar{3}}\;{}^{10}$	20)	${}^{2}\;{}^{0}\;{}^{\bar{3}}\;{}^{\overline{10}}\;{}^{6}\;{}^{10}$	10)	${}^{2}\;{}^{0}\;{}^{\bar{2}}\;{}^{2}\;{}^{\bar{1}}$
	5.1 1 6 1 $\bar{4}$		3.1 0 $\bar{1}$ 5 4		2.2 $\bar{1}$ $\bar{1}$ 2

x = 5.11606, –3.61606   x = 3.09854, –3.76521   x = 2.1892, –1.5225

14.1b x < –1

  4   Solve $x^2 - 5x = 16$.

This has a root at about $x = -2$, which leaves a remainder of 2.
$D_1 = 2x - 5$, so $D_1(-2) = -9$ is the divisor:

$$
\begin{array}{r}
1\,6\,.\,0\ \ 0\ \ 0\ \ 0\ \ 0\ \ 0\ \ 0 \\
\overline{9)}\quad {\scriptstyle 2\ \ 2\ \ 7\ \ 3\ \ 1\ \ \bar{4}\ \ 1} \\
\hline
\overline{2}\,.\,\overline{2}\ \ \overline{1}\ \ \overline{7}\ \ 0\ \ 0\ \ {}_{|}0
\end{array}
$$

After the initial diagonal is done: $20 \div \overline{9} = \overline{2}$ rem 2 for the second diagonal.
Then $20 - \left(\overline{2}\right)^2 = 16$, $16 \div \overline{9} = \overline{1}$ rem 7.
And so on.

So $x = \mathbf{-2.216990}$ or $x = \mathbf{7.216990}$ to 6 D.P.

Of course it would have been easier in this case to find the positive root first.
There are various ways of transforming polynomial equations so that the roots of the transformed equation bear some specific relationship to the original equation. We can get equations in which the signs of the roots are all changed, in which the roots are a given multiple or reciprocal or increased or reduced by a given number, for example. See Reference 5, Chapter 8.

So, in Example 4 above it is easy to convert $x^2 - 5x - 16 = 0$ to $x^2 + 5x - 16 = 0$ to change the signs of the roots (we change the sign of alternate terms beginning with the second term). We may now find the (positive) solution to $x^2 + 5x - 16 = 0$ and change the sign to get a root of the given equation.

Other cases, for example where the roots are close (as in $x^2 - 4x + 3.8 = 0$) or large (e.g. $x^2 - 4x = 530$) can be solved by transforming the roots, but more work is needed in this area.

14.1c 0 < x < 1

If x is small the x term in $x^2 + mx = n$ becomes dominant and so we use the coefficient of x as the divisor.

With the usual notation: $(a/b/c...)^2 + m(a/b/c...) = n$.

So $n = ma / mb + \mathbf{a^2} / mc + \mathbf{2ab} / md + \mathbf{2ac + b^2} / ...$ - - - (4)

We do not use derivatives here and we do not need to know the first figure of the answer.
From $n = ma / ...$ we can get the first figure of x by dividing n by m.
We then subtract successive duplexes (bold terms in (4) above) and divide by m at each step.

⟨5⟩ Solve $x^2 + 4x = 1.5$.

This can be written as $x = \dfrac{1.5 - x^2}{4}$.

We set up the initial chart and divide 4 into 15 to get 3 remainder 3:

$$
\begin{array}{r}
1\,.\,5\ 0\ 0\ 0\ 0\ 0\ 0 \\
4)\quad {}^{3} \\
\hline
0\,.\,3
\end{array}
$$

Then we take the duplex of 3, $D(3) = 9$, from 30 to get 21 and $21 \div 4 = 5$ rem 1: which we put down.

Then $10 - D(35) = 10 - 30 = -20$, $-20 \div 4 = \bar{5}$ rem 0: written down.

Then $0 - D(35\bar{5}) = 0 - \bar{5} = 5$, $5 \div 4 = 2$ rem $\bar{3}$.*

And so on.

$$
\begin{array}{r}
1\,.\,5\ \ 0\ \ 0\ \ 0\ \ 0\ \ 0\ \ 0 \\
4)\quad {}^{3}\ {}^{1}\ {}^{0}\ {}^{\bar{3}}\ {}^{8}\ {}^{7} \\
\hline
0\,.\,3\ 5\ \bar{5}\ 2\ 0\ 7
\end{array}
$$

* Note in this step we may not put the obvious answer, 1 remainder 1, as we want to keep the next answer digit small.

So $x = \mathbf{0.345207}$ and $x = -4 - 0.345207 = \mathbf{-4.345207}$ to 6 D.P.

✎ **Practice C**   Solve:

a $x^2 + 5x = 1.5$ **b** $x^2 - 7x + 2 = 0$ **c** $x^2 + 3x - 2 = 0$ **d** $x^2 - 4x + 2 = 0$

a	b	c	d
$1\,.\,5\ 0\ 0\ 0\ 0\ 0\ 0$	$2\,.\,0\ 0\ 0\ 0\ 0\ 0\ 0$	$2\,.\,0\ 0\ 0\ 0\ 0\ 0\ 0$	$2\,.\,0\ 0\ 0\ 0\ 0\ 0\ 0$
5) $\quad 0\ 1\ 2\ \bar{3}\ 2\ 2$	7) $\quad \bar{1}\ \bar{1}\ 4\ 0\ \bar{4}\ 2\ \bar{1}$	3) $\quad 5\ 7\ 7\ 9\ 13\ 10$	4) $\quad \bar{4}\ 0\ 4\ 1\ \bar{2}\ 4$
$0\,.\,3\ \bar{2}\ 4\ \bar{1}\ \bar{2}\ 2$	$0\,.\,3\ 0\ \bar{2}\ 4\ 4\ \bar{2}\ \bar{1}$	$0\,.\,5\ 6\ 1\ 5\ 5\ 3$	$0\,.\,6\ \bar{1}\ \bar{4}\ \bar{2}\ \bar{1}\ \bar{4}$
$x = 0.283882, -5.283882$	$x = 0.2984379, 6.7015621$	$x = 0.561553, -3.561553$	$x = 0.585786, 3.414214$

14.1d $0 < x < 1$ and x^2 Coefficient >1

We now have: $k(a/b/c...)^2 + m(a/b/c...) = n$.

So $n = ma / mb + ka^2 / mc + 2abk / md + (2ac + b^2)k / ...$

This shows, as we might have expected, that the method is the same as above except that we multiply all duplexes by k (the coefficient of x^2) before deducting them.

 6   Solve $2x^2 + 7x = 3$.

The divisor is 7 (the coefficient of x) and all duplexes are multiplied by 2:

$$
\begin{array}{r}
3\,.\,0 \;\; 0 \;\; 0 \;\; 0 \;\; 0 \;\; 0 \;\; 0 \;\; 0 \\
7)\quad {\scriptstyle 2 \;\; 2 \;\; 10 \;\; \bar{4} \;\; 8 \;\; 1 \;\; 1} \\
\hline
0\,.\,4 \;\; \bar{2} \;\; 6 \;\; 0 \;\; 0 \;\; 1 \;\; \bar{1}
\end{array}
$$

The steps are: $30 \div 7 = 4$ rem 2.
$\qquad\qquad 20 - 2 \times 4^2 = -12,\; -12 \div 7 = \bar{2}$ rem 2.
$\qquad\qquad 20 - 2 \times (2 \times 4 \times \bar{2}) = 52,\; 52 \div 7 = 6$ rem 10.
$\qquad\qquad$ Etc.

So $x = \mathbf{0.3860009}$ and $x = -3.5 - 0.3860009 = \mathbf{-3.8860009}$ to 7 D.P.

14.1e −1 < x < 0

 7   Solve $x^2 + 4x = -1.5$.

We discover a root at about $x = -0.4$.

$$
\begin{array}{r}
\bar{1}\,.\,\bar{5} \;\; 0 \;\; 0 \;\; 0 \;\; 0 \;\; 0 \;\; 0 \\
4)\quad {\scriptstyle 1 \;\; 2 \;\; 0 \;\; 0 \;\; \bar{4} \;\; \bar{1}} \\
\hline
0\,.\,\bar{4} \;\; \bar{2} \;\; 1 \;\; 1 \;\; 4 \;\; \bar{1}
\end{array}
$$

We can begin with $\overline{15} \div 4 = \bar{4}$ rem 1.
Then $10 - \left(\bar{4}\right)^2 = -6,\; -6 \div 4 = \bar{2}$ rem 2.
And so on.

So $x = \mathbf{-0.418861}$ or $\mathbf{-3.581139}$ to 6 D.P.

This method is extended to the solution of cubic equations later in this lesson and developed further in Lesson 18 for calculating inverse sines and inverse cosines and solving transcendental equations.

14.1f x LARGE

8   Solve $x^2 + 3x = 187920$.

Here x has three digits before the decimal point so that the x-term dominates, and we therefore treat this as the square root of 187920 initially.

$$
\begin{array}{r}
1\ 8\ 7\ 9\ 2\ 0 \\
8)\quad \underline{2\ 3\ 2\ 1\ \ } \\
\underline{4\ 3\ 2\ .0\ 0}
\end{array}
$$

So the first figure is 4, twice this is 8 and the remainder is 2.
Next, as usual, we divide 27 by 8 and put down 3 remainder 3.
So far we have ignored the 3x in the equation and in fact we need to subtract 3x from 920 (in 187920). So we will take 3×4, 3×3 and 3×2 (three times the digits of the answer 432) from the 9, 2, 0 respectively.

Next we take D(3) from 39 as usual and also take 3×4 as well, to get 18; 18 ÷ 8 = 2 rem 2.

Now take D(32) from 22 and also 3×3 to get 1; 1 ÷ 8 = 0 rem 1.
Finally D(320) + 3×2 = 10, which exhausts the remaining 10. And all remaining duplexes are zero so **x = 432** exactly.

14.2 HIGHER ORDER EQUATIONS

14.2a CUBE ROOT

Finding a cube root is equivalent to solving an equation of the form $x^3 = n$.
And if, as before, x = a/b/c/d/e... then $(a/b/c/d/e...)^3 = n$.

Now using the expansion of $(a + b + c + d + e \ldots)^3$ and the oblique lines to separate successive orders of magnitude we have:

a^3 /
$3a^2b$ /
$3a^2c + 3ab^2$ /
$3a^2d + 6abc + b^3$ /
$3a^2e + 6abd + 3ac^2 + 3b^2c$ /
$3a^2f + 6abe + 6acd + 3b^2d + 3bc^2$ /
. . .
= n   - - - (5)

Notice that the first term in each order after the first is $D_1(a)$ multiplied by b, c, d, etc., where $D_1 = 3x^2$ and $D_1(a) = 3a^2$. And so $D_1(a)$, as before, is used as a constant divisor in each step of the calculation.

The other terms, in bold above, are the successive subtraction terms required at each step.

 Solve $x^3 = 70.1$.

The first figure of the answer is found to be a = 4 and this leaves a remainder from 70 of 6.
Also $D_1(a) = 3 \times 4^2 = 48$ and this is used as the divisor. So the initial chart looks like this:

$$
\begin{array}{r}
70\ .1\ 0\ 0\ 0\ 0\ 0 \\
48)\quad{}^{6} \\
\hline
4
\end{array}
$$

Now looking at the second order term $3a^2b$ in (5) above we have only to divide 61 by 48 to get b. So b = 1 and there is a remainder of 13:

$$
\begin{array}{r}
70\ .1\ 0\ 0\ 0\ 0\ 0 \\
48)\quad{}^{6}\ {}^{13} \\
\hline
4\ .1
\end{array}
$$

Looking now at $3a^2c + 3ab^2$ in (5) we subtract $3ab^2 = 12$ from 130 to get 118 and divide by 48 to get 2 remainder 22.

$$
\begin{array}{r}
70\ .1\ 0\ 0\ 0\ 0\ 0 \\
48)\quad{}^{6}\ {}^{13}\ {}^{22}\ {}^{27}\ {}^{48}\ {}^{27} \\
\hline
4\ .1\ 2\ 3\ 2\ 5
\end{array}
$$

The remaining steps are similar: deduct the value of the next set of terms, in bold in (5), from the latest dividend, divide by 48 and put down answer digit and remainder.

Practice D   Find the cube root:

a 7   b 60   c 10   d 2

a 7.000000	b 60.000000	c 10.000000	d 2.000000
12) $^{\bar{1}}$ ^{2} ^{2} $^{\bar{3}}$ ^{9} ^{0}	48) $^{\bar{4}}$ ^{8} ^{20} $^{\overline{15}}$ ^{3} ^{18}	12) ^{2} ^{8} ^{14} ^{31} ^{49} ^{79}	3) ^{1} ^{1} $^{\bar{5}}$ $^{\bar{5}}$ ^{13} $^{\bar{2}}$
2.$\bar{1}$ 1 3 $\bar{1}$ 3	4.$\bar{1}$ 1 5 $\bar{1}$ $\bar{3}$	2.1 5 4 4 3	1.3 $\bar{4}$ 0 $\bar{1}$ 2
= 1.91293	= 3.91487	= 2.15443	= 1.25992

14.2b CUBIC EQUATIONS

Expanding $(a/b/c/d...)^3 + k(a/b/c/d...)^2 + m(a/b/c/d...) = n$

we get $a^3 + ka^2 + ma / 3a^2b + 2abk + bm / 3a^2c + 3ab^2 + 2ack + b^2k + cm / ...$

$= a^3 + ka^2 + ma / b(3a^2 + 2ak + m) / c(3a^2 + 2ak + m) + 3ab^2 + b^2k / ...$

$= a^3 + ka^2 + ma /$
  $bD_1(a) /$
  $cD_1(a) + \mathbf{3ab^2 + b^2k} /$
  $dD_1(a) + \mathbf{6abc + b^3 + 2bck} /$
  $eD_1(a) + \mathbf{6abd + 3ac^2 + 3b^2c + 2bdk + c^2k} /$
  $fD_1(a) + \mathbf{6abe + 6acd + 3b^2d + 3bc^2 + 2bek + 2cdk} /$
  $. . .$
$= n$

Here we have the same pattern.
We decide the first figure, a, and the remainder and we find $D_1(a)$.
We use $D_1(a)$ as a divisor and the subtraction terms above, in bold, to gradually exhaust n.

10   Solve $x^3 - 3x^2 + 7x = 23$.

We find $a = 3$ and there is a remainder of 2.

$D_1 = 3x^2 - 6x + 7$ and so $D_1(3) = 16$, our divisor.

So we start with:

```
         2 3 . 0  0  0  0  0
   16)        ²
        ─────────────────────
         3 .
```

The next step is to divide 20 by 16 and put down 1 remainder 4 (see next diagonal below).

```
         2 3 . 0  0  0  0  0
   16)        ²  ⁴  ²  ⁵̄  ⁰
        ─────────────────────
         3 . 1  2  0  5̄
```

Next we deduct $3ab^2 + b^2k$ from 40 to get $40 - 6 = 34$. Then $34 \div 16 = 2$ rem 2.
Then, $6abc + b^3 + 2bck = 36 + 1 - 12 = 25$, $20 - 25 = -5$, $-5 \div 16 = 0$ rem $\overline{5}$.
And so on.

This can be extended to higher order polynomials.

A SIMPLIFICATION

The subtraction terms get rather cumbersome and this can be simplified.
The subtraction terms are given, in bold, by:

$a^3 + ka^2 + ma$ /
$\mathbf{bD_1(a)}$ /
$\mathbf{cD_1(a) + 3ab^2 + b^2k}$ /
$\mathbf{dD_1(a) + 6abc + b^3 + 2bck}$ /
$\mathbf{eD_1(a) + 6abd + 3ac^2 + 3b^2c + 2bdk + c^2k}$ /
$\mathbf{fD_1(a) + 6abe + 6acd + 3b^2d + 3bc^2 + 2bek + 2cdk}$ /
$\cdots$
$= n$

We note that $D_1(a) = 3a^2 + 2ka + m,$
$\quad\quad \frac{1}{2}D_2(a) = 3a + k,$
$\quad\quad \frac{1}{6}D_3(a) = 1.$

This last line is superfluous for cubics but indicates how the method works for higher order equations.

This means the subtraction terms listed above can be written:

$a^3 + ka^2 + ma$ /
$\mathbf{bD_1(a)}$ /
$\mathbf{cD_1(a) + b^2\frac{1}{2}D_2(a)}$ /
$\mathbf{dD_1(a) + 2bc\frac{1}{2}D_2(a) + b^3\frac{1}{6}D_3(a)}$ /
$\mathbf{eD_1(a) + (2bd + c^2)\frac{1}{2}D_2(a) + 3b^2c\frac{1}{6}D_3(a)}$ /
$\mathbf{fD_1(a) + (2be + 2cd)\frac{1}{2}D_2(a) + (3b^2d + 3bc^2)\frac{1}{6}D_3(a)}$ /
$\cdots$
$= n$

And this means we can put $D_1(a)$, $\frac{1}{2}D_2(a)$, $\frac{1}{6}D_3(a)$ as special multipliers on one side and the duplex and triplex terms become more manageable. This result is easily proved using Taylor's theorem. See Reference 5, Chapter 12.

The solution given in Example 10 above would look the same using the higher derivatives, the only difference being that the quantities subtracted at each step would be obtained differently.

A CUBIC WITH $0 < x < 1$

For this we use the method shown in Sections 14.1c, d and e.
As with the quadratics the coefficient of x is used as a divisor.

In general for $x^3 + kx^2 + mx = n$ or $mx + kx^2 + x^3 = n,$

we have m(abcd...) + k(abcd...)^2 + (abcd...)^3 = n.

And n = ma / mb + a^{2}k / mc + 2abk + a^3 / md + 2ack + b^{2}k + 3a^{2}b / . . .

So   n = ma / mb + **a^{2}k** / mc + **2abk** + a^3 / md + **(2ac + b^2)k** + **3a^{2}b** / . . . and again we see that the subtracted duplexes are multiplied by the coefficient of x^2.

(11)   Solve **8x – 2x^2 + x^3 = 2.**

$$
\begin{array}{r}
2 . \; 0 \quad 0 \quad 0 \quad 0 \quad 0 \\
\overline{4} \quad 2 \quad \overline{3} \quad \overline{7} \\
8) \quad \overline{} \\
\hline
0 . \; 3 \quad \overline{3} \quad \overline{5} \quad 2
\end{array}
$$

The steps are: $20 \div 8 = \mathbf{3}$ rem $\overline{4}$.

$$\overline{40} - -18 = -22, \quad -22 \div 8 = \overline{3} \text{ rem } 2.$$

$$20 - \left(2 \times 3 \times \overline{3} \times (-2) + 3^3\right) = -43, \quad -43 \div 8 = \overline{5} \text{ rem } \overline{3}.$$

And so on.

✎ **Practice E**   Find the root near the integer given:

a x^3 + x^2 – 4x = 25 (a = 3)   **b** x^3 – 2x^2 – 3x = 54 (a = 5)

a	25 . 0 0 0 0 0
29)	1 10 13 14 21
	3 . 0 3 4 1

x = 3.0341

b	54 . 0 0 0 0 0 0
52)	$\overline{6}$ $\overline{8}$ 11 7 $\overline{2}$
	5 . $\overline{1}$ $\overline{2}$ 1 1

x = 4.8811

14.2c QUINTICS

Here we need the expansion of:

(a+b+c+d+e+...)^5 = a^5 +
  5a^{4}b +
  5a^{4}c + 10a^{3}b^2 +
  5a^{4}d + 20a^{3}bc + 10a^{2}b^3 +
  5a^{4}e + 10a^{3}c^2 + 20a^{3}bd + 30a^{2}b^{2}c + 5ab^4 +
  . . .

The same methods as before can be applied.

12   Solve $x^5 + 3x^3 + x = 70$.

There is a root around $x = 2$.
Using $a = 2$, we get a remainder of 12.

And as $D_1 = 5x^4 + 9x^2 + 1$, $D_1(2) = 117$, which is our divisor.

Rather than consider the general quintic we can, for the purposes of this particular equation consider only $(abc...)^5 + j(abc...)^3 + (abc...) = n$.

This gives:

$a^5 + ja^3 + a / 5a^4b + j3a^2b + b / 5a^4c + 10a^3b^2 + j(3a^2c + 3ab^2) + c / 5a^4d + 20a^3bc + 10a^2b^3 + j(3a^2d + 6abc + b^3) + d / \ldots$

$= a^5 + ja^3 + a / b(5a^4 + j3a^2 + 1) / c(5a^4 + 3ja^2 + 1) + 10a^3b^2 + 3jab^2) / d(5a^4d + 3ja^2 + 1) + 20a^3bc + 10a^2b^3 + 6jabc + jb^3) / \ldots$

$= \ a^5 + ja^3 + a /$
$\quad bD_1(a) /$
$\quad cD_1(a) + 10a^3b^2 + 3jab^2) /$
$\quad dD_1(a) + 20a^3bc + 10a^2b^3 + 6jabc + jb^3) /$
$\quad \ldots$
$= n$

$$
\begin{array}{r}
70 \,.\, 0 \quad 0 \quad 0 \quad 0 \\
117) \quad {}^{12} \quad {}^{3} \quad {}^{49} \quad {}^{58} \\
\hline
2 \,.\, 1 \quad \bar{1} \quad 5 \quad \bar{3}
\end{array}
$$

We have $a = 2$, the divisor is 117 and the remainder is 12.
Then $120 \div 117 = 1$ rem 3.
Now $10a^3b^2 + 3jab^2 = 98$. $30 - 98 = -68$, $-68 \div 117 = \bar{1}$ rem 49.
And so on.

It is worth noting that the division can be simplified by using *On the Flag* division $\left(117 = 12\bar{3}\right)$, and we can also spread 2-digit numbers over two columns:

$$
\begin{array}{r}
\overline{95} \quad \bar{9} \\
{}^{15} \quad {}^{3} \\
\bar{9} \quad \bar{8} \\
\bar{3}\ |70\,.\,0 \quad 0 \quad 0 \quad 0 \quad 0 \\
12| \quad {}^{12} \quad {}^{0} \quad {}^{6} \quad {}^{4} \quad \bar{1} \\
\hline
2 \,.\, 1 \quad \bar{1} \quad 5 \quad \bar{3}
\end{array}
$$

Having put down the first digit of the answer and the remainder we next divide 12 into 12 and put down 1 remainder 0.
Now we must bring in the subtraction terms $10a^3b^2 + 3jab^2$ which total 98. But these can be written in two columns as shown in the row above the dividend. From this $\bar{9}$ then we must

subtract the product of the last answer digit with the flagged digit (straight division method) and this gives $\overline{9} - 1 \times \overline{3} = \overline{6}$. This $\overline{6}$ we divide by 12 and put down 0 remainder $\overline{6}$ (see alternative method below) or $\overline{1}$ remainder 6, as shown above.

The remaining steps follow similar lines.

Alternatively:

$$
\begin{array}{cccccc}
 & & & & {}^{97} & 0 \\
 & & & \overline{4} & \overline{3} & \\
 & & \overline{9} & \overline{8} & & \\
\overline{3}\ |70.\ \ 0 & 0 & 0 & 0 & 0 \\
12| & {}^{12} & {}_{0} & {}^{\overline{6}} & {}^{\overline{12}} & {}_{7} \\
\hline
 & 2\ .\ 1 & 0 & \overline{5} & \overline{4}
\end{array}
$$

✎ **Practice F**   Find the root near the integer given:

a $x^5 - 3x^3 + x = 15\ (a = 2)$ 　　　**b** $x^5 - 3x^4 - 3x - 10 = 0\ (a = 3)$

a	15 . 0 0 0 0 0		b	−10 . 0 0 0 0
45)	⁵ ⁵ $\overline{12}$ $\overline{22}$ ²³		78)	$\overline{1}$ $\overline{10}$ $\overline{22}$ ¹⁴
	2 . 1 0 $\overline{3}$ 3			3 . 0 $\overline{1}$ $\overline{3}$
x = 2.0973			x = 2.987	

The fact that the second digit is zero in this last equation (**b** in Practice F) means that all the subtraction terms in the next two steps are zero, and we can just divide by 78.

Although the subtraction terms can make the calculation slow if many decimal places are required, the first few figures can be obtained quite easily by this method.

LESSON 15
CALCULUS METHODS

SUMMARY
This lesson shows various applications of Vedic Mathematics in calculus.
15.1 Partial Fractions – expressing fractions in 'partial' form.
15.2 Integration by 'Parts' – the one-line Vedic method.
15.3 Derivatives of a Product
15.4 Derivative of Quotients
15.5 Differential Equations – 1 – using *By the Completion or Non-Completion*.
15.6 Differential Equations – 2 – using *Vertically and Crosswise*.
15.7 Limits – geometric and arithmetic limits.

15.1 PARTIAL FRACTIONS

These are of particular use in differentiating and integrating fractions.

 Express $\dfrac{2x-3}{(x-2)(x+1)}$ as partial fractions.

We have to find values of A and B for which

$$\frac{2x-3}{(x-2)(x+1)} \equiv \frac{A}{x-2}+\frac{B}{x+1}.$$

For A we substitute in the LHS the transposed value in As denominator (i.e. 2) but omitting the part that is As denominator on the LHS: that is put $x = 2$ in $\dfrac{2x-3}{x+1}$.

Therefore $A = \frac{1}{3}$.

For B we similarly substitute Bs transposed value (-1), into the LHS, but omitting the $(x + 1)$: that is put $x = -1$ in $\dfrac{2x-3}{x-2}$.

Therefore $B = \frac{5}{3}$.

So $\dfrac{2x-3}{(x-2)(x+1)} \equiv \dfrac{1}{3(x-2)}+\dfrac{5}{3(x+1)}.$

The reason for this can be seen by multiplying the original identity by (x–2) and putting x=2 [$\frac{2x-3}{x+1} = A + \frac{B(x-2)}{x+1}$] and by multiplying by (x+1) and putting x=–1.

2   Express $\dfrac{3}{(x+2)(x+3)(2x-1)}$ in partial fractions.

Put $\dfrac{3}{(x+2)(x+3)(2x-1)} \equiv \dfrac{A}{x+2} + \dfrac{B}{x+3} + \dfrac{C}{2x-1}$.

For A put $x = -2$: $A = \dfrac{3}{(-2+3)(-4-1)} = -\frac{3}{5}$.

For B put $x = -3$: $B = \dfrac{3}{(-3+2)(-6-1)} = \frac{3}{7}$.

For C put $x = \frac{1}{2}$: $C = \dfrac{3}{(\frac{1}{2}+2)(\frac{1}{2}+3)} = \frac{12}{35}$.

So $\dfrac{3}{(x+2)(x+3)(2x-1)} \equiv \dfrac{-3}{5(x+2)} + \dfrac{3}{7(x+3)} + \dfrac{12}{35(2x-1)}$.

3   Express $\mathbf{E} \equiv \dfrac{x^2-2}{(x+3)(x-1)}$ in partial fractions.

We observe that the denominator will divide once into the numerator.

That is, $\mathbf{E} \equiv 1 + \dfrac{A}{x+3} + \dfrac{B}{x-1}$.

For A put $x = -3$: $A = \dfrac{(-3)^2-2}{-3-1} = -\frac{7}{4}$.

For B put $x = 1$: $B = \dfrac{1^2-2}{1+3} = -\frac{1}{4}$.

So $\mathbf{E} \equiv 1 - \dfrac{7}{4(x+3)} - \dfrac{1}{4(x-1)}$.

4   Express $\mathbf{E} \equiv \dfrac{x^3+3x^2+1}{(x+2)(x-3)}$ as partial fractions.

We can divide the numerator by the denominator using straight division (see Lesson 10):

$$x^2 - x - 6 \; \underline{\left|\; \begin{array}{l} x^3 + 3x^2 + 0x + 1 \\ \hline x + 4 \end{array}\right.}$$

So $\mathbf{E} \equiv x + 4 + \dfrac{A}{x+2} + \dfrac{B}{x-3}$.

We can then substitute the transposed values (−2 and 3) into the original expression (or we could use the remainder from the above division*):

For A put $x = -2$: $A = \frac{(-2)^3 + 3(-2)^2 + 1}{-2 - 3} = -1$.

For B put $x = 3$: $B = \frac{3^3 + 3 \times 3^2 + 1}{3 + 2} = 11$.

So $E \equiv x + 4 - \frac{1}{x+2} + \frac{11}{x-3}$

Explanation

The reason that we can substitute into either the original numerator or the remainder after division as in these last two examples is that the numerator is some multiple of the denominator plus the remainder, but substitution of the transposed value in the denominator brings it to zero (by the remainder theorem).

* Had we continued the division above so that we had the remainder ($10x+25$) we could have

put $x=-2$ in $\frac{10x + 25}{x - 3}$ to get A and put $x=3$ in $\frac{10x + 25}{x + 2}$ to get B.

5   Repeated factor: $E \equiv \dfrac{3x}{(x+2)(x-1)^2}$.

Put $\dfrac{3x}{(x+2)(x-1)^2} \equiv \dfrac{A}{x+2} + \dfrac{B}{(x-1)^2} + \dfrac{C}{x-1}$.

For A put $x = -2$: $A = \frac{3(-2)}{(-2-1)^2} = -\frac{2}{3}$.

For B put $x = 1$: $B = \frac{3(1)}{1+2} = 1$.

For C put $x = 0$ (say): $0 = \frac{A}{0+2} + \frac{B}{(0-1)^2} + \frac{C}{0-1}$, $C = \frac{2}{3}$.

All this can be done **mentally**.

So $E \equiv \dfrac{-2}{3(x+2)} + \dfrac{1}{(x-1)^2} + \dfrac{2}{3(x-1)}$.

6   Quadratic factor: $E \equiv \dfrac{2}{(x^2+1)(x-1)} \equiv \dfrac{Ax+B}{(x^2+1)} + \dfrac{C}{(x-1)}$.

Putting $x = 1$, $C = \frac{2}{1+1} = 1$.

Putting $x = 0$, $B - 1 = -2$, $B = -1$.

Putting $x = 2$, $\frac{2A-1}{5} + 1 = \frac{2}{5 \times 1}$, $A = -1$.*

So $E \equiv \dfrac{-x-1}{x^2+1} + \dfrac{1}{x-1}$.

*Alternatively we can differentiate $2 = (Ax + b)(x - 1) + c(x^2 + 1)$ twice to get $2A + 2C = 0$ and so $A = -1$.

✎ **Practice A**   Express as partial fractions:

a $\dfrac{4x+21}{(x-1)(x+4)}$

b $\dfrac{5}{(x+3)(x-2)}$

c $\dfrac{3x}{(x-1)(x-2)(x-3)}$

d $\dfrac{x^2+2x+3}{(x+3)(x-2)}$

e $\dfrac{x^3+2x^2+3x+4}{(x+1)(x+3)}$

f $\dfrac{2x^3+x^2-3x+1}{(x-1)(x+4)}$

g $\dfrac{9}{(x-1)(x+2)^2}$

h $\dfrac{1}{x(x-1)^2}$

i $\dfrac{10-11x}{(x-4)(x^2+1)}$

---

a $\dfrac{5}{x-1} - \dfrac{1}{x+4}$

b $\dfrac{1}{x-2} - \dfrac{1}{x+3}$

c $\dfrac{3}{2(x-1)} - \dfrac{6}{x-2} + \dfrac{9}{2(x-3)}$

d $1 - \dfrac{6}{5(x+3)} + \dfrac{11}{5(x-2)}$

e $x - 2 + \dfrac{1}{x+1} + \dfrac{7}{x+3}$

f $2x + 5 + \dfrac{1}{5(x-1)} + \dfrac{99}{5(x+4)}$

g $\dfrac{1}{x-1} - \dfrac{3}{(x+2)^2} - \dfrac{1}{x+2}$

h $\dfrac{1}{x} + \dfrac{1}{(x-1)^2} - \dfrac{1}{x-1}$

i $\dfrac{-2}{x-4} + \dfrac{2x-3}{x^2+1}$

15.2 INTEGRATION BY PARTS

  Find $\mathbf{I} = \int(x^2 +1)e^{2x}\,\mathbf{dx}$.

The integration of this product would normally be done by 'parts', using the formula:
$\int u \frac{dv}{dx} dx = uv - \int v \frac{du}{dx} dx.$

In the Vedic method one part of the product is differentiated until zero is reached and the other part is integrated the same number of times:

$$\int(x^2 +1)e^{2x}\,dx$$

$$2x \quad \tfrac{1}{2}e^{2x}$$

$$2 \quad \tfrac{1}{4}e^{2x}$$

$$0 \quad \tfrac{1}{8}e^{2x}$$

The integral can then be written straight down by affixing a minus sign on the even-positioned terms in the first column, i.e. the second, fourth etc. derivatives and cross-multiplying as shown below:

$$\int \left(x^2+1\right)e^{2x}\,dx \;=\; (x^2+1)\left(\tfrac{1}{2}e^{2x}\right) - 2x\left(\tfrac{1}{4}e^{2x}\right) + 2\left(\tfrac{1}{8}e^{2x}\right) + c$$

$$-2x \searrow \tfrac{1}{2}e^{2x}$$
$$2 \searrow \tfrac{1}{4}e^{2x}$$
$$-0 \searrow \tfrac{1}{8}e^{2x}$$

By the usual method this example would require two applications of the cumbersome standard formula. But with the Vedic method the answer can be put straight down no matter how many cycles would normally be required.

8 Find $I = \int x^5 e^x dx$.

Here we give the answer immediately (instead of five applications of the 'parts' formula):

$$I = \int x^5 \; e^x \, dx = x^5 e^x - 5x^4 e^x + 20x^3 e^x - 60x^2 e^x + 120xe^x - 120e^x + c$$
$$-5x^4 \; e^x$$
$$20x^3 \; e^x$$
$$-60x^2 \; e^x$$
$$120x \; e^x$$
$$-120 \; e^x$$
$$0 \; e^x$$

In fact, especially for easy cases like this, the vertical derivatives and integrals do not need to be written down. We write down the first product (the first part of the product multiplied by the integral of the second part) and just differentiate the first part of this first term of the answer and integrate the second part. We continue like this, inserting the minus when appropriate, until we reach zero.

✎ **Practice B**   Find

a $\int x^3 e^{\frac{x}{3}} dx$ b $\int x^2 \sin x\,dx$ c $\int x.x\,dx$ d $\int 2.x dx$

---

a $2x^3 e^{\frac{x}{3}} - 12x^2 e^{\frac{x}{3}} + 48xe^{\frac{x}{3}} - 96e^{\frac{x}{3}} + c$ b $-x^2\cos x + 2x\sin x + 2\cos x + c$

c $\frac{x^3}{3}+c$ d $x^2 + c$

TRUNCATING

The process can be truncated at any point, and this can be useful.

$$\int \left(x^2 + 1\right)e^{2x}\, dx = (x^2 + 1)\left(\tfrac{1}{2}e^{2x}\right) - \int 2x\left(\tfrac{1}{2}e^{2x}\right)dx \, .$$

$$-2x \searrow \tfrac{1}{2}e^{2x}$$
$$2 \qquad \tfrac{1}{4}e^{2x}$$
$$-0 \qquad \tfrac{1}{8}e^{2x}$$

In this example we stop after one diagonal product and multiply horizontally. Such a horizontal product always terminates the process with an integral.

Alternatively:

$$\int \left(x^2 + 1\right)e^{2x}\, dx = (x^2 + 1)\left(\tfrac{1}{2}e^{2x}\right) - 2x\left(\tfrac{1}{4}e^{2x}\right) + \int 2\left(\tfrac{1}{4}e^{2x}\right)dx$$

$$-2x \searrow \tfrac{1}{2}e^{2x}$$
$$2 \searrow \tfrac{1}{4}e^{2x}$$
$$-0 \qquad \tfrac{1}{8}e^{2x}$$

Find $I = \int x^4 \ln x\, dx$.

We need put down only one row:

$$\ln x \qquad x^4$$
$$\tfrac{1}{x} \searrow \tfrac{x^5}{5}$$

$$\therefore I = \frac{x^5}{5}\ln x - \int \frac{1}{x} \times \frac{x^5}{5} dx = \frac{x^5}{5}\ln x - \int \frac{x^4}{5} dx = \frac{x^5}{5}\ln x - \frac{x^5}{25} + c$$

Another type that requires two applications of the usual formula is also easily solved.

Find $I = \int e^x \sin x\, dx$.

Here we truncate after two rows:

$$e^x \searrow \sin x$$
$$-e^x \searrow -\cos x$$
$$e^x \underline{\quad} -\sin x$$

$$\therefore I = -e^x \cos x + e^x \sin x + \int e^x \left(-\sin x\right)dx$$

$$\therefore I = \tfrac{1}{2}e^x\left(\sin x - \cos x\right) + c$$

Since we have the original integral, I, appearing on the RHS we can take it over to the left to get: $2I = e^x\left(\sin x - \cos x\right) + c$.

✒ **Practice C**   Find

a $\int x \ln x \, dx$

b $\int x^3 \ln\left(x^3\right) dx$

c $\int(2x+1)\ln\left(x^2+x\right) dx$

d $\int x(1+x)^7 \, dx$

e $\int e^x \cos x \, dx$

---

a $\tfrac{x^2}{2}\ln x - \tfrac{x^2}{4} + c$

b $\tfrac{x^4}{4}\ln x^3 - \tfrac{3x^4}{16} + c$

c $\left(x^2+x\right)\ln\left(x^2+x\right) - x^2 - x + c$

d $\tfrac{x(1+x)^8}{8} - \tfrac{(1+x)^9}{72} + c$

e $\tfrac{e^x}{2}(\sin x + \cos x) + c$

15.3 BINOMIAL AND MACLAURIN THEOREMS

This combining of differentiation and integration can be seen in operation in other areas. For example the Binomial Theorem and MacLaurin's Theorem.

The Binomial Theorem is given as: $(a+b)^n = a^n + na^{n-1}b + \frac{n(n-1)}{2!}a^{n-2}b^2 + \frac{n(n-1)(n-2)}{3!}a^{n-3}b^3 \ldots$

But if this is re-written as: $(a+b)^n = a^n.1 + na^{n-1}b + n(n-1)a^{n-2}\frac{b^2}{2!} + n(n-1)(n-2)a^{n-3}\frac{b^3}{3!}\ldots$
we can see successive derivatives of a^n (with respect to a) in each term followed by successive integrals of 1 (with respect to b).

This makes it easy to expand binomials, giving the expansion term by term, instead of the very cumbersome method of substituting into the standard formula and simplifying.

 12 $(2+3x)^{-3} = 2^{-3}.(3x)^0 - 3.2^{-4}.(3x)^1 + 12.2^{-5}\tfrac{(3x)^2}{2} - 60.2^{-6}.\tfrac{(3x)^3}{6}\ldots$

This still needs to be simplified but it is much more satisfying and useful in actual practice to get the terms sequentially and by a simple pattern, and the simplifications can be carried out mentally.

MacLaurin's Theorem gives:
$$f(x) = f(0) + f'(0)x + f''(0)\tfrac{x^2}{2} + f'''(0)\tfrac{x^3}{6} \ldots$$

Here again we see successive derivatives of f(0) and successive integrals of 1, both with respect to x.

Since MacLaurin's Theorem can be used to derive the Binomial Theorem it is not surprising that the same pattern is present in both.

13   Use MacLaurin's Theorem to obtain a series expansion for e^{2x}.

$$e^{2x} = e^{2.0} + 2e^{2.0}x + 4e^{2.0}\tfrac{x^2}{2} + 8e^{2.0}\tfrac{x^3}{6} + \ldots$$
$$= 1 + 2x + 2x^2 + \tfrac{4}{3}x^3 + \ldots$$

So we can put down $e^{2.0}$ initially for f(0) and differentiate as if the zero were an x.
This is easy to do in practice and means we can put the series straight down, term by term, each being obtained from the previous one, as with the Binomial Theorem above.

15.4 DERIVATIVES OF A PRODUCT

14   **Find the 1st, 2nd and 3rd derivatives of $x^5 \times e^{2x}$.**

Here we make use of the *Vertically and Crosswise* formula.
We write the two parts of the product, x^5 and e^{2x} one vertically beneath the other, and put their derivatives next to them:

$$\begin{array}{cc} x^5 & 5x^4 \\ & \\ e^{2x} & 2e^{2x} \end{array}$$

Then by cross-multiplication $D_1 = x^5 \times 2e^{2x} + 5x^4 \times e^{2x}$.

For the second derivative we put the first and second derivatives and multiply vertically and crosswise:

$$\begin{array}{ccc} x^5 & 5x^4 & 20x^3 \\ & & \\ e^{2x} & 2e^{2x} & 4e^{2x} \end{array}$$

Then $D_2 = x^5 \times 4e^{2x} + 2 \times 5x^4 \times 2e^{2x} + 20x^3 \times e^{2x}$.

The extra factor, 2, that comes into the middle term here is from Pascal's triangle; in fact the three terms are multiplied by 1, 2, 1 respectively.

For the third derivative we differentiate three times:

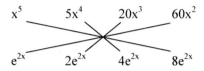

The four products are multiplied by 1, 3, 3, 1 respectively:

$$D_3 = x^5 \times 8e^{2x} + 3 \times 5x^4 \times 4e^{2x} + 3 \times 20x^3 \times 2e^{2x} + 60x^2 \times e^{2x}.$$

This process is equivalent to Leibniz' theorem, which says that the nth derivative of a product uv is given by:

$$(uv)_n = u_0 v_n + \binom{n}{1} u_1 v_{n-1} + \binom{n}{2} u_2 v_{n-2} + \dots$$

This gives us the product, of course, but does not bring out the underlying vertical and crosswise pattern, which makes the Vedic method much more direct and practical.

There are similarities here with the *Vertically and Crosswise* method for finding the product of two numbers, and the corresponding method for the product of three numbers is similar to that of obtaining derivatives of products of three functions.

15.5 DERIVATIVE OF A QUOTIENT

 Find $\dfrac{d}{dx}\left(\dfrac{x^5}{e^{2x}}\right)$.

As with the product we put the derivatives next to the functions:

$$\begin{array}{cc} x^5 & 5x^4 \\ & \times \\ e^{2x} & 2e^{2x} \end{array}$$

And instead of adding the products we subtract them, and divide by the square of the denominator function:

$$\frac{d}{dx}\left(\frac{x^5}{e^{2x}}\right) = \frac{5x^4 \cdot e^{2x} - x^5 \cdot 2e^{2x}}{\left(e^{2x}\right)^2} = \frac{x^4}{e^{2x}}(5-2x).$$

This is similar to division of complex numbers (see Page 123).
Note that we start with the top right-hand term of the four.

  If $y = \dfrac{ax+b}{cx+d}$ find y_1.

$$y_1 = \frac{a(cx+d)-(ax+b)c}{(cx+d)^2} = \frac{ad-bc}{(cx+d)^2}.$$

Note here that the numerator of y_1 is the determinant $\begin{vmatrix} a & b \\ c & d \end{vmatrix}$.

17 If $y = \dfrac{ax^2+bx+c}{dx^2+ex+f}$ find y_1. $y_1 = \dfrac{(ae-bd)^2 x^2 + 2(af-cd)x + (bf-ce)}{\left(dx^2+ex+f\right)^2}$

This result can be generalised for the derivative of the quotient of two polynomials of the same order.

18 If $y = \dfrac{1+3e^x}{2+5e^x}$ find y_1. $y_1 = \dfrac{(3\times2-1\times5)e^x}{\left(2+5e^x\right)^2}$

19 If $y = \dfrac{2+7\sin x}{3+5\sin x}$ find y_1. $y_1 = \dfrac{(7\times3-2\times5)\cos x}{\left(3+5\sin x\right)^2}.$

And in general:

20 If $y = \dfrac{af(x)+bg(x)}{cf(x)+dg(x)}$, $y_1 = \dfrac{(bc-ad)(fg_1-gf_1)}{\left(cf+dg\right)^2}$

[for zero gradients: $f\,g_1 = g\,f_1$]

See the note on Page 219.

21 Locate the maxima and minima of $y = \dfrac{x}{1+x^2}$.

We differentiate numerator and denominator of this fraction to form a new fraction which we equate to the original one:*

$$\frac{x}{1+x^2} = \frac{1}{2x} \qquad\qquad \dots (1)$$

By cross-multiplication we then solve this equation: $2x^2 = 1 + x^2$ $\therefore x = \pm 1$.

To find the corresponding y values we can substitute these values of x into the right-hand side of equation (1), and get **(1,½)** and **(−1,−½)** for the coordinates of the two turning points.

This problem would normally be solved by using the formula for differentiation of a quotient, equating the result to 0, solving the equation, and substituting the result into $y = x/(1 + x^2)$.

* This is explained as follows. If the quotient is $\dfrac{d}{dx}\left(\dfrac{f(x)}{g(x)}\right)$, the usual method to locate

maxima and minima gives: $\dfrac{g(x).f'(x) - f(x).g'(x)}{[g(x)]^2} = 0$.

Therefore $g(x).f'(x) = f(x).g'(x)$ and $\dfrac{f(x)}{g(x)} = \dfrac{f'(x)}{g'(x)}$.

15.6 DIFFERENTIAL EQUATIONS - 1

USING BY THE COMPLETION OR NON-COMPLETION

Again we use subscripts to denote derivatives.
So y_1 and y_2 etc. indicate the first and second etc. derivatives of y with respect to x.

22 Solve $xy_1 + 2y = 3x$.

We recognise here that we would have a perfect first derivative of a product (i.e. x^2y) on the LHS if we multiplied it by x:

i.e. $x^2y_1 + 2xy = 3x^2$
$\therefore (x^2y)_1 = 3x^2$

$\therefore x^2y = x^3 + c$.

Similarly for $xy_1 + ay = f(x)$, a>0, we multiply through by x^{a-1}:

$x^a y_1 + ax^{a-1}y = f(x).x^{a-1}$.

Therefore $(x^a y)_1 = x^{a-1}f(x)$.

And $x^a y = \int x^{a-1}f(x)dx$.

 Solve $xy_1 - y = x$.

Dividing through by x^2 gives the perfect derivative of a quotient:

$\frac{xy_1-y}{x^2} = \frac{1}{x}$, $\left(\frac{y}{x}\right)_1 = \frac{1}{x}$, $\frac{y}{x} = \int \frac{1}{x}dx$.

So $y = x\ln x + cx$.

 Solve $x^2 y_2 + 4xy_1 + 2y = x$.

Here we have the second derivative of a product:

$(x^2 y)_2 = x$.

So $x^2 y = \frac{x^3}{6} + cx + d$.

 Solve $x^2 y_2 + 3xy_1 + y = x$.

Here we add $xy_1 + y$ to both sides: $x^2 y_2 + 4xy_1 + 2y = x + xy_1 + y$.

Both sides now contain a perfect derivative of a product:
$xy_1 + y = (xy)_1$ on the RHS, and
$x^2 y_2 + 4xy_1 + 2y = (x^2 y)_2$ on the LHS.

So $(x^2 y)_2 = (xy)_1 + x$.

Integrating: $(x^2 y)_1 = xy + \frac{x^2}{2} + c$.

Then $x^2 y_1 + 2xy = xy + \frac{x^2}{2} + c$.

So that $xy_1 + y = \frac{x}{2} + \frac{c}{x}$ and $(xy)_1 = \frac{x}{2} + \frac{c}{x}$.

Therefore $xy = \frac{x^2}{4} + c\ln x + d$.

✎ **Practice D**   Solve the following differential equations:

a $xy_1 + y = x$

b $xy_1 + 2y = x$

c $y_1(x+1) + y = 1 - x$

d $xy_2 + 2y_1 = x$

e $x^2y_2 + 6xy_1 + 6y = x$

---

a $(xy)_1 = x$

$\quad xy = \dfrac{x^2}{2} + c$

b $x^2y_1 + 2xy = x^2$

$\quad (x^2y)_1 = x^2$

$\quad x^2y = \dfrac{x^3}{3} + c$

c $[(x+1)y]_1 = 1 - x$

$\quad (x+1)y = x - \dfrac{x^2}{2} + c$

d $xy_2 + y_1 + 0y = x$

$\quad (xy)_2 = x$

$\quad xy = \dfrac{x^3}{6} + cx + d$

e $x^3y_2 + 6x^2y_1 + 6xy = x^2$

$\quad x^2y = \dfrac{x^3}{6} + cx + d$

15.7 DIFFERENTIAL EQUATIONS - 2

USING VERTICALLY AND CROSSWISE

 27   Solve $2y + 3y' = 18 + 8x$, where $y'(0) = 4$.   - - - (1)

Here, and throughout this section, $y' = \dfrac{dy}{dx}$ and $y'(0) = \dfrac{dy}{dx}$ evaluated with $x = 0$. An explanation of the steps will be given shortly, but the complete working and solution appears finally as follows:

$$\begin{array}{ccccc} 3 & 4 & 0 & 0 & 0 \end{array}$$
$$y = a + bx + cx^2 + dx^3 + ex^4 + \ldots \qquad \text{- - - (2)}$$

$$y' = b + 2cx + 3dx^2 + 4ex^3 + 5fx^4 + \ldots \qquad \text{- - - (3)}$$
$$\begin{array}{ccccc} 4 & 0 & 0 & 0 & 0 \end{array}$$

So the solution is $y = 3 + 4x$.

Explanation

By Maclaurin's Theorem a series expansion can be used for y, as in equation (2). Differentiating gives Equation (3), successive coefficients of x being arranged in successive columns. Purely for purposes of explanation we   will   now   use   the following lay-out:

Coefficients		Column			
	1	2	3	4	
2	$y = a$	$+ bx +$	$cx^2 +$	$dx^3 + \dots$	Row 1
3	$y' = b$	$+ 2cx +$	$3dx^2 +$	$4ex^3 + \dots$	Row 2
	18	$+ 8x$			Row 3

The left-hand side of Equation (1) translates into $2 \times$ Row 1 $+ 3 \times$ Row 2, and the coefficients '2' and '3' have here been placed in a column on the left as a reminder. To facilitate the working, the right-hand side terms of Equation (1) have been placed in a third row. Thus for each successive column we have:

$$2 \times \text{Row } 1 + 3 \times \text{Row } 2 = \text{Row } 3,$$

in accordance with Equation (1). And each successive column yields the next of the unknowns, a, b, c, d, ...
The sutra here is *By Alternate Elimination and Retention.*

Since $y'(0) = 4$, **b = 4**, from Row 2.

Write this in place, as shown in the complete solution.

To find 'a', Column 1 (absolute terms only) gives us: $2a + 3b = 18$.

Since b is known to equal 4, the mental procedure is, reduce 18 by 3×4, giving 6, and divide by 2 to obtain **a = 3**. Now write '3' above 'a' in Row 1.

So far we have:
$$
\begin{array}{c}
 3 \quad 4 \\
y = a + bx + cx^2 + \dots \\
y' = b + 2cx + 3dx^2 + \dots \\
 4
\end{array}
$$

Similarly, in Column 2: $2b + 3 \times 2c = 8$
$$2c = 8 - 2 \times 4 = 0$$
$$c = 0, \text{ etc.}$$

The same procedure shows that all subsequent terms are zero, and

$y = 3 + 4x$ exactly.

The next example introduces a non-linearity, namely the term y^2.

28   Solve $y'' + y^2 = 1 + 2x^2 + x^4$, where $y(0) = 0$ and $y'(0) = 0$.   - - - (4)

The working can be written down as follows:

Column:	I	II	III	IV	V	VI	VII	VIII	IX	X
	0	0	$\frac{1}{2}$	0	$\frac{1}{6}$	0	$\frac{1}{40}$	0	$-\frac{1}{336}$	0

$$y = a + bx + cx^2 + dx^3 + ex^4 + fx^5 + gx^6 + hx^7 + ix^8 + jx^9 + \ldots \text{-(5)}$$
$$y'' = 2c + 6dx + 12ex^2 + 20fx^3 + 30gx^4 + 42hx^5 + 56ix^6 + 72jx^7 + \ldots \quad \text{- -(6)}$$

Column:	I	II	III	IV	V	VI	VII	VIII	IX	X
	1	0	2	0	$\frac{3}{4}$	0	$-\frac{1}{6}$	0		

Explanation

From the boundary conditions we have **a = 0** and **b = 0**.
As before, we work with coefficients of x, in succession, each step yielding another of the values of b, c, d, . . .

To conform with the left-hand side of Equation (4), the successive terms for y^2 are given by the successive duplexes (or dwandwa-yogas, see Lesson 7 for the term 'duplex') of Equation (5).

For 'c': From Column 1, $2c + a^2 = 1$
since we are eliminating all except the absolute terms. And since $a^2 = 0$, the mental procedure is, reduce 1 by 0 to obtain the value of 2c. Hence we put $2c = 1$ and **c = ½**, as shown in the complete solution.

For 'd': We now eliminate all terms from Equation (1) except for the coefficients of x. The dwandwa-yoga of y^2 here is $2ab = 2 \times 0 \times 0$, and from Column II we have, $2ab + 6d = 0$, and therefore **d = 0**.

For 'e': (Column III) The dwandwa-yoga is now $2ac + b^2$, and we have, $2 \times 0 \times \frac{1}{2} + 0^2 + 12e = 2$, so we write '2' below 12e, and '$\frac{1}{6}$' above e.

For 'f': (Column IV) Since the coefficient of x^3 in Equation (1) is zero, the term in y'' equals minus the dwanda-yoga term, i.e. $-2ad - 2bc$, which is zero; hence **f = 0**. And so the solution continues. Had y(0) not been zero there would have been two solutions. As it is, the two solutions coincide.

Note: these two examples come from the book "Vertically and Crosswise" (Reference 5) and are the work of Andrew Nicholas, as also are Examples 16 to 20, on Derivative of a Quotient. above.

✎ **Practice E**   Solve the following differential equations:

a $y' + 2y + 6 = 4x + 16$ **b** $y'' + 2y' + 6y = 14x + 4$

c $2y + 3y' + 6y^2 = 5\exp(x) + 6\exp(2x)$

---

a $y = 4 + 2x$ **b** $y = 1 + 4x$
c $y = \exp(x)$

15.8 LIMITS

Some geometrical theorems are easy to prove using limits. The relevant Sutra is *Only the Last Terms*.

 Proof of the tangent-secant theorem.

We make use of the theorem which states that if two chords AB and CD of a circle meet outside the circle at X as shown below on the left, then AX.BX = CX.DX.

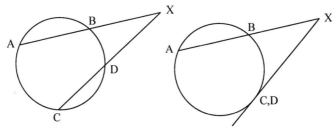

Imagine the line XDC turning anti-clockwise about X. Then we can see that the points C and D approach each other until, when the line is a tangent, they coincide.

CX and DX are now equal and so AX.BX = CX.DX becomes AX.BX = $(CX)^2$ which is the tangent-secant theorem.

If further, we allow ABX to become a tangent, we can show that tangents to a circle from a point outside are equal.

 Proof of the Alternate Segment Theorem

We begin with the theorem that angles in the same segment are equal. That is, in the diagram below angles BDC and BAC are equal.

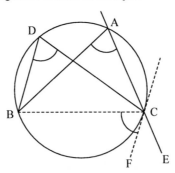

Extending AC, we observe what happens to angle BAC as A moves around the circle clockwise towards C.

Careful observation shows that the line ACE becomes the tangent CF, and that the angle BAC becomes the angle BCF. Therefore angle BCF is equal to the angle BDC, which proves the alternate segment theorem.

31   The Cyclic Quadrilateral Property

In the last example A had arrived at C, and angles BDC and BCF were shown to be equal.

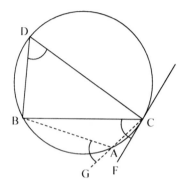

Suppose that we now allow A to continue its journey around the circle. As A emerges from C angle BCF becomes angle BAG and these angles are equal by the alternate segment property. It follows that angles BDC and BAC are supplementary (they add up to 180°) and this is the cyclic quadrilateral property.

Finally an arithmetical example of the use of a limit.

32   Which is greater $\dfrac{4}{7}$ or $\dfrac{5}{8}$?

We notice a pattern in the four digits which allows us to continue the series:

$$\frac{0}{3} \quad \frac{1}{4} \quad \frac{2}{5} \quad \frac{3}{6} \quad \frac{4}{7} \quad \frac{5}{8} \quad \frac{6}{9} \quad \frac{7}{10} \quad \frac{8}{11} \cdots \cdots \frac{100}{103} \cdots$$

The series is clearly approaching the value 1 from below and so $\dfrac{5}{8}$ is greater than $\dfrac{4}{7}$.

In practice we do not have to write these fractions out, we simply make use of the pattern present, an approach not encouraged by the current system.

Alternatively we can trace the series backwards in which case the fractions approach zero.

We can also use the *Vertically and Crosswise* method for subtracting fractions as given earlier.

LESSON 16
APPLIED MATHEMATICS

SUMMARY

This lesson shows how to use triples for tackling problems in applied mathematics.

16.1 Simple Harmonic Motion
16.2 Projectiles
16.3 Forces in Equilibrium
16.4 Work and Moment

16.1 SIMPLE HARMONIC MOTION

The equation $x = \sin t$, and its successive derivatives, can be represented by triples:

$$
\begin{aligned}
x &= \sin t : &\quad t) &\; - ,\; x ,\; 1 \\
\dot{x} &= \cos t : &\quad t) &\; \dot{x} ,\; - ,\; 1 \\
\ddot{x} &= -\sin t : &\quad t) &\; - ,\; -\ddot{x} ,\; 1 \\
\dddot{x} &= -\cos t : &\quad t) &\; -\dddot{x} ,\; - ,\; 1
\end{aligned}
$$

etc.

Note that the x moves to and fro between the first and second positions of the triple, and that the sign changes when it moves to the right.

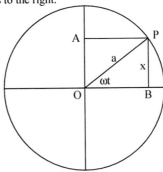

Suppose a point P moves with constant speed around a circle of radius a, as shown above.
PA and PB are perpendiculars from P onto the vertical and horizontal diameters.
The motion of A and B is called Simple Harmonic Motion.

If x is the height of P measured upwards from O and the angle is measured anticlockwise from OB then we can see that **x = asinωt.** This describes the motion of A.

This equation and its first two derivatives give:

	-,	x,	a	- - - (1)
ωt	$\dot{x}$,	-,	aω	- - - (2)
	-,	$-\ddot{x}$,	aω²	- - - (3)

Using these three triples it is an easy matter to solve problems in Simple Harmonic Motion by simply finding missing elements in this chart. We do not need the complex formulae usually associated with this topic, though these can be easily obtained from the chart.

There are various important and useful observations that can be made from the above chart and these will be illustrated in the following examples. But note here that these three triples are equal as the angle is the same in each (ωt), and that the third element of each triple shows that the second triple is ω times the first and the third is ω times the second.

A particle oscillates in a horizontal line about a fixed point O such that its distance, x, from O at time t is given by **x = 5sin2t.**
Find (a) the velocity and acceleration when x =3,
(b) x and $\dot{x}$ when $\ddot{x}$ = 1.

(a) From the given equation we know that a = 5 and ω = 2.
And we are given x = 3, so the chart is

```
        | -      3    5
   2t | $\dot{x}$      -    -
        | -    $-\ddot{x}$   -
```

Completing the triple in the first line we can put ± 4 down, and the last elements of the other two triples are found by multiplying 5 by ω and then by ω again, giving 10 and 20:

```
        | ± 4    3    5
   2t | $\dot{x}$      -    10
        | -    $-\ddot{x}$   20
```

It now becomes clear that since the second triple is double the first (as 10 is double 5), $\dot{x}$ = ± 8.
We now have the first two triples, and $-\ddot{x}$ in the last line:

```
        | ± 4    3    5
   2t | ± 8    6    10
        | -    $-\ddot{x}$   20
```

Since the bottom triple is double the middle one this gives us $-\ddot{x}$ = 12 and so:
$\ddot{x}$ = −12. We could also obtain $-\ddot{x}$ from the first triple by doubling 3 twice.

(b) We have $\ddot{x} = 1$ so this can be put in the middle of the last triple, and this triple can then be completed:

$$
\begin{array}{r|rrrr}
 & | & - & x & 5 \\
2t| & & \dot{x} & - & 10 \\
 & | & \pm\sqrt{399} & -1 & 20 \\
\end{array}
$$

Now we can see that we have to divide $\pm\sqrt{399}$ by 2 to get $\dot{x}$, and divide -1 by 4 to get x. So $x = -\frac{1}{4}$ and $\dot{x} = \pm\frac{\sqrt{399}}{2}$.

Note here that since we are dealing with triples the last element of any triple gives a maximum and minimum value.
For example, from the above chart: $x_{max} = 5,$
$$\dot{x}_{max} = 10,$$
$$\ddot{x}_{min} = -20.$$

2   A particle is describing linear S.H.M. with a period of 4 seconds. Given that the greatest speed is 3m/s find the amplitude of the path and the speed of the particle when it is $\frac{2}{\pi}$ m from the centre.

If the period is 4 seconds then $\omega = \frac{2\pi}{4} = \frac{\pi}{2}$.
So if a is the required amplitude we have:

$$
\begin{array}{l|lll}
 | & - & - & a \\
 | & - & - & \frac{a\pi}{2} \\
 | & - & - & - \\
\end{array}
$$

But since $\frac{a\pi}{2}$ is the maximum speed, we have $\frac{a\pi}{2} = 3$ and $a = \frac{6}{\pi}$.

Inserting this value and the
given $\frac{2}{\pi}$ we now have:

$$
\begin{array}{l|lll}
 | & - & \frac{2}{\pi} & \frac{6}{\pi} \\
 | & - & - & 3 \\
 | & - & - & - \\
\end{array}
$$

Seeing the ratio 1:3 in the first line
we can now complete the second triple:

$$
\begin{array}{l|lll}
 | & - & \frac{2}{\pi} & \frac{6}{\pi} \\
 | & \pm\sqrt{8} & 1 & 3 \\
 | & - & - & - \\
\end{array}
$$

So $\dot{x} = \pm\sqrt{8}$.

3   A particle oscillating with linear S.H.M. has an amplitude of 3m. When $\sqrt{5}$ m from the centre of oscillation its speed is 10ms^{-1}. Find the maximum speed of the particle.

The chart when $x = \sqrt{5}$ m is:

$$
\begin{array}{l|lll}
 | & - & \sqrt{5} & 3 \\
 | & 10 & - & - \\
 | & - & - & - \\
\end{array}
$$

and the first element of the first triple is therefore ± 2.

Since this gives a ratio between the first two triples of 1:5 we can set up a chart for x = 0 (when the speed of the particle is maximum):

$$
\begin{array}{|ccc}
3 & 0 & 3 \\
15 & 0 & 15 \\
- & - & - \\
\end{array}
$$

The maximum speed is therefore clearly **15ms⁻¹**.

4   Two particles P and Q perform linear S.H.M. with the same parameters as Example 1, as shown in the chart below. When P first reaches B, where OB = 3m, Q passes through O, the mean position.

$$
\begin{array}{c}
\quad\quad\quad Q \quad Q' \quad\quad P \quad P' \\
\text{———}|\text{—}|\text{————}|\text{—}|\text{——} \\
\quad\quad\quad O \quad X \quad\quad B \quad C
\end{array}
$$

$$
2t \begin{array}{|ccc}
- & x & 5 \\
\dot{x} & - & 10 \\
- & -\ddot{x} & 20 \\
\end{array}
$$

Find (a) the distance travelled by Q when P first reaches C, where OC = 4m.
      (b) the time for P to cover the distance BC.

We know that $\omega = 2$ and $a = 5$.

(a) The two "distance" triples for P at B and at C   are   (4),3,5   and   (3),4,5   respectively.

Subtracting these two triples:

$$
\begin{array}{ccc}
3 & 4 & 5 \\
4 & 3 & 5 \\
\hline
24 & 7 & 25 \\
\end{array} -
$$

gives a triple whose angle gives the time taken for P to travel from B to C, and Q to travel from O to X, say, where OX is the required distance.

We can now divide this triple by 5, so that its last element is equal to a.
This gives the equal triple   4.8, 1.4, 5   which can be thought of as a "distance" triple in which x = 1.4. So **OX = 1.4m**.

(b) We need the angle in the triple 24,7,25.
This is a known triple (see Reference 4) so we can put:
2t = 0.2838, and so **t = 0.1419s**.

For problems where Simple Harmonic Motion starts at an extremity of the motion it is sometimes useful to use a system based on $x = a\cos \omega t$ rather than $x = a\sin \omega t$.

The general chart in this case would be:

$$\begin{array}{c|ccc} & x & - & a \\ \omega t & - & -\dot{x} & a\omega \\ & -\ddot{x} & - & a\omega^2 \end{array}$$

Distances are measured from the mean position in both systems, but in this second system time is measured from an extremity.

5 A particle describes linear S.H.M. with period 12 seconds between two points A and B. Given that the particle is 0.5m from A after 2 seconds find its velocity 4 seconds after leaving A.

A period of 12 seconds means that $\omega = \frac{\pi}{6}$.
It would be convenient in this example to use the second system with time being measured from position A.

Then the chart for t = 2 would be:

$$\begin{array}{c|ccc} & 0.5 & - & a \\ \frac{\pi}{3} & - & - & - \\ & - & - & - \end{array}$$

Since the triple for $\frac{\pi}{3}$ is $1, \sqrt{3}, 2$ we can see by proportion that a = 1.

Now consider the chart for t = 4:

$$\begin{array}{c|ccc} & - & - & - \\ \frac{2\pi}{3} & - & -\dot{x} & \frac{\pi}{6} \\ & - & - & - \end{array}$$

The triple for $\frac{2\pi}{3}$ is $-1, \sqrt{3}, 2$ and again by proportion we find that $\dot{x} = -\frac{\pi\sqrt{3}}{12}$.

As mentioned earlier the standard formulae for Simple Harmonic Motion can be established from the initial general chart:

$$\begin{array}{c|ccc} & - & x & a \\ \omega t & \dot{x} & - & a\omega \\ & - & -\ddot{x} & a\omega^2 \end{array} \quad \begin{array}{l} ---(1) \\ ---(2) \\ ---(3) \end{array}$$

Multiplying (1) by ω^2 so that the elements may be equated to those in (3) we get $\ddot{x} = -\omega^2 x$. And multiplying (1) by ω and equating the first elements in (1) and (2) we get $\dot{x} = \omega\sqrt{a^2 - x^2}$.

Other formulae, not normally used, are also available by equating other elements.

✐ **Practice A**

a A particle oscillates in a horizontal line about a fixed point such that its distance, xm, from the fixed point at time t seconds is given by x = 2sin3t.
Find the velocity and acceleration when x = 1m.

b A particle oscillates in a horizontal line about a fixed point such that its distance, xm, from the fixed point at time t seconds is given by $x = 2\sin 3t$.
Find its distance from the fixed point and its acceleration when $\dot{x} = 3$m/s.

c If the equation of motion is $x = 5\sin 2t$, with the same units as above find when the particle is 4m from the origin and when $\dot{x} = 8$.

---

a $\pm 3\sqrt{3} ; -9$ b $\pm\sqrt{3} ; \pm 9\sqrt{3}$ c   0.4636; 0.32175

16.2 PROJECTILES

A particle moving under a constant gravitational force would have an "acceleration triple":

$$A)\ 0,\ -g,\ -$$

meaning that the acceleration, a, is zero in a horizontal direction and equal to $-g$ (g is the acceleration due to gravity) in a vertically upwards direction.

Integrating this with respect to time gives the "velocity triple":

$$V)\ w,\ u-gt,\ -$$

where w is the initial velocity in the horizontal direction and u is the initial velocity in the vertical direction.

Integrating again we obtain the "distance triple":

$$S)\ wt,\ ut-\tfrac{1}{2}gt^2,\ -$$

assuming that time is measured from when the particle was at the origin of coordinates.

These three triples contain the usual formulae for this type of motion in a compact and accessible form that is easily derived from first principles.

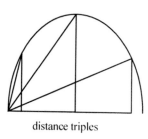

distance triples

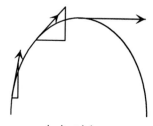

velocity triples

Putting the three triples together we may write:

A | 0   − g   g
V | w   u − gt   speed at time t
S | wt   ut − ½gt²   distance from origin at time t

in which we complete the three triples (third column), and in which, we use the letters A, V and S to represent the angles in these triples.

6 A particle is projected at **200ms⁻¹** at an angle of elevation of **tan⁻¹(4/3)**.
Find (a) its greatest height,
  (b) its range on a horizontal plane,
  (c) its speed after 7 seconds,
  (d) when its velocity is at tan⁻¹(5/12) to the horizontal,
  (e) after how long the velocity is perpendicular to its original velocity.

Using g = 10ms⁻² and finding the components of the initial velocity to be:
$\frac{3}{5}$× 200 = 120 and $\frac{4}{5}$× 200 = 160 the general chart here is:

A | 0   − 10   -
V | 120   160 − 10t   -
S | 120t   160t − 5t²   -

a) The greatest height will be when the vertical component of the velocity is zero. That is 160 − 10t = 0. So t = 16s.

Putting this value into the vertical component of the distance triple we get **1280m** as the greatest height.

b) The range will be twice the base of the distance triple just discussed, so it is **3840m**.

c) The speed is given by the third element of the velocity triple. Putting t = 7 we get 120 and 90 as the first two elements of this triple so that the third element is **150ms⁻¹**.

d) Here the velocity triple given is 12,5,13 and this is equated to the general velocity triple.
So we can write $\frac{120}{160-10t} = \frac{12}{5}$, from which we find that **t = 11s**.

e) A triple perpendicular to 120, 160, - is 160, −120, -, but since the first element is always 120 we multiply this through by $\frac{3}{4}$ to obtain 120, −90, - as the perpendicular velocity triple.
Comparing this with the general velocity triple we can write:
160 − 10t = −90.
From which **t = 25s**.

7 A particle is projected with a velocity of **40√2 m/s** at an angle of **45°** from the edge of a cliff. The particle is sighted from the point of projection when at its greatest height. Find the time that elapses from then until its angle of elevation, as seen from the point of projection, has decreased by the angle in the triple **4,3,5**.

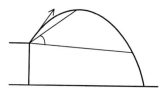

Since the triple for 45° is $1,1,\sqrt{2}$, the initial velocity triple is $40,40,40\sqrt{2}$.
So the general chart is:

```
A |  0      -10        -
V |  40     40 - 10t    -
S |  40t    40t - 5t²   -
```

At the greatest height we have $40 - 10t = 0$, so $t = 4s$.
The distance triple at this time is therefore 160, 80, - , which cancels to 2, 1, -.
And from this we should subtract the 4,3,5 triple:

```
         2    1    -
         4    3    -   —
        11   -2    -
```

We see from this answer that the particle is seen below the horizontal.
At this time its direction is given by 11, –2, -, though these are not the right distances.
This is not a problem however as we are going to equate the ratio of distances to that in the general distance triple: $\frac{40t}{40t-5t^2} = \frac{11}{-2}$ from which $t = \frac{104}{11}$ **s.**

8 A particle is projected at **30m/s** at an angle of **arctan$\frac{3}{4}$** to the horizontal. When has the direction of its velocity changed by the angle in the triple **12,5,13**?

The general chart is:

```
A |  0      -10        -
V |  24     18 - 10t    -
S |  24t    18t - 5t²   -
```

Here the original direction is given by 4,3,5 and this is to be reduced by 12,5,13.
We therefore subtract these triples:

```
        4    3    5
       12    5   13   —
       63   16   65
```

Since this is the final velocity direction we need to find the value of t for which it is equal to the general velocity triple: $\frac{63}{16} = \frac{24}{18-10t}$ from which $t = \frac{25}{21}$ **s.**

There are various advantages in using the triple system here, including:
(a) the use of distance triples and velocity triples, and the significance of their last element,
(b) the use of addition and subtraction of triples,
(c) the structuring of the various equations in a single chart, which becomes even more useful when two or more projectiles occur in the same problem (see exercise below).

✎ **Practice B** (use $g = 10m/s^2$)

a A particle is projected at $\arctan\frac{3}{4}$ with a speed of 100m/s.

Find (i)   its speed and position after 2 seconds,
     (ii) the change in direction of the projectile's motion from $t = 2$ to $t = 3s$,
     (iii) the change in the angle of elevation of the projectile from $t = 2$ to $t = 3s$ as seen from its point of projection.

b Two particles are projected in the same vertical plane, at the same instant, from the same point and with a speed of 20m/s. They are projected on horizontal ground at angles of 30° and 60°.
(i)   Write down the general chart for each projectile.
(ii) Find the position of each projectile when the lower one hits the ground.

c Two particles A and B are projected in the same vertical plane, at the same instant and from the same point, one with an initial speed of 26m/s at an angle of $\arctan\frac{5}{12}$ and the other with an initial speed of 30m/s and at an angle of $\arctan\frac{3}{4}$. Find the position of B when A is at its greatest height and their distance apart when $t = 2s$.

---

a   (i) $40\sqrt{5}$; 160, 100, -   (ii) 19, 2, -   (iii) 173, 8, -
b   (i) 0   −10   -   0   −10   -
         $10\sqrt{3}$ 10−10t   -   10 $10\sqrt{3}$ −10t   -
         $10\sqrt{3}$ t   10t−5t²   -   10t $10\sqrt{3}$ t −5t² -
    (ii) $\left(20\sqrt{3},0\right)$; $\left(20, 20\sqrt{3} - 20\right)$
c   (24,13);   16m

16.3 FORCES IN EQUILIBRIUM

Various methods are available for solving problems with forces in equilibrium including resolution of forces in perpendicular directions, the triangle of forces and Lami's theorem.

If two of three forces acting on a body are perpendicular then a triple of forces results and simple proportion can provide the solution. And, as Example 12 shows, even when none of the forces are perpendicular (or when more than three forces are involved) this triple method can still be used.

9 An object of weight **20N** is attached to one end of a string AC **2m** long. The other end, A, of the string is fixed and a horizontal force is applied at C so that the system hangs in equilibrium as shown, with C **120cm** from the vertical through A. Find the magnitude of the force and the tension in the string.

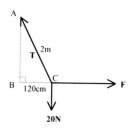

The triangle ABC shown is the triple 120 - 200 which is equal to 3,4,5.
Since the three forces are parallel to the sides of this triangle ABC also serves as a triple of forces.

So the triple of forces **F   20   T**
              is equal to **3   4   5.**

And since the middle element of the first is 5 times the middle element of the second we can see that **F = 15N** and **T = 25N**.

10 Wires of length 8m and 6m are attached at each end of a beam 10m long. The other ends are attached to a third wire from which a weight of 20N hangs. Find the tensions in the three wires.

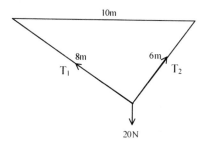

The diagram shows the arrangement and it is clear that 6, 8, 10 is a triple so that the tensions T_1 and T_2 are perpendicular. $T_3 = 20N$, so the hypotenuse of the triple of forces is 20N. It follows that the three forces are 12, 16, 20N.
And since T_2 is greater than T_1 the three forces are **12N, 16N** and **20N** respectively.

11 A rod AE of weight **21N** and length **10m** is hinged at A and is supported as shown by a horizontal wire DE where D is **7m** vertically above A. Find the tension in the wire.

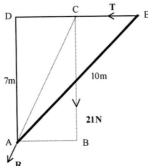

The three forces (tension T, weight 21N, and the hinge reaction R) acting on the rod are in equilibrium and so must all pass through a point. This point is C, the mid point of DE.

Thus triangle ABC can represent a triple of forces.

From triangle ADE we see that $DE = \sqrt{51}$ m and that AB is therefore $\frac{\sqrt{51}}{2}$ m.

So the triple of forces is   T   21   R
and its dimensions are $\frac{\sqrt{51}}{2}$ 7   -

The ratio of the middle elements here clearly gives $T = \frac{3\sqrt{51}}{2}$ **N.**

12 A particle of weight 50N rests on a smooth slope inclined at 30° to the horizontal. It is supported in this position by a force F which is inclined at 60° to the horizontal. Find F.

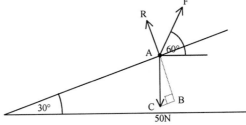

The best way to solve this is probably to resolve forces parallel to the plane, but the triple method can be used for this by resolving F into components along and perpendicular to the plane.

The triangle ABC can be viewed as a triple of forces in which

the triple of forces is $R + \frac{F}{2}$ $\frac{F\sqrt{3}}{2}$ 50
and the dimensions are $\sqrt{3}$ 1   2

Looking at the ratios in the last two columns $\frac{F\sqrt{3}}{2} = 25$ and $F = \frac{50}{\sqrt{3}}$ **N.**

✏ **Practice C**

a A weight of 50N is suspended by a string attached to a fixed point. The weight is pulled aside by a force F until the string is inclined at 30° to the vertical. Find F and the tension in the string.

b A sphere of weight 20N and radius r rests against a smooth vertical wall supported by a string of length r attached to a point on the sphere and to the wall. Find the tension in the string.

c A ladder of weight 30N, on rough horizontal ground, leans against a smooth vertical wall at an angle of arctan($\frac{12}{7}$) to the horizontal. Find the magnitude of the reaction at each end of the ladder.

d A uniform rod AB of length 13m and weight 6N is hinged at A to a vertical wall. A horizontal force F is applied at B so that B is 5m vertically below A. Find F and the magnitude of the force at the hinge.

a $\frac{50}{\sqrt{3}}$; $\frac{100}{\sqrt{3}}$ **b** $\frac{40}{\sqrt{3}}$ **c** $\frac{210}{24}$ (top); $\frac{25\times30}{24}$ (bottom)   **d** $\frac{36}{5}$; $\frac{6}{5}\sqrt{61}$

16.4 WORK AND MOMENT

13 Given $F = 5i + 4j$ and $r = 3i + 2j$
find (a) the work done when the force F moves through the vector r,
and (b) the moment about the origin of the force F acting through the point with position vector r.

$$\begin{array}{cc} F = & 5i + 4j \\ r = & 3i + 2j \\ \hline & 23 \quad 2 \end{array}$$

Using the method of triple subtraction we get
$5 \times 3 + 4 \times 2 = 23$J as the work done,
and $4 \times 3 - 5 \times 2 = 2$Nm for the moment.

This triple method can be extended to 3-dimensional space in which we use 'quadruples' like 2,3,6,7 (in which $2^2 + 3^2 + 6^2 = 7^2$). Finding the moment of a force in 3-dimensional space and the work done is a more striking illustration of the effectiveness of the triple method since there is no need to evaluate a 3 by 3 determinant, which is the usual method (see Reference 4).

LESSON 17
TRIGONOMETRIC FUNCTIONS

SUMMARY

Here we have derivatives and series expansions of trigonometric functions and their inverses, and also evaluating sine, cosine and inverse tangent.

17.1 Derivatives – of the six trig functions and some variations.

17.2 Series Expansions

17.3 Inverse Trigonometric Functions – derivatives and series expansions.

17.4 Evaluating Trigonometric Functions – sine, cosine and inverse tangent.

17.1 DERIVATIVES

To obtain the derivative of a function f(x), where x is an angle (measured in radians), we look at the change produced in that function by a small change in x of, say, dx.

 To prove $\dfrac{d\sin x}{dx} = \cos x$.

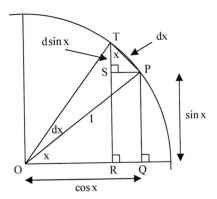

In the unit circle above $\cos x$ and $\sin x$ are as shown and since $\angle OPS = x$, then $\angle STP \approx x$, as $\angle OPT$ is approximately a right angle.

Since $RT = \sin(x+dx)$ the change in $\sin x$ resulting from the increase of dx in x is ST. We denote this by $d\sin x$.

Also the arc TP = dx.

Now in triangle STP, $\cos x = \dfrac{ST}{TP} \approx \dfrac{d\sin x}{dx}$.

And as $dx \to 0$ this approximation tends to equality.

So $\dfrac{d\sin x}{dx} = \cos x$. Or using limit notation: $\text{Lim}_{dx\to 0}\,\dfrac{d\sin x}{dx} = \cos x$.

We observe the change that a small increase in x produces in the function being differentiated.

Similarly, from the same diagram, $\sin x = \dfrac{SP}{TP} = \dfrac{-d\cos x}{TP} \approx \dfrac{-d\cos x}{dx}$.

Here we have a decrease in $\cos x$ as x increases, hence the minus sign.

Therefore $\dfrac{d\cos x}{dx} = -\sin x$.

Sin(x+a)

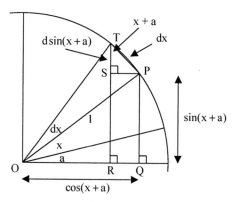

Here a is a constant.

Similarly we see in the small triangle STP that $\dfrac{d\sin(x+a)}{dx} = \cos(x+a)$.

4   **Sin2x**

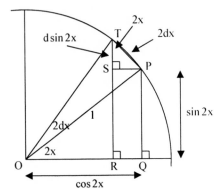

An increase of dx in x means an increase of 2dx in 2x.

We therefore get, from $\triangle STP$, $\cos 2x \approx \dfrac{d\sin 2x}{2dx}$ and so in the limit:

$$\frac{d\sin 2x}{dx} = 2\cos 2x.$$

Similarly the diagram shows $\dfrac{d\cos 2x}{dx} = -2\sin 2x$.

And it can also be seen that $\dfrac{d\sin nx}{dx} = n\cos nx$.

5   **Sin(x²)**

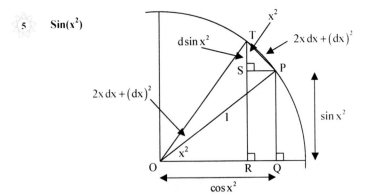

We need the increase in $\sin x^2$ resulting from an increase of dx in x. If x becomes x+dx then x^2 becomes $(x+dx)^2$ and the increase is: $(x+dx)^2 - x^2 = 2xdx + (dx)^2$.

From the small triangle STP we can then see that $\cos x^2 \approx \dfrac{d\sin x^2}{2xdx + (dx)^2}$.

And as $dx \to 0$ we get $\cos x^2 = \dfrac{d\sin x^2}{2xdx}$. So that $\dfrac{d\sin x^2}{dx} = 2x\cos x^2$.

6   Tangent and Secant

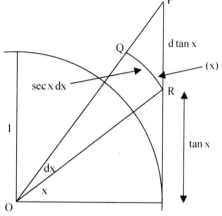

In the diagram OR = $\sec x$ and if QR is an arc centred on O and radius $\sec x$ then the length of the arc is $\sec x\,dx$.

PR is the increase in $\tan x$ due to the increase dx. So PR = $d\tan x$.

The angle QRP is approximately equal to x and approaches x as $dx \to 0$.

So in the limit we get $\sec x = \dfrac{d\tan x}{\sec x\,dx}$ and $\dfrac{d\tan x}{dx} = \sec^2 x$.

Similarly PQ = $d\sec x$ and so $\tan x = \dfrac{d\sec x}{\sec x\,dx}$ giving $\dfrac{d\sec x}{dx} = \sec x\tan x$.

7   Cosecant and Cotangent

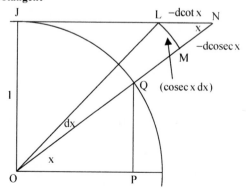

Here OQ is extended to meet the tangent at J at N.
Then JN = cot x and ON = cosec x .

LM is an arc centred on O, radius OL. So the length of the arc LM is approximately cosec x dx and tends to cosec x dx as dx → 0

The change in cosec x (which is −d cosec x) and cot x (which is −d cot x) are then as shown.

Then again in the limit we get $\cot x = \dfrac{-d\cosec x}{\cosec x\, dx}$, so that $\dfrac{d\cosec x}{dx} = -\cosec x \cot x.$

And $\cosec x = \dfrac{-d\cot x}{\cosec x\, dx}$, so that $\dfrac{d\cot x}{dx} = -\cosec^2 x.$

17.2 SERIES EXPANSIONS

Cosine x

It follows from Section 17.1 that $\dfrac{d^2 \cos x}{dx^2} = -\cos x.$

And since we know that $\cos 0 = 1$ it follows that if a polynomial, series expansion for cos x exists it starts with 1 and each succeeding term can be found by integrating the previous term twice and changing the sign.

So integrating 1 twice and changing the sign we get $-\dfrac{x^2}{2}.$

Integrating $-\frac{x^2}{2}$ twice and changing the sign gives $+\dfrac{x^4}{4!}.$

And so on. So $\mathbf{cos x} = 1 - \dfrac{x^2}{2!} + \dfrac{x^4}{4!} - \dfrac{x^6}{6!} \ldots + (-1)^n \dfrac{x^{2n}}{(2n)!}$

"Well, I may say at this point that whatever kind of question there may be, in whatever chapter it may be, simple equations, quadratic equations, cubic, bi-quadratic, and various other subjects of algebra, geometry, plane trigonometry, spherical trigonometry, calculus, and so on, the question must come under one of the sixteen rules. All that we have to do is, let me repeat, to recognize and identify the particular type and apply the Sutra relative to that particular type.
From "Vedic Metaphysics", Page 180.

9   Similarly for **sine x**. We know that $\dfrac{d^2 \sin x}{dx^2} = -\sin x$.

We also know that $\sin x \approx x$ for small x so that x will be the first term of the series. We therefore integrate x twice and change the sign, and continue this process as before.

So $\sin x = x - \dfrac{x^3}{3!} + \dfrac{x^5}{5!} \ldots + (-1)^n \dfrac{x^{2n+1}}{(2n+1)!}$

Alternatively, since $\dfrac{d \sin x}{dx} = \cos x$ we can get $\sin x$ by integrating the series for $\cos x$ term by term.

Or we can integrate the nth term of the series for $\cos x$: $\int (-1)^n \dfrac{x^{2n}}{(2n)!} dx = (-1)^n \dfrac{x^{2n+1}}{(2n+1)!}$.

10   For **tangent x** we can proceed as follows.

We know from Example 6 that $\dfrac{d \tan x}{dx} = \sec^2 x$ and $\sec^2 x = 1 + \tan^2 x$.

So $\tan x = \int (1 + \tan^2 x) dx = x + \int \tan^2 x\, dx$.

We can therefore find a series for $\tan x$ by finding the duplex of the first 1, 2, 3 etc. terms and integrating.
The first term is x.

$D(x) = x^2$. $\int x^2 dx = \dfrac{x^3}{3}$. So the second term is $\dfrac{x^3}{3}$.

Then $D(x + \dfrac{x^3}{3}) = \dfrac{2x^4}{3}$ and $\int \dfrac{2x^4}{3} dx = \dfrac{2x^5}{15}$. which is the third term.

Similarly $D\left(x + \dfrac{x^3}{3} + \dfrac{2x^5}{15} \right) = \left(\dfrac{4}{15} + \dfrac{1}{9} \right) x^6$. and $\int \dfrac{17x^6}{45} dx = \dfrac{17x^7}{315}$.

So $\tan x = x + \frac{1}{3} x^3 + \frac{2}{15} x^5 + \frac{17}{315} x^7 + \ldots$

Alternatively we could use $\tan x = \dfrac{\sin x}{\cos x}$ and divide the series for $\sin x$ by the series for $\cos x$ using straight division:

$$\left.1-\frac{x^2}{2}+\frac{x^4}{4!}-\frac{x^6}{6!}\cdots\;\right|\;x-\frac{x^3}{3!}+\frac{x^5}{5!}\cdots$$

$$x+\tfrac{1}{3}x^3+\tfrac{2}{15}x^5+\ldots$$

The steps are:

$x \div 1 = x.$

$1\times(-\tfrac{1}{2})=-\tfrac{1}{2},\;\; -\tfrac{1}{3!}--\tfrac{1}{2}=\tfrac{1}{3}.$

$1\times\tfrac{1}{4!}+\tfrac{1}{3}\times(-\tfrac{1}{2})=-\tfrac{1}{8},\;\tfrac{1}{5!}--\tfrac{1}{8}=\tfrac{2}{15}.$

Etc.

Other series can be found by using straight division: $\sec x$ and $\csc x$ for example.

Though not a trig. function we can include the series for e^x here.

 Using the fact that $e^0 = 1$ and that $\dfrac{de^x}{dx}=e^x$ we can also get a series expansion for e^x by integrating 1, integrating the result, integrating that result and so on.

$$e^x = 1+x+\frac{x^2}{2!}+\frac{x^3}{3!}+\frac{x^4}{4!}+\cdots$$

17.3 INVERSE TRIGONOMETRIC FUNCTIONS

17.3a DERIVATIVES

 Prove $\dfrac{d\tan^{-1}\left(\frac{x}{a}\right)}{dx}=\dfrac{a}{a^2+x^2}.$

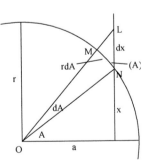

Suppose A is the angle whose tangent is $\dfrac{x}{a}$, where a is a constant.

That is $A = \tan^{-1}\left(\frac{x}{a}\right)$ or $\tan A = \frac{x}{a}$.

In triple terms we have: A) a, x, r where r is the hypotenuse.

Since we want to find $\dfrac{d\tan\left(\frac{x}{a}\right)}{dx}$ or $\dfrac{dA}{dx}$ we are interested in the increase in A, i.e. dA,

resulting from an increase of dx in x. This is shown geometrically above.

As $dx \to 0$ the triangle LMN tends to a right-angled triangle with the angle A at N.

From triangle LMN we see that in the limit $\cos A = \dfrac{rdA}{dx}$.

Therefore, since $\cos A = \dfrac{a}{r}$, $\dfrac{dA}{dx} = \dfrac{a}{r} \times \dfrac{1}{r} = \dfrac{a}{r^2} = \dfrac{a}{a^2 + x^2}$.

And so $\dfrac{d\tan^{-1}\left(\frac{x}{a}\right)}{dx} = \dfrac{a}{a^2 + x^2}$.

13 Prove $\dfrac{d\sin^{-1}\left(\frac{x}{a}\right)}{dx} = \dfrac{1}{\sqrt{a^2 - x^2}}$.

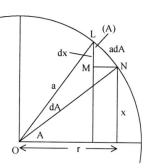

Now let $A = \sin^{-1}\left(\frac{x}{a}\right)$ (a again being constant), described by the triple: A) r, x, a.

x is increased by dx and dA is the resulting increase in A.

As $dx \to 0$ triangle LMN tends to a right-angled triangle with angle A at L and hypotenuse equal to $a\,dA$.

Then in the limit $\cos A = \dfrac{dx}{adA}$.

Therefore $\dfrac{dA}{dx} = \dfrac{1}{a\cos A} = \dfrac{1}{r} = \dfrac{1}{\sqrt{a^2 - x^2}}$. So $\dfrac{d\sin^{-1}\left(\frac{x}{a}\right)}{dx} = \dfrac{1}{\sqrt{a^2 - x^2}}$.

17.3b SERIES

14   Find a series expansion for **tan^{-1} x**.

Since from above $\dfrac{d\tan^{-1}x}{dx} = \dfrac{1}{1+x^2}$ then $\tan^{-1}x = \int \dfrac{1}{1+x^2}dx.$

This means we can get a series for tan^{-1}x by finding a series for $\dfrac{1}{1+x^2}$ and integrating it.

By straight division:

$$1+x^2 \;\Big|\; \dfrac{1}{\;1-x^2+x^4-x^6+...}$$

Then $\int (1-x^2+x^4-x^6+...)dx = x-\tfrac{1}{3}x^3+\tfrac{1}{5}x^5-\tfrac{1}{7}x^7+...$ which is the required series.

So $\tan^{-1}x = x-\tfrac{1}{3}x^3+\tfrac{1}{5}x^5-\tfrac{1}{7}x^7+\ldots$

15   Similarly for **sin^{-1}x**, we know that $\sin^{-1}x = \int \dfrac{1}{\sqrt{1-x^2}}dx.$

So we obtain a series for $\dfrac{1}{1-x^2}$, take its square root and integrate.

$$1-x^2 \;\Big|\; \dfrac{1}{\;1+x^2+x^4+x^6+...}$$

So $\dfrac{1}{1-x^2} = 1+x^2+x^4+x^6+...$

For the square root:

$$
\begin{array}{l}
\;\; 1 + x^2 + x^4 + \; x^6 + \ldots \\
2)\;\; \underline{\qquad -\tfrac{1}{4} \qquad \tfrac{3}{8} \qquad\quad} \\
\;\; 1+\tfrac{1}{2}x^2+\tfrac{3}{8}x^4+\tfrac{5}{16}x^6+\ldots
\end{array}
$$

And integrating this result we get: $\sin^{-1}x = x+\tfrac{1}{6}x^3+\tfrac{3}{40}x^5+\tfrac{5}{102}x^7\ldots$

These series can be used to evaluate angles given $\sin x$, $\cos x$ or $\tan x$.

We can get other series by using:

$$\int \frac{1}{\sqrt{x^2+a^2}}dx = \sinh^{-1}\left(\tfrac{x}{a}\right),$$

$$\int \frac{1}{\sqrt{x^2-a^2}}dx = \cosh^{-1}\left(\tfrac{x}{a}\right),$$

$$\int \frac{a}{a^2-x^2}dx = \tanh^{-1}\left(\tfrac{x}{a}\right).$$

Though it is not a trig. function we may take one further example.

 16   Find a series for **ln(1+x)**.

This can be found from the result $\ln(1+x) = \int \frac{1}{1+x}dx$.

That is we obtain a series for $\frac{1}{1+x}$ and integrate it.

$$
\begin{array}{c|l}
1+x & 1 \\
 & \overline{} \\
 & 1-x+x^2-x^3+\ldots
\end{array}
$$

Integrating this result gives: **$\ln(1+x) = x - \tfrac{1}{2}x^2 + \tfrac{1}{3}x^3 - \tfrac{1}{4}x^4 + \ldots$**

 17   Find a polynomial expansion up to the term in x^3 for $(1+x)^3 e^x$.

Setting the two series out one below the other we can obtain the product from left to right.

$$
\begin{array}{lllllll}
1 & + 3x & + & 3x^2 & + & x^3 \\
1 & + x & + & \tfrac{x^2}{2} & + & \tfrac{x^3}{6} & +\ldots \\
\hline
\multicolumn{7}{l}{1+(1+3)x+(\tfrac{1}{2}+3+3)x^2+(\tfrac{1}{6}+\tfrac{3}{2}+3+1)x^3\ldots} \\
= 1 & + 4x & + & \tfrac{13}{2}x^2 & + & \tfrac{17}{3}x^3\ldots
\end{array}
$$

The *Vertically and Crosswise* pattern automatically collects together like powers of x.

Where powers of x are missing in a series we can insert zero. So for an expression for $e^x \cos x$ we can write $\cos x$ as $1 + 0x - \tfrac{x^2}{2!} + 0x^3 + \tfrac{x^4}{4!} + \ldots$

17.4 EVALUATING TRIGONOMETRIC FUNCTIONS

By using the left to right methods and the series expansions for sinx, cosx and inverse tanx, these functions can be evaluated for any angle. See Lesson 18 for inverse sine, inverse cosine and tangent.

17.4a COSINE

The series expansion for $\cos x$ is:

$\cos x = 1 - \frac{x^2}{2!} + \frac{x^4}{4!} - \frac{x^6}{6!} + \frac{x^8}{8!} - \ldots$ where x is in radians (see Example 8).

If we write this as $\cos x = 1 + A + B + C + D + \ldots$

we see that $B = \frac{A^2}{6}, C = \frac{AB}{15}, D = \frac{AC}{28}$ etc.

This means that once we have obtained the value of $\frac{x^2}{2}$ the next term is obtained by squaring this and dividing by 6, the next by multiplying the two previous terms and dividing by 15, and so on.

 Find **cosine 0.2** radians.

We set up a chart as shown:

$$
\begin{array}{r|l}
1 - \frac{x^2}{2} & 1 \cdot 0\ \bar{2} \\
\frac{x^4}{24}\ \ 6 & .0\ 0\ 0\ 0\ 6\ 6\ 6\ 6\ 6 \\
-\frac{x^6}{720}\ \ 15 & \qquad\qquad \bar{1}\ 3\ 1\ 3\ 1\ 3\ 1\ 3 \\
\hline
\cos 0.2 = & 1 \cdot 0\ \bar{2}\ 0\ 0\ 6\ 6\ 5\ 7\ 7\ 7
\end{array}
$$

row 1
row 2
row 3
row 4

We require the figures in row 4 and these are the sum of the figures in rows 1, 2 and 3, as can be seen by looking at the left-hand side. As explained above the divisors in rows 2 and 3 are 6 and 15 and it may be useful to have these written down.

We put 1 in row 1, followed by $\frac{-0.2^2}{2} = 0.0\bar{2}$.

Then square the decimal part of row 1 and divide by 6 to obtain row 2:

$0.02^2 = 0.0004;\quad 0.0004 \div 6 = 0.0000\dot{6}$.

Then multiply rows 1 and 2 and divide by 15:

$\bar{2} \times 6 = \overline{12};\ \overline{12} \div 15 = \bar{1}\ r3;$ put down $\bar{1}_3$

then $\bar{2} \times 6 = \overline{12};\ \overline{12} +$ carried 3 (as 30) = 18; 18 ÷ 15 = 1 r3; etc.

We then add the columns up. In fact the next term in the series comes in at the tenth decimal place, so that the last figure should be 8.

∴ **cos 0.2 = 0.980066578 to 9 D.P.**

19   **Cosine 0.3** radians = **0.95533649** to 8 D.P.

This is similar:

$1-\frac{x^2}{2}$		1 . 0 $\overline{4}$ $\overline{5}$		row 1
$\frac{x^4}{24}$	6	. 3 $_{\overline{2}}$3 $_{27}$ 3 5		row 2
$-\frac{x^6}{720}$	15	$\overline{1}$ $_{30}$ 3$\overline{1}$ $_2$		row 3
cos 0.3 =		1 . 0 $\overline{4}$ $\overline{5}$ 3 3 6 5 $\overline{1}$		row 4

Row 1: $\frac{-0.3^2}{2}=0.0\overline{45}$

Row 2:   we need to square $\overline{45}$, so we find the duplexes in turn, and divide each of
them by 6: D($\overline{4}$) = 16: 16÷6 = 3 r$\overline{2}$, put $3_{\overline{2}}$.

     D($\overline{45}$) = 40: 40 + carried $\overline{2}$ (as $\overline{20}$) = 20: 20÷6 = 3 r2, put 3_2.

     D($\overline{5}$) = 25. 25 + 20 = 45. 45 ÷ 6 = 7_3.

     The carried 3 is 30 in the next column, so 30 ÷ 6 = 5.

Row 3:   we multiply rows 1, 2: $CP\begin{pmatrix} \overline{4} \\ 3 \end{pmatrix}=\overline{12}, \; \overline{12}\div 15 = \overline{1}_3,$

     where CP means the cross-product:

     e.g. $CP\begin{pmatrix} a \\ b \end{pmatrix}=ab.\; CP\begin{pmatrix} a & b \\ c & d \end{pmatrix}=ad+bc,$ etc.

     $CP\begin{pmatrix} \overline{4} & \overline{5} \\ 3 & 3 \end{pmatrix}=\overline{27}.\; \overline{27}+30 = 3.\; 3\div 15 = 0_3$

     $CP\begin{pmatrix} \overline{4} & \overline{5} \\ 3 & 7 \end{pmatrix}=\overline{43}.\; \overline{43}+30 = \overline{13}.\; \overline{13}\div 15 = \overline{1}_2$

     Finally adding the columns and removing the bar figures gives the answer.

20   **Cosine 0.1982.**

$Cos\,0.1982 = cos\,0.20\overline{2}2$

$1-\frac{x^2}{2}$		1 . 0 $\overline{2}$ 0 4 $\overline{4}$ $\overline{2}$ 4		row 1
$\frac{x^4}{24}$	6	1 $_{\overline{2}}$ $\overline{3}$ $_{\overline{2}}$ $\overline{6}$ 0 3 $_{\overline{2}}$		row 2
$-\frac{x^6}{720}$	15	$\overline{1}$ $_1$		row 3
cos 0.20$\overline{2}$2 =		1 . 0 $\overline{2}$ 0 5 $\overline{7}$ $\overline{8}$ 6		row 4

∴ **Cos 0.1982** = 0 . 9 8 0 4 2 2 6

To obtain the figures of row 1 we take successive duplexes of 0.20$\overline{2}$2 divide by 2
and change the sign:

$D(2) = 4, 4 \div 2 = 2$, put down $\overline{2}$; $D(20) = 0, 0 \div 2 = 0$, put down 0;

$D(20\overline{2}) = \overline{8}, \overline{8} \div 2 = \overline{4}$, put down 4; $D(20\overline{2}2) = 8, 8 \div 2 = 4$, put down $\overline{4}$;

$D(0\overline{2}2) = 4, 4 \div 2 = 2$, put down $\overline{2}$; $D(\overline{2}2) = \overline{8}, \overline{8} \div 2 = \overline{4}$, put down 4;

For row 2, take duplexes in row 1 and divide by 6:

$D(\overline{2}) = 4, 4 \div 6 = 1_{\frac{-}{3}}$; $D(\overline{2}0) = 0, 0 + \overline{20} = \overline{20}, \overline{20} \div 6 = \overline{3}_{\frac{-}{3}}$;

$D(\overline{2}04) = \overline{16}, \overline{16} + \overline{20} = \overline{36}, \overline{36} \div 6 = \overline{6}_0$; $D(\overline{2}04\overline{4}) = 16, 16 + 0 = 16, 16 \div 6 = 3_{\frac{-}{2}}$.

For row 3, take cross-products of rows 1 and 2 and divide by 15:

$CP\begin{pmatrix} \overline{2} \\ 1 \end{pmatrix} = \overline{2}$ and $CP\begin{pmatrix} \overline{2} & 0 \\ 0 & 3 \end{pmatrix} = 6$, and combining these gives $\overline{2}6 = \overline{14}, \overline{14} \div 15 = \overline{1}_1$.

Next add rows 1, 2, 3 to get **cos 0.1982 = 0.9804226 to 7 D.P.**

17.4b SINE

The series expansion for $\sin x$ (see Example 9) is:

$$\sin x = x - \frac{x^3}{3!} + \frac{x^5}{5!} - \frac{x^7}{7!} + \ldots$$

Writing this as $\sin x = A - B + C - D + \ldots$.

we see that $B = \frac{Ax^2}{6}$, $C = \frac{Bx^2}{20}$, $D = \frac{Cx^2}{42}$ etc.

This means that we can obtain x^2 and then evaluate each term by multiplying the previous term by x^2 and dividing by 6, 20, 42 etc.

 21   **Sine 0.2**.

$(x^2$		0 . 0	4)										row 0
x		0 . 2											row 1
$-\frac{x^3}{3!}$	6	. 0	0	$\overline{1}_2$	$\overline{3}_2$	$\overline{3}_2$	$\overline{3}_2$	$\overline{3}_2$	$\overline{3}_2$	$\overline{3}_2$			row 2
$\frac{x^5}{5!}$	2						2	6	6	6			row 3
$-\frac{x^7}{7!}$	42									$\overline{2}_{20}$			row 4
sin 0.2 =		0 . 2	0	$\overline{1}$	3	3	$\overline{1}$	3	3	1			row 5

First we find that $x^2 = 0.04$

For row 2, we multiply rows 0 and 1 and divide by 6:

$4\times2 = 8$, $8 \div 6 = 1$ r 2, put down 1_2 (we can change the signs of rows 2 and 4 later).

Take the carried 2, as 20, $20 \div 6 = 3_2$ etc.

For row 3, multiply rows 0 and 2 and divide by 2:
$4\times1 = 4$, $4 \div 2 = 2$
$4\times3 = 12$, $12 \div 2 = 6$, etc.

For row 4, multiply rows 0 and 3 and divide by 42:
$4\times26 = 104$, $104 \div 42 = 2_{20}$

Then change the signs of rows 2 and 4 and add the columns up.

∴ sin 0.2 = 0.19866933 to 8 D.P.

 Sine 0.3 .

$$
\begin{array}{l|l}
(x^2 & 0\,.\,1\ \ \bar{1}) \\
x & 0\,.\,3 \\
-\dfrac{x^3}{3!}\quad 6 & .\,0\ \ 0\ \ \bar{4}\,_3\,5 \\
\dfrac{x^5}{5!}\quad 2 & \qquad\qquad 2\ \ 0_1\ \ 2\ \ 5 \\
-\dfrac{x^7}{7!}\quad 42 & \qquad\qquad\qquad\qquad\qquad \bar{4} \\
\hline
\sin 0.3 = & 0\,.\,3\ \ 0\ \ \bar{4}\ \ \bar{5}\ \ 2\ \ 0\ \ 2\ \ 1
\end{array}
$$

 Sine 0.23 .

Here we have 2 digits after the decimal point.

$$
\begin{array}{l|l l}
(x^2 & .\,0\ \ 5\ \ 3\ \ \bar{1}) & \text{row 0} \\
x & 0\,.\,2\ \ 3 & \text{row 1} \\
-\dfrac{x^3}{3!}\quad 6 & .\,0\ \ 0\ \ \bar{2}_{\bar2}\,0_1\,\bar{3}_{\bar1}\,\overset{+}{2}\,_{\bar1}\overset{+}{2}\,_2\bar{3}\ \ \bar{3} & \text{row 2} \\
\dfrac{x^5}{5!}\quad 20 & \qquad\qquad\qquad 5\ \ 3\ \ 6_1\ \ 4_1 & \text{row 3} \\
-\dfrac{x^7}{7!}\quad 42 & \qquad\qquad\qquad\qquad\qquad \bar{7}_{\overline{14}} & \text{row 4} \\
\hline
\sin 0.23 = & 0\,.\,2\ \ 3\ \ \bar{2}\ \ 0\ \ \bar{3}\ \ 7\ \ 5\ \ 3\ \ \bar{6}
\end{array}
$$

For row 2 we multiply rows 0 and 1 and divide by 6:

$$CP\binom{5}{2} = 10,\ 10 \div 6 = 2_{\bar{2}}$$

$$CP\binom{5\quad 3}{2\quad 3} = 21,\ 21 + \overline{20} = 1,\ 1 \div 6 = 0_1.$$

$$CP\binom{3\quad \bar{1}}{2\quad 3} = 7,\ 7 + 10 = 17,\ 17 \div 6 = 3_{\bar{1}}.$$

$$CP\begin{pmatrix}\overline{1}\\3\end{pmatrix}=\overline{3}.\ \overline{3}+\overline{10}=\overline{13},\ \overline{13}\div6=\overline{2}_{\overline{1}}.$$

For row 3 multiply rows 0 and 2 and divide by 2:

$$CP\begin{pmatrix}5\\2\end{pmatrix}=10.\ 10\div2=5.$$

$$CP\begin{pmatrix}5&3\\2&0\end{pmatrix}=6,\ 6\div2=3.$$

$$CP\begin{pmatrix}5&3&\overline{1}\\2&0&3\end{pmatrix}=13,\ 13\div2=6_{1}.$$

$$CP\begin{pmatrix}5&3&\overline{1}\\0&3&2\end{pmatrix}=\overline{1},\ \overline{1}+10=9,\ 9\div2=4_{1}.$$

For row 4: $CP\begin{pmatrix}5\\5\end{pmatrix}=25$ and $CP\begin{pmatrix}5&3\\5&3\end{pmatrix}=30$ together these give 280.
$280\div42=7_{\overline{14}}.$

$\therefore\ \textbf{sin\,0.23 = 0.22797752 to 8 D.P.}$

The solution converges well for small angles. For larger angles we can always use the nearest quadrant boundary. This means that the most awkward cases are when the angle is near $\frac{\pi}{4}$ radians. So we tackle one more sine where the angle is close to this, and also has four figures after the decimal point.

24   **Sine 0.7132 = 0.654257 to 6 D.P.**

```
(x²       0 . 5 ₁̄ 1 ₆̄ 1̄ ₇ 3 ₆̄ 5̄ 3 4 2)
 x        0 . 7   1   3   2
  -x³/3!  6        6̄ ₁̄ 0 2 5̄ ₁̄ 3⁺ ₁̄ 8⁺ ₁̄
   x⁵/5!  20              1 10 5 6 4 ₁̄ 2̄ 2
  -x⁷/7!  42                         2̄ ₈ 1⁺ ₁₄̄
─────────────────────────────────────────────
sin 0.7132 =  0 . 7  5̄  4  2  5  7
```

We have to be careful if we want to avoid large figures here.
The squaring in the first line is similar to that in Example 7, Page 102.

25   **Sine 1.331 = 0.97138550** to 8 D.P.

$\sin 1.331 = \cos\left(\frac{\pi}{2} - 1.331\right) = \cos 0.2398 = \cos 0.240\overline{2}:$

$$
\begin{array}{c|l}
1 - \frac{x^2}{2} \quad 20 & 1 . 0_4\ \overline{3}_{\overline{4}}\ \overset{+}{1}\ _{\overline{4}}\ \overset{+}{2}\ _{\overline{8}}\ \overset{+}{5}\ _4\ \overline{2}\ _0\ 0\quad\ \overline{2} \\
\quad\ \frac{x^4}{24} \quad\ 6 & \qquad\qquad\quad 1\ _3\ 4\ _0\overline{2}\ _1\ \overline{3}\ _2\ 8\ _{\overline{2}} \\
\quad -\frac{x^6}{720} \quad 15 & \qquad\qquad\qquad\qquad\qquad\quad \overline{3}\ _4\ 4\ _{\overline{8}} \\
\hline
\sin 1.331\ =\ 1\ .\ 0\quad \overline{3}\quad 1\quad\ 3\quad 9\quad \overline{4}\quad\ \overline{5}\quad\ 0
\end{array}
$$

In the first line of this calculation we have used 20 as a divisor because the duplexes obtained give some large numbers if divided by 2.

For the first line:
D(2) = 4, 4 ÷ 20 = 0 r 4, put 0_4
D(24) = 16, 16 + 40 = 56, 56 ÷ 20 = $3_{\overline{4}}$
$D(240) = 16,\ 16 - 40 = \overline{24},\ \overline{24} \div 20 = \overline{1}_{\overline{4}}$
$D\left(240\overline{2}\right) = \overline{8},\ \overline{8} - 40 = \overline{48},\ \overline{48} \div 20 = \overline{2}_{\overline{8}}$
$D\left(40\overline{2}\right) = \overline{16},\ \overline{16} - 80 = \overline{96},\ \overline{96} \div 20 = \overline{5}_4$
etc.

17.4c INVERSE TANGENT

The series (see Example 14) is: $\tan^{-1}x = x - \frac{x^3}{3} + \frac{x^5}{5} - \frac{x^7}{7} + ...$

26   Find **tan⁻¹0.2** .

$$
\begin{array}{c|l}
x & 0 . 2 \\
-\frac{x^3}{3} & \quad\ .\ 0\ \ 0\ \ \overline{3}\ \ 3\ \ 3\ \ 3\ \ 3 \\
\frac{x^5}{5} & \qquad\qquad\qquad 6\ \ 4 \\
-\frac{x^7}{7} & \qquad\qquad\qquad\qquad\quad \overline{2}\ \ 2 \\
\hline
\tan^{-1}0.2 = & 0\ .\ 2\quad 0\quad \overline{3}\quad 3\quad 9\quad 5\quad 5
\end{array}
$$

Here it is very easy to evaluate the terms of the series and add them up:
$\frac{0.2^3}{3} = \frac{0.008}{3} = 0.002\dot{6} = 0.003\overline{\dot{3}}$ and so on.

27   **$Tan^{-1}0.342$.**

$$
\begin{array}{l|cccc c}
x & 0.3 & 4 & 2 & & 1 \\
-\frac{x^3}{3} & & & \overline{1} & 3 \,_1 \,\overline{4}\,_{\overline{1}} & 2 \\
\frac{x^5}{5} & & & & 1\,_{\overline{2}}\ \overline{1}\,_0 & 3 \\
\hline
\tan^{-1}0.342 = 0.3 & 3 & 0 & \overline{5} & & 4 \\
\hline
(x^2 = & 0.1\,_{\overline{1}}\ 2\,_{\overline{6}}\ \overline{3}\,_{\overline{2}}\ ) & & & & 5
\end{array}
$$

We first find x^2 in row 5.

For row 2 we multiply rows 1 and 5 and divide by 3:

$CP\begin{pmatrix}3\\1\end{pmatrix}=3,\ 3\div3=1.$

$CP\begin{pmatrix}3&4\\1&2\end{pmatrix}=10,\ 10\div3=3_{1\cdot}$

$CP\begin{pmatrix}3&4&2\\1&2&3\end{pmatrix}=1,\ 1+10=11,\ 11\div3=4_{\overline{1}\cdot}$

For row 3, multiply rows 2 and 5, multiply the result by 3, and divide by 5:

$D(1)=1,\ CP\begin{pmatrix}3\\1\end{pmatrix}=3,\ 3\div5=1_{\overline{2}\cdot}$

$D(12)=4,\ CP\begin{pmatrix}3&4\\1&4\end{pmatrix}=16,\ 16+\overline{20}=\overline{4},\ \overline{4}\div5=\overline{1}_{1\cdot}$

Change the signs of the figures in row 2, and add up the columns.

∴ **$tan^{-1}0.342 = 0.3295$.**

 28   **$Tan^{-1}20$.**

This angle is close to 90°, and,
as can be seen from the diagram,
we can find it by first finding
$\tan^{-1}\frac{1}{20}$ and then subtracting
the result from $\frac{\pi}{2}$.

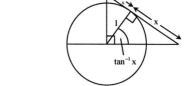

$$
\begin{array}{l|cccccc}
x & 0.0 & 5 & & & & \\
-\frac{x^3}{3} & & 0 & 0 & 0 & 0 & \overline{4}\ \ \overline{2} \\
\hline
\tan^{-1}0.05 = & 0.0 & 4 & 9 & 9 & 5 & 8
\end{array}
$$

∴ **$tan^{-1}20 = 1.570796 - 0.049958 = 1.520838$.**

LESSON 18
TRIGONOMETRIC AND TRANSCENDENTAL EQUATIONS

SUMMARY
This lesson shows how the left-to-right method can be used for solving a variety of types of equation.

18.1 Polynomial equations – solution of quadratic and cubic equations.

18.2 Trigonometric Equations – finding inverse sine, inverse cosine, tangent, inverse hyperbolic sine.

18.3 Transcendental Equations – solution, including Kepler's Equation.

Once we are able to calculate from left to right and combine operations many new possibilities arise. We can calculate trig. functions and solve transcendental equations for example.

18.1 POLYNOMIAL EQUATIONS

The following method is shown in Lesson 14 (with different examples) but is also included here as it leads neatly to finding inverse sines, cosines etc. and the solution of transcendental equations. It works well when a root of a polynomial is small (between +1 and −1) and is equivalent to an iterative method. But it is totally efficient: normally with iterative methods a huge amount of superfluous work is done, but here only those digits which are required are found.

There are also methods of changing the roots of equations: to increase or reduce them by a given value, multiply them by a factor, to get reciprocal roots or change their sign, etc. (see Reference 5). This allows us to transform a given equation to one on which this technique can be applied.

 1 Solve $x^2 - 5x + 1 = 0$.

This equation is easily rearranged to give $x = 0.2 + \dfrac{x^2}{5}$.

If we then set out a table as follows:

$$
\begin{array}{c|cccccc}
0.2 & 0 & . & 2 & 0 & 0 & 0 & 0 \\
\frac{x^2}{5} & & & & & & & \\
\hline
x & 0 & . & 2 & & & & \\
\end{array}
$$

We know that the first two lines must add up to the third and we can bring **0.2** down into the answer line.

The middle row is for $\frac{x^2}{5}$ so we find the first figure of this from the first figure of x (= 0.2).
This we do by finding the duplex of 2 and dividing it by 5: $D(2) = 2^2 = 4$, $4 \div 5 = 1$ rem $\bar{1}$, and this is placed as shown below.

$$
\begin{array}{l|llllll}
0.2 & 0.2 & 0 & 0 & 0 & 0 \\
\frac{x^2}{5} & & 1 & {}_{\bar{1}} & & \\
\hline
x & 0.2 & 1 & & &
\end{array}
$$

The $\bar{1}$ remainder is worth –10 in the next column.
We also bring the **1** down into the answer to give x = 0.21 so far.

Next we take the duplex of the first two figures of x, combine them with the remainder (–10) and divide by 5 again: $D(21) = 4$, $4 - 10 = -6$, $-6 \div 5 = \bar{1}$ rem $\bar{1}$:

$$
\begin{array}{l|llllll}
0.2 & 0.2 & 0 & 0 & 0 & 0 \\
\frac{x^2}{5} & & 1 & {}_{\bar{1}}\bar{1} & {}_{\bar{1}} & \\
\hline
x & 0.2 & 1 & \bar{1} & &
\end{array}
$$

and we bring the $\bar{1}$ down into the answer.

This process is repeated as many times as required: obtain the latest duplex, add any remainder, divide by 5, put down answer and remainder and bring the next answer figure down into the answer.

In the next step: $D(21\bar{1}) = \bar{3}$, $-3 - 10 = -13$, $-13 \div 5 = \bar{3}$ rem 2, put it down, bring $\bar{3}$ down into the answer.
Then $D(D(2\bar{1}\bar{3}) = \overline{14}$, $\overline{14} + 20 = 6$, $6 \div 5 = 1$ rem 1, put it down and bring **1** into the answer.

$$
\begin{array}{l|llllll}
0.2 & 0.2 & 0 & 0 & 0 & 0 \\
\frac{x^2}{5} & & 1 & {}_{\bar{1}}\bar{1} & {}_{\bar{1}}\bar{3} & {}_{2}1 & {}_{1} \\
\hline
x & 0.2 & 1 & \bar{1} & \bar{3} & 1
\end{array}
$$

So we get **x = 0.20871** to 5 decimal places.

In fact, quadratic equations with reciprocal roots are of the form $ax^2 + bx + a = 0$, which is the form of the example above. The other root can therefore be found by finding the reciprocal of the answer found. Or, as explained in Lesson 14, we can take the found answer from minus the coefficient of x in the quadratic equation: x = – –5 – 0.20871 = **4.79129** to 5 D.P.

Solve $2x^3 - 4x^2 - 10x + 3 = 0$.

If we rearrange this equation to get $x = 0.3 - \dfrac{2x^2}{5} + \dfrac{x^3}{5}$

we see that there is a root at about $x = 0.3$.
We therefore proceed as before:

0.3	0 . 3		1
$-\frac{2x^2}{5}$	$\bar{3}\,_3\,0\,_{\bar{6}}\,0\,_6\,\bar{5}\,_{\bar{1}}$		2
$\frac{x^3}{5}$	$4\,_1\,1\,_{\bar{1}}\,2\,_{\bar{2}}$		3
$x =$	0 . 3 $\bar{3}$ 4 1 $\bar{3}$		4

Bring down **0.3** into the answer.
We need to square x, multiply by 2, divide by 5 and change the sign:

$D(3) = 9, 9 \times 2 = 18, 18 \div 5 = 3$ r3, put $\bar{3}_3$.

Bring down $\bar{3}$.
$D(3\bar{3}) = \overline{18}, \overline{18} \times 2 = \overline{36}, \overline{36} + 30 = \bar{6}, \bar{6} \div 5 = 0_{\bar{6}}$.

Row 3: we change the sign of the figures in row 2, multiply by x (i.e. by row 4), and divide by 2:
$CP\begin{pmatrix} 3 \\ 3 \end{pmatrix} = 9, 9 \div 2 = 4_1$.

Etc.
And **x = 0.27407** to 5 d.p.

Alternatively we could use $x = 0.3 - 0.4x^2 + 0.2x^3$.

18.2 TRIGONOMETRIC EQUATIONS

Solve **sine x = 0.2**.

Here we find the inverse sine of 0.2.

Using the series expansion for $\sin x$ from Lesson 17: $\sin x = x - \dfrac{x^3}{3!} + \dfrac{x^5}{5!} - \ldots$

$\therefore x = \sin x + \dfrac{x^3}{3!} - \dfrac{x^5}{5!} + \ldots$

And since we are given $\sin x = 0.2$ we have $\therefore x = 0.2 + \dfrac{x^3}{3!} - \dfrac{x^5}{5!} + \ldots$

Notice here that in the sequence $x, \dfrac{x^3}{3!}, \dfrac{x^5}{5!}, \ldots$ the first term is multiplied by x^2 and divided by 6 to get the second term, the second is multiplied by x^2 and divided by 20 to get the third and so on.

This means it is worth calculating x^2 as we go along (see row 5 below).
And the divisors 6 and 20 are placed near the beginning of rows 2 and 3 (actually divisors 6 and 2 are used).

We can therefore find x in a similar way to the previous examples:

$\sin x$	0	.	2	0							1
$\frac{x^3}{3!}$	6					1_2	3_2	5_2			2
$-\frac{x^5}{5!}$	2										3
$x =$	0	.	2	0	1	3	5				4
$(x^2 =$	0	.04	0	4		)					5

The answer appears in row 4, and rows 2, 3 and 5 are formed digit by digit as x is found.

4   Find $\cos^{-1} 0.123$.

Since this angle is close to $90°$, we can find $\sin^{-1} 0.123$ and subtract the result from $\frac{\pi}{2}$:

$\sin x$		0	.	1	2	3				
$\frac{x^3}{3!}$	6						$3_{\bar{1}}$	$1_{\bar{1}}$	2_0	
$x =$		0	.	1	2	3	3	1	2	
$(x^2 =$		.0	$_1$1	$_4$	5_0	$2_{\bar{2}}$	$0_3)$			

$\therefore \cos^{-1} 0.123 = \frac{\pi}{2} - 0.123312 = \mathbf{1.447484}.$

5   Find $\cos^{-1} 0.8$.

Since, from Lesson 17, $\cos x = 1 - \frac{x^2}{2!} + \frac{x^4}{4!} - \frac{x^6}{6!} + \frac{x^8}{8!} - \ldots$
$\therefore x^2 = 2(1 - \cos x) + \frac{x^4}{12} - \frac{x^6}{360} + \ldots$

And if we let $y = x^2$ we have: $\quad y = 2(1 - \cos x) + \frac{y^2}{12} - \frac{y^3}{360} + \ldots$
so that we can evaluate y and take its square root (see Lesson 11) to find x.

So if $\cos x = 0.8$, then: $y = 2(1-0.8) + \dfrac{y^2}{12} - \dfrac{y^3}{360} + \ldots.$

$2(1-\cos x)$	$0 \ . \ 4$				row 1
$\dfrac{y^2}{12}$ 12		$1_4 \ 4_0 \ 3_3 \ \bar{1}_2$			2
$-\dfrac{y^3}{360}$ 3		$\bar{2}_2 \ 0_3$			3
$y = x^2 =$	$0 \ . \ 4$	$1_5 \ 4_6 \ 1_9 \ \bar{1}_5$			4
$x =$	$0 \ . \ 6$	$4 \ \ 3 \ \ 5$			5

First we bring **0.4** down into row 4.
Row 2: $D(4) = 16$, $16 \div 12 = 1_4$

Bring down **1** into row 4
Row 2: $D(41) = 8$, $8 + 40 = 48$, $48 \div 12 = 4_0$

Bring down **4** into row 4
Row 2: $D(414) = 33$, $33 + 0 = 33$, $33 \div 12 = 3_{\bar{3}}$

Row 3: multiply rows 2 and 4 and divide by 3:

$$CP\binom{1}{4} = 4, \ 4 \div 3 = 2 \ r\bar{2}, \text{ put } \bar{2}_{\bar{2}} \text{ as this term is negative.}$$

Bring down **1** into row 4
Row 2: $D(4141) = 16$, $16 + \overline{30} = \overline{14}$, $\overline{14} \div 12 = \bar{1}_{\bar{2}}$

Row 3: $CP\begin{pmatrix} 1 & 4 \\ 4 & 1 \end{pmatrix} = 17, \ 17 + \overline{20} = \overline{3}, \ \overline{3} \div 3 = 0_{\bar{3}}.$

Bring $\bar{1}$ into row 4
We then find the square root of row 4 using the usual Vedic method.

Alternatively we can find $\sin^{-1} 0.6$.

 Find **tangent 0.3**.

We have, from Section 17.3b: $\tan^{-1} x = x - \frac{1}{3}x^3 + \frac{1}{5}x^5 - \frac{1}{7}x^7 + \ldots$

$\therefore \ x = \tan^{-1} x + \frac{1}{3}x^3 - \frac{1}{5}x^5 + \frac{1}{7}x^7 + \ldots$

$\tan^{-1}x$	$0 \ . \ 3$	0			1
$\dfrac{x^3}{3}$ 3		$1_0 \ 0_1 \ \bar{1}_0$			2
$-\dfrac{x^5}{5}$ 5		$\bar{1}_{\bar{2}} \ {}^{+}4_0$			3
$x =$	$0 \ . \ 3$	$1 \ \ \bar{1} \ \ 3$			4
$(x^2 =$	$0 \ . \ 1_{\bar{1}}$	$0_{\bar{4}} \ \bar{4}_{\bar{5}}$		$)$	5

Put **0.3** in the answer.
Row 5: $D(3) = 1_{\bar{1}}$

Row 2: $CP\begin{pmatrix} 3 \\ 1 \end{pmatrix} = 3,\ 3 \div 3 = 1_0$, put **1** in the answer.

Row 5: $D(31) = 6,\ 6 + \overline{10} = \overline{4}$, put $0_{\bar{4}}$

Row 2: $CP\begin{pmatrix} 3 & 1 \\ 1 & 0 \end{pmatrix} = 1,\ 1+0 = 1,\ 1 \div 3 = 0_1$

Row 3: multiply rows 2 and 5, multiply by 3 and divide by 5:

$$CP\begin{pmatrix} 1 \\ 1 \end{pmatrix} = 1,\ 1 \times 3 = 3,\ 3 \div 5 = 1_{\bar{2}}$$

Put $\overline{1}$ in the answer.
Row 5: $D(3\,\overline{1}1) = \overline{5},\ \overline{5} + \overline{40} = \overline{4}_{\bar{5}}$

Row 2: $CP\begin{pmatrix} 3 & 1 & \overline{1} \\ 1 & 0 & \overline{4} \end{pmatrix} = \overline{13},\ \overline{13} + 10 = \overline{3},\ \overline{3} \div 3 = \overline{1}_0$

Row 3: $CP\begin{pmatrix} 1 & 0 \\ 1 & 0 \end{pmatrix} = 0,\ 0 \times 3 = 0,\ 0 + \overline{20} = \overline{20},\ \overline{20} \div 5 = \overline{4}_0$ *

Put **3** in the answer.

*Note that we multiply by 3 and add the carried figure **before** dividing by 5.

Find **sinh⁻¹0.5432**.

The expansion for hyperbolic sine (a derivation is indicated in Lesson 17) gives:

$$\therefore 0.5432 = x + \frac{x^3}{3!} + \frac{x^5}{5!} + \ldots$$

$$\therefore x = 0.5432 - \frac{x^3}{3!} - \frac{x^5}{5!} - \ldots$$

sinh x	0 . 5	4	3	2				1
$-\frac{x^3}{3!}$ 6			$\overline{2}_3\ \overline{3}_3\ \overline{4}_0\ \overset{+}{3}_{\bar{2}}$					2
$-\frac{x^5}{5!}$ 2				$\overline{3}_0\ \overline{1}_{\bar{1}}$				3
x =	0 . 5	2	0	$\overline{5}$	2			4
(x^2 =	0 . 3 $_{\bar{5}}$	$\overline{3}_0$	0_4	$\overline{1}_0$			)	5

18.3 TRANSCENDENTAL EQUATIONS

These are equations whose roots are transcendental i.e. they are not the roots of any finite polynomial equation with rational coefficients.

One example is $x + \sin x = 1$.

8 Solve $x + \sin x = 1$.

Using the series expansion for $\sin x$: $\quad x + x - \dfrac{x^3}{3!} + \dfrac{x^5}{5!} - \ldots = 1$.

$\therefore x = 0.5 + \dfrac{x^3}{12} - \dfrac{x^5}{240} + \dfrac{x^7}{2 \times 7!} - \ldots$

Note that there is again a simple ratio between consecutive terms of the RHS. So, as before, we bring down the first digit, 5, evaluate the first digit of x^3 and divide it by 12, and so on.

```
0.5        │ 0 . 5                                 1
 x³/12   12│        1 ₃ 1 ₁ 1 ₂ 2 ₅                2
-x⁵/240   2│               1̄ ₁ 5̄ ₁                 3
x =        │ 0 . 5   1   1   0   3̄                 4
(x² =      │ 0 . 3 ₅ 4̄ ₀ 1 ₁ 1 ₂ 1̄ ₁      )       5
```

The method, which follows similar steps to those from the previous lesson, is quick and efficient if x is small and can be extended to any number of decimal places.

With the extra flexibility offered by the vinculum device the figures can always be kept small and manageable.

"*And as regards the time required by the students for mastering the whole course of Vedic Mathematics as applied to all its branches, we need merely state from our actual experience that 8 months (or 12 months) at an average rate of 2 or 3 hours per day should suffice for completing the whole course of mathematical studies on these Vedic lines instead of 15 or 20 years required according to the existing systems of Indian and also of foreign universities.*"
From "Vedic Mathematics", Page xvii.

KEPLER'S EQUATION

The next example shows the solution of Kepler's Equation, an equation of great importance in positional astronomy. This is:

$$M = E - e\sin E$$

where M and E are the mean and eccentric anomalies respectively of a planet in its orbit and e is the eccentricity of the orbit.

The eccentricity, e, is a measure of the oblateness of the ellipse and can be defined by
$$e^2 = 1 - \frac{b^2}{a^2}$$
where a and b are the lengths of the semi-major and semi-minor axes:

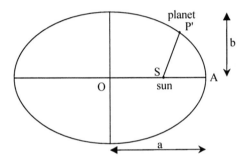

The velocity of a planet in an elliptical orbit is variable and the mean anomaly, M, is the angle shown in the diagram below assuming the planet travelled at constant speed in a circular orbit that was completed in the same time as the actual planet, and started at A at the same instant.

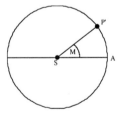

M is found from $\dfrac{M}{2\pi} = \dfrac{d}{T}$ where d is the number of days since the planet passed A (called the perihelion) and T is the time for one full orbit.

The eccentric anomaly, E, is as shown in the diagram below where Q lies on a circle of radius a.

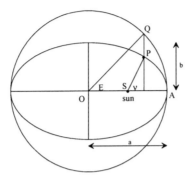

v is the true anomaly of the planet at P and there is a fairly simple formula for getting v once E is known.

So the problem is to find E given M and e in the equation $M = E - e\sin E$.

Kepler's equation looks very simple, but as we require E the equation is a transcendental one, which means E cannot be made the subject of the equation without having an infinite number of terms on the right-hand side.

Many methods have been proposed to solve this equation including one by Kepler himself. The Vedic method which follows is extremely efficient, using each digit of the answer as they are obtained to get the next digit. Modern calculating devices make the solution rapid, using the Newton-Raphson, or some other, iterative technique. But their methods, though extremely fast are not efficient and there is also sometimes a need for quick pencil and paper solutions. See Reference 3 Chapter 3 for more on this.

We will take M = 0.30303 radians and e = 0.016722, which is the eccentricity of the Earth's orbit.

 Solve $\mathbf{0.30303 = E - 0.016722\sin E}$.

$$\therefore E = 0.30303 + 0.016722(E - \tfrac{E^3}{3!} + \tfrac{E^5}{5!} - \ldots)$$

M	0 . 3	0	3	0	3	0	0			1
eE		1 ₄	5 ₃	2 ₆	5 ₁	2 ₁	1 ₃			2
$-\frac{eE^3}{3!}$ 6				1̄ ᵢ	2 ᵢ	1̄ ₃	5̄ ₀			3
$\frac{eE^5}{5!}$ 2						4 ₀				4
E =	0 . 3	1	2̄	1	0	1	0			5
(E² =	. 1 ᵢ	0 ₄	5̄ ᵢ	1̄ ₂	3 ₄	)				6

where $e = 0.016722 = 0.02\overline{3}3\overline{2}2$.

Bring **0.3** into the answer row.

Row 2: we multiply e and E, $CP\begin{pmatrix} 2 \\ 3 \end{pmatrix} = 6 = 1_{\overline{1}}$

Bring **1** into the answer row.

Row 2: $CP\begin{pmatrix} 2 & \overline{3} \\ 3 & 1 \end{pmatrix} = \overline{7},\ \overline{7} + \overline{40} = \overline{5}_3$

Bring $\overline{2}$ down into the answer row.

Row 2: $CP\begin{pmatrix} 2 & \overline{3} & \overline{3} \\ 3 & 1 & \overline{2} \end{pmatrix} = \overline{16},\ \overline{16} + 30 = 2_{\overline{6}}$

Row 3: we find E^2 (row 6) then multiply rows 2 and 6, divide by 6 and change the

sign: $CP\begin{pmatrix} 1 \\ 1 \end{pmatrix} = 1,\ CP\begin{pmatrix} 1 & \overline{5} \\ 1 & 0 \end{pmatrix} = \overline{5}$, giving $\overline{15} = 5$,

$5 \div 6 = 1\,r\,\overline{1}$, put $\overline{1}_{\overline{1}}$

Bring **1** down into the answer.
Etc.

We get **E = 0.3081010** to 7 decimal places.

Although M, and therefore E, take all values between 0 and 2π,
by using the angle to the nearest quadrant boundary we can always
arrange that the quantity we calculate is less than about $\frac{\pi}{4}$.
For example, if M = 3 radians, so that $E \approx 3$, we let $E = \pi - A$:

$\therefore M = \pi - A - e\sin(\pi - A)$

$\quad = \pi - A - e\sin A$.

from which we can find A and then E, since $E = \pi - A$.

Transcendental equations occur in a wide range of situations including the prediction of
eclipses (see Reference 7).

10   Solve $x + e^x = 2$.

Using the expansion for e^x we get:

$x + 1 + x + \frac{x^2}{2!} + \frac{x^3}{3!} + \frac{x^4}{4!} + \frac{x^5}{5!} + \ldots = 2$

$\therefore x = 0.5 - \dfrac{x^2}{4} - \dfrac{x^3}{12} - \dfrac{x^4}{48} - \dfrac{x^5}{240} - \ldots$

0.5		0 .	5							1
$-\frac{x^2}{4}$ 4				$\bar{5}$ 5	$\overset{+}{1}$ $\bar{}$	0 6				2
$-\frac{x^3}{12}$ 3				$\bar{1}$	3 $\bar{}$	$\bar{2}$ 1				3
$-\frac{x^4}{48}$ 4					$\bar{1}$ $\bar{}$	2 3				4
$-\frac{x^5}{240}$ 5						$\bar{1}$ 0				5
x =		0 .	5	$\bar{6}$	3	$\bar{1}$				6

Bring down **0.5** to row 6.

Row 2: $D(5) = 25$, $25 \div 4 = 5$ r5, put $\bar{5}_5$

Row 3: we multiply rows 2 and 6 and divide by 3, $CP\begin{pmatrix}\bar{5}\\5\end{pmatrix} = \overline{25}$

$\overline{25} \div 3 = \bar{7} r \bar{4}$, put $\bar{13}_{\bar{4}}$

Bring down $\bar{6}$.

Row 2: $D(\bar{56}) = \overline{60}$, $\overline{60} + 50 = \overline{10}$, $\overline{10} \div 4 = \bar{1}$ r6, put $1_{\bar{6}}$

Row 4: we multiply rows 3 and 6 and divide by 4, $CP\begin{pmatrix}\bar{1}\\5\end{pmatrix} = \bar{5}$, $\bar{5} \div 4 = \bar{1}_1$

Bring down **3** into the answer.
Etc.

So **x = 0.4429** to 4 D.P.

11   Solve $3x = \cos x$.

$x = \dfrac{1}{3} - \dfrac{x^2}{6} + \dfrac{x^4}{72} - \dfrac{x^6}{2160} + \ldots$

$\frac{1}{3}$		0 . 3	3	3	3	3	3		1
$-\frac{x^2}{6}$ 6				$\bar{1}$ $_3$	$\bar{7}$ $_0$	$\overset{+}{3}$ $_{\bar{2}}$			2
$\frac{x^4}{72}$ 2						1 $_{\bar{1}}$			3
x =		0 . 3	2	$\bar{4}$	7				4

REFERENCES

1. Sri Bharati Krsna Tirthaji, "Vedic Mathematics", published by Motilal Banarsidass, 1965. ISBN 81-208-0163-6.

2. "Celebrating Perfection in Education", Maharishi University Press 1997. ISBN 81-7523-013-4.

3. Williams K. R. *Discover Vedic Mathematics*. Inspiration Books, 1984. ISBN 978-1-902517-20-9.

4. Williams K.R. *Triples*. Inspiration Books, 1984. ISBN 978-1-902517-19-3.

5. Nicholas A. P., K. Williams, J. Pickles. *Vertically and Crosswise*. Inspiration Books, 1984. ISBN 978-1-902517-21-6.

6. Sri Bharati Krsna Tirthaji, "Vedic Metaphysics", published by Motilal Banarsidass, 1978. ISBN 0-89581-472-2.

7. Williams K. R. *Astronomical Applications of Vedic Mathematics*. Inspiration Books, 2000. ISBN 978-1-902517-22-3.

VEDIC MATHEMATICS SUTRAS

1	एकाधिकेन पूर्वेन Ekādhikena Pūrveṇa	*By One More than the One Before*
2	निखिलं नवतश्चरमं दशतः Nikhilaṃ Navatascaramaṃ Dasataḥ	*All from 9 and the Last from 10*
3	ऊर्ध्वतिर्यग्भ्यामं Ūrdhva Tiryagbhyāṃ	*Vertically and Crosswise*
4	परावर्त्य योजयेत् Parāvartya Yojayet	*Transpose and Apply*
5	शून्यं साम्यसमुच्चये Sūnyaṃ Sāmyasamuccaya	*If the Samuccaya is the Same it is Zero*
6	आनुरूप्ये शून्यं अन्यत् (Ānurūpya) Sūnyamanyat	*If One is in Ratio the Other is Zero*
7	संकलन व्यवकलनाभ्यां Saṅkalana Vyavakalanābhyāṃ	*By Addition and by Subtraction*
8	पूरणापूरणाभ्यां Pūraṇāpūraṇābhyām	*By the Completion or Non-Completion*
9	चलनकलनाभ्याम् Calana Kalanābhyām	*Differential Calculus*
10	यावदूनं Yāvadūnam	*By the Deficiency*
11	व्यष्टिसमष्टिः Vyaṣṭisamaṣṭiḥ	*Specific and General*
12	शेषाण्यङ्केन चरमेण Seṣanyaṅkena Carameṇa	*The Remainders by the Last Digit*
13	सोपान्त्यद्वयमन्त्यं Sopāntyadvayamantyam	*The Ultimate and Twice the Penultimate*
14	एकन्यूनेन पूर्वेन Ekanūnena Pūrveṇa	*By One Less than the One Before*
15	गुणितसमुच्चयः Guṇitsamuccayaḥ	*The Product of the Sum*
16	गुणकसमुच्चयः Guṇakasamuccayaḥ	*All the Multipliers*

SUB-SUTRAS

1	आनुरूप्येण Ānurūpyeṇa	*Proportionately*
2	शिष्यते शेषसंज्ञः Siṣyate Seṣamjñaḥ	*The Remainder Remains Constant*
3	आधमाधेनान्त्यमन्त्येन Ādyamādyenāntyamantyena	*The First by the First and the Last by the Last*
4	केवलैः सप्तकं गुण्यात् Kevalaiḥ Saptakaṃ Guṇyāt	*For 7 the Multiplicand is 143*
5	वेष्टनम् Veṣṭanam	*By Osculation*
6	यावदूनं तावदुनं Yāvadūnaṃ Tāvadūnaṃ	*Lessen by the Deficiency*
7	यावदूनं तावदूनीकृत्य वर्गं च योजयेत् Yāvadūnaṃ Tāvadūnīkṛtya Vargañca Yojayet	*Whatever the Deficiency lessen by that amount and set up the Square of the Deficiency*
8	अन्त्ययोर्दशकेऽपि Antyayordasake'pi	*Last Totalling 10*
9	अन्त्ययोरेव Antyayoreva	*Only the Last Terms*
10	समुच्चयगुणितः Samuccayaguṇitaḥ	*The Sum of the Products*
11	लोपनस्थापनाभ्यां Lopanasthāpanābhyām	*By Alternate Elimination and Retention*
12	विलोकनं Vilokanam	*By Mere Observation*
13	गुणितसमच्चुयः समुच्चयगुणितः Guṇitsamuccayaḥ Samuccayaguṇitaḥ	*The Product of the Sum is the Sum of the Products*
14	ध्वजाङ्क Dhvajāṅka	*On the Flag*

INDEX OF THE VEDIC FORMULAE

SUTRAS

By One More than the One Before 36-, 125-

All from 9 and the Last from 10 12-, 18-

Vertically and Crosswise 19, 56, 67-, 80, 99, 107, 122, 135, 137-, 174-, 212-, 217-

Transpose and Apply 79-, 86, 205-

When the Samuccaya is the Same it is Zero 89-

If One is in Ratio the Other is Zero 83, 85-

By Addition and by Subtraction 82, 125, 171

By the Completion or Non-Completion 215-

Differential Calculus 84, 191-, 205-, 222-, 234-

By the Deficiency 18

Specific and General

The Remainders by the Last Digit

The Ultimate and Twice the Penultimate 94

By One Less than the One Before 13, 46

The Product of the Sum 10

All the Multipliers

INDEX OF THE VEDIC FORMULAE

SUB-SUTRAS

INDEX

<u>INDEX</u>

OTHER VEDIC MATHEMATICS BOOKS

Teacher's Manual – Elementary
This is similar to the intermediate book but covers a lesser range (aimed at teachers of grades 3 to 7). It contains many topics that are not in the other Manuals that are suitable for this age range and many topics that are also in Manual 2 are covered in greater detail here. ISBN 978-1-902517-16-2

Teacher's Manual – Intermediate
This is similar to the elementary book but covers a greater range (aimed at teachers of grades 5 to 10) including divisibility, square roots, applications of triples, further equations, combined operations etc. ISBN 978-1-902517-17-9

The Cosmic Computer - Abridged Edition
This is a shortened version of the full course described next. It contains some of the most striking Vedic methods. It is beautifully illustrated with full colour cover and is perfect bound (paperback). A good introduction to Vedic Mathematics. Authors: Kenneth Williams and Mark Gaskell. 216 pages. Almost A4 in size. 1997. ISBN 978-0-9531782-0-9

The Cosmic Computer Course
This covers Key Stage 3 (age 11-14 years) of the National Curriculum for England and Wales. It consists of three textbooks, a Teacher's Guide and an Answer Book. Much of the material in Book 1 is suitable for children as young as eight and this is developed from here to topics such as Pythagoras' Theorem and Quadratic Equations in Book 3. The Teacher's Guide contains a Summary of each Book, a Unified Field Chart (showing the whole subject of mathematics and how each of the parts are related), hundreds of Mental Tests (these revise previous work, introduce new ideas and are carefully correlated with the rest of the course), Extension Sheets (about 16 per book) for fast pupils or for extra classwork, Revision Tests, Games, Worksheets etc.

Discover Vedic Mathematics
This has sixteen chapters each of which focuses on one of the Vedic Sutras or sub-Sutras and shows many applications of each. It goes into some detail, showing variations and giving explanations and proofs.. Also contains solutions to GCSE and 'A' level examination questions. Author: K. Williams, 216 pages. 1984. ISBN 978-1-902517-20-9.

Triples
This book shows applications of Pythagorean Triples (like 3,4,5). A simple, elegant system for combining these triples gives unexpected and powerful general methods for solving a wide range of mathematical problems, with far less effort than conventional methods use. The easy text fully explains this method which has applications in trigonometry (you do not need any of those complicated formulae), coordinate geometry (2 and 3 dimensions) transformations (2 and 3 dimensions), simple harmonic motion, astronomy etc. etc. Author: K. Williams, 176 pages. ISBN 978-1-902517-19-3

Vertically and Crosswise
This is an advanced book of sixteen chapters on one Sutra ranging from elementary multiplication etc. to the solution of non-linear partial differential equations. It deals with (i) calculation of common functions and their series expansions, and (ii) the solution of equations, starting with simultaneous equations and moving on to algebraic, transcendental and differential equations. Authors: A. P. Nicholas, K. Williams, J. Pickles, 200 pages, paperback, 1999. ISBN 978-1-902517-21-6.

The Natural Calculator
This book focuses on mental mathematics and has a detailed introduction outlining its merits. There are nine chapters, mainly on multiplication but including addition, subtraction and division. Author: K. Williams, 100 pages, paperback. ISBN 978-1-902517-15-5

For further details and other books please visit http://www.vedicmaths.org